Jan. 2023

MW01094994

J,

I hope you enjoy this
book. I follow these authors
through the Discovery Institute
& I think you will enjoy their
thinking.

YOUR DESIGNED BODY

Your friend,

Forrest

YOUR DESIGNED BODY

STEVE LAUFMANN

HOWARD GLICKSMAN

SEATTLE   DISCOVERY INSTITUTE PRESS   2022

Description

Consider your body. Every day it must solve hundreds of hard engineering problems simultaneously, or else you'll die. While you're going about your daily business, your body stores, retrieves, translates, and manages software for thousands of proteins, switches, setpoints, thresholds, feedback loops, coordinate systems, counters, and timers. It disassembles thousands of different complex molecules, converts them into their building blocks, absorbs the building blocks, then reassembles them into the legions of chemicals and proteins that keep you going.

Your body also safely transports hazardous chemicals to where they're needed, without spilling them in places where they'd do harm, and employs them as it orchestrates thousands of complex processes and movements, some nearly instantaneous. At the same time it defends itself against threats large and small, and reproduces its own parts to replace those that are wearing out. And this is only a tiny portion of what your body must do to remain alive—all without conscious input from you.

In *Your Designed Body*, systems engineer Steve Laufmann and physician Howard Glicksman explore this extraordinary system of systems encompassing thousands of ingenious and interdependent engineering solutions. They present a compelling case that no gradual evolutionary pathway could have achieved this, and that instead it must be the handiwork of a masterful designer-engineer.

Library Cataloging Data

Your Designed Body by Steve Laufmann and Howard Glicksman

Cover design by Brian Gage. Interior by Mike Perry.

474 pages, 6 x 9 x 1 in, & 1.4 lb. 229 x 152 x 24 mm. & 0.63 kg.

Library of Congress Control Number: 2022947487

ISBN-978-1-63712-020-0 (paperback), 978-1-63712-021-7 (Kindle), 978-1-63712-022-4 (EPUB)

BISAC: SCI036000 SCIENCE/Life Sciences/Human Anatomy & Physiology

BISAC: SCI027000 SCIENCE/Life Sciences/Evolution

BISAC: TEC073000 TECHNOLOGY & ENGINEERING/Systems Engineering

Publisher Information

Discovery Institute Press, 208 Columbia Street, Seattle, WA 98104

Internet: discoveryinstitutepress.com

Published in the United States of America on acid-free paper.

First edition, November 2022

Advance Praise

Your Designed Body is the latest dramatic chapter in the ongoing story of scientific discovery inspired by the theory of intelligent design. The book is a masterful synthesis of modern medicine and engineering, revealing a human body brimming not only with biological information and ingenious molecular machines, but also with exquisitely engineered systems and subsystems that resemble but exceed the most advanced engineering techniques of our best engineers. Laufmann and Glicksman draw on the mainstream and increasingly fruitful discipline of systems biology, but they push the exploration into wondrous new territory. Those who cling to the old paradigm of Darwinian materialism risk missing out on a most fantastic voyage of discovery.

—Stephen C. Meyer, PhD, philosopher of science and bestselling author of *Darwin's Doubt* and *Return of the God Hypothesis*

The machinery, integration, and control in human physiology is truly astounding. *Your Designed Body* provides an excellent and systematic overview of the biological engineering and does so with great insight. The authors are particularly good at raising the relevant questions about how all of this engineering came to be. Evidence of design and intent are everywhere, and as soon as foresight or planning becomes involved in a process, any attempt at a naturalistic explanation is torpedoed. It is all good, but I particularly enjoyed the way the authors tackled claims about "botched design" as well as the implications of following the evidence to its obvious conclusion.

—David Galloway, MD DSc FRCS FRCP FACS FACP; former President, Royal College of Physicians and Surgeons of Glasgow; Honorary Professor of Surgery, College of Medical, Veterinary & Life Sciences, University of Glasgow; author of *Design Dissected*

Steve Laufmann and Howard Glicksman have written a fascinating description of the basic truth about the human body—a truth that I have also seen in my own research on blood flow in the brain. The human body is an elegantly engineered system, complete with intracellular nanotechnology, organ-level interconnectivity, and whole-body integration of countless delicate and precise systems. The bookshelves in my office are full of engineering texts that are indispensable to understand how the body works, and most of the cutting-edge basic research in neuroscience of my medical colleagues and students depends critically on the implicit assumption that the human body is an engineered system. The modern science of human biology and physiology is reverse engineering, plain and simple. *Your Designed Body* tells the captivating story of how modern medical science reveals the engineering marvels inside our skin. It's a magnificent and much-needed accomplishment—the indispensable book on the intelligent design of the human body.

—Michael Egnor, MD, Professor of Neurosurgery and Pediatrics at
State University of New York, Stony Brook; former Director of Pediatric
Neurosurgery; member of the Scientific Advisory Board of the Hydrocephalus
Association; named one of New York's best doctors by *New York Magazine*

A wonderful book! Over my 40+ years of teaching and discussing with engineering students and friends the implications of God's design, I have had some of my best discussions with those in the medical profession. Doctors and engineers provide complementary perspectives. As engineer Steve Laufmann and physician Howard Glicksman wonderfully tell, the human body provides an almost inexhaustible and continually unfolding array of complex and designer-orchestrated systems that continue to be tapped for inspiration by the astute and discerning engineer. *Your Designed Body* is a worthy and thorough addition to any person who seeks to discover, understand, and discuss the details of the human body's marvelous design. Particularly helpful for knowledge and preparing to enter into discussion with the skeptic is the chapter on so-called "botched designs." The book will no doubt inspire and inform numerous conversations, discoveries, and designs in the future.

—Anthony Lyle Donaldson, PhD, founding dean and current Professor
of Electrical and Computer Engineering of the Gordon and Jill
Bourns College of Engineering at California Baptist University

Your Designed Body is an excellent overview of the evidence demonstrating how the human body is the result of engineering design. The authors accomplish this by combining the knowledge and experience of both an engineer and physician. In the book they define a theory of biological design, which is primarily based on the concept of organisms being the product of intentional engineering. The book includes a comprehensive description of attributes of the human body characteristic of engineering, including foresight, coherence, interdependence, fine tuning, modularity, and many others. Laufmann and Glicksman evaluate the possibility that these characteristics are the result of a random unguided process such as Darwinian materialistic evolution, and they show that to be extremely unlikely. They also effectively refute arguments that there are many poorly designed elements of the human body. The authors conclude that the source of the engineering is a designer-engineer who must be an intelligent agent.

—Eric Cassell, systems engineer, longtime engineering consultant for NASA and the Federal Aviation Administration (FAA), author of *Animal Algorithms: Evolution and the Mysterious Origin of Ingenious Instincts*

In *Your Designed Body* an accomplished pair of experts—a physician and a systems engineer—take us on a brilliant tour of the mind-boggling interactive complexity of the human body. They make a compelling case that only an intelligent agent could possibly have accommodated the millions of design constraints needed to produce a living, breathing, moving, thinking, and reproducing organism like us. Readers whose eyes have not been blinded by a materialistic worldview will see irrefutable evidence that our bodies are indeed designed.

—William S. Harris, PhD, Professor of Internal Medicine, Sanford School of Medicine, University of South Dakota; Founder of OmegaQuant Analytics, LLC; President of the Fatty Acid Research Institute

Your Designed Body is an excellent addition to the rapidly growing library of scientific discussions and books that show us how all aspects of the human being, from conception to death and from macroscopic to sub-microscopic, reflect incomprehensible forethought, irreducible complexity, and complex design. The authors show there is incomprehensible complexity upon complexity upon complexity within the human body. Everything is too coincidental to be a coincidence (per Yogi Berra). In a sense, Glicksman and Laufmann discard the "what came first, the chicken or the egg" conundrum. Instead, they make it clear that one needs both at the same time to make (any) life. Some examples are a man and a woman (the ultimate irreducible complexity), an egg and a sperm, and digestion, transportation, and metabolism with nutrients like carbohydrates and fats. There are uncountable "chicken-and-egg" scenarios found at all levels. Naturalism (Darwinism) fails miserably to explain these phenomena.

—Geoffrey Simmons, MD, former Governor of the American Academy of Disaster Medicine (AADM), author of *What Darwin Didn't Know* and *Billions of Missing Links*

CONTENTS

INTRODUCTION

I sing the body electric.

—WALT WHITMAN

THE HUMAN BODY IS AMAZING. EVEN A CURSORY LOOK SHOWS US that a lot is going on. Hands that wield a sledgehammer during the day can play evocative piano sonatas in the evening. In a triathlon, the same body swims, bicycles, and runs—three very different activities—in rapid succession and with extreme endurance. The same body that completed that triathlon can also climb a mountain (though perhaps on a different day).

Our bodies keep a constant internal temperature, manage our water levels effectively, and keep us going even when we eat the wrong foods.

When we stand up, our blood pressure adjusts almost instantly to keep blood flowing to the brain. We know when we need food and water. Even with our eyes closed, we can sense the position of all our body parts and make detailed adjustments in movement.

Our eyes differentiate the nuances across an amazing spectrum of colors. The same eyes that work in painfully bright light can also see in almost total darkness. How do they turn light (photons) into information (electrical impulses), and how does our brain turn that into images?

Our ears face similar challenges, only they turn sound (pressure waves) into electrical signals. Further, they're configured such that our minds can generate a three-dimensional understanding of the objects around us, just by the sounds those objects emit (or block).

When we cut our finger, the blood quickly stops and the wound scabs over and heals. When we get sick, our bodies generally do an excellent job of fixing the problem and getting well again.

While our bodies are neither the fastest, nor the biggest, nor the strongest in the animal kingdom, they are without question the most versatile. The human body's range of capabilities boggles the mind.

On top of all this, we can make *new* people. Anyone who has experienced the birth of a child knows that in this astonishing process something special happens.

What is a fitting response to such wonders?

Several years ago, I (Steve Laufmann) was perusing an online discussion board frequented by some fellow enterprise and systems architects when one post caught my attention. The writer observed that human-designed systems architectures can't compare to the amazing architectures we see in living organisms. This comment sparked an energetic discussion. Of particular interest to me, one responder agreed that these biological systems would indeed be amazing architectures, but since they resulted from entirely random, unguided Darwinian processes, as he believed, they could not be considered architecture. After all, architects know that good architectural design takes hard work and never happens by accident.

Huh?

Surely the architecture—the quality of the engineering in any system, including a living system—is evident in the resulting system, independent of who, or what, did the architectural work. And from a systems perspective, it's clear that living systems have extraordinarily hard problems to solve, else they can't be alive. For example, many single-celled organisms can intake oxygen from the surrounding environment, but how do the cells in a large multi-cellular body (like a human's) get oxygen when most of them have no access to the external environment?

It takes complex, multi-part systems to solve problems of this kind—to make a large and complex body work. And such systems only happen when there's a suitable architectural framework to define how they fit together—and how they work together. In the example above, a naïve architecture would likely fail to get the necessary oxygen to each and every cell, or would make any of a million other similar errors that would render life impossible.

The human body is unquestionably a marvel of engineering, but what is the source of the engineering? We've all been told that we are cosmic accidents, built gradually over eons by the purposeless forces of nature. We also have been told that we are purposely made. Which is it?

To shed light on the question we intend a detailed examination of the human body. The exploration will benefit from two distinct, complementary perspectives:

- A medical perspective—to understand the sophisticated and extraordinarily precise functional capacities, dynamics, and coordination of the body's many interconnected systems.
- An engineering perspective—to explore the exquisite engineering of these systems: the mechanical, pneumatic, hydraulic, and electrical systems, the control systems, the internal signaling and coordination mechanisms, the information processing systems, and much more.

Throughout, we'll base our observations and arguments on incontrovertible medical and engineering knowledge.

We'll also consider claims that one or another part of the human body is poorly engineered. The past several years have seen a growing move to denigrate and demote the human body's architecture. According to this argument, the human body is actually not so well designed. Rather, it's filled with the many errors and evolutionary dead ends you'd expect if it resulted from billions of small, random, purposeless mutations threshed by natural selection. This argument for blind evolution is commonly known as the argument from poor design. We'll look at a few examples of this line of argument in the course of the book and take a deeper dive into the matter in Chapter 23, after we've explored many recurring design principles and patterns in the human body.

We will argue that the exquisite architecture and engineering-design of the human body reveal daunting hurdles to any causal explanation—hurdles that can no longer be ignored. In the final chapters we will unpack a theory of biological causation rooted in the lessons of engineering and systems biology, and compare it to the modern evolutionary paradigm.

There's no question that our view will be controversial. It challenges the reigning paradigm for biological origins. But dominant paradigms aren't always the best paradigms. The history of science is replete with dominant paradigms that were overthrown when new evidence drove new theories to the fore.

In such cases, the champions of the dominant paradigms do not generally cede the field quickly or magnanimously. This is perhaps the central message of historian of science Thomas Kuhn's famous work *The Structure of Scientific Revolutions*. The Nobel Prize-winning physicist Max Planck put it this way: "A new scientific truth does not triumph by convincing its opponents and making them see the light, but rather because its opponents eventually die, and a new generation grows up that is familiar with it."[1] Or, as his point is often paraphrased informally, "Science advances one funeral at a time."

That's a bit more pessimistic than the reality. Already there have been some high-level public conversions to the design paradigm in the scientific and broader academic community, as well as a growing number of young scientists who are privately supportive but are keeping a low profile because they are at vulnerable points in their careers. Planck's observation, however, is true in the main.

Psychologist James Dobson tells a story from early in his career, when he worked in a clinic with patients who had varying levels of detachment from reality. One patient believed he had been dead for some time. Dobson tried everything he could think of to convince this poor guy that he was actually alive. Nothing worked. After much thought, he devised a foolproof approach. He asked, "Do dead men bleed?" The patient was outraged, "Of course dead men don't bleed. That's absurd." Dobson then pulled out a needle and pricked the man's finger. Staring at the drop of blood oozing from his skin, the man exclaimed, "Well, I'll be darned... Dead men *do* bleed."

An amusing story, all the more so because it illustrates a common foible of humans. When faced with evidence that challenges long-held assumptions, a person may not let go of the assumption that is most reasonable to let go of. Instead, he may let go of the one he cherishes the least.

As you examine the evidence laid out in these pages, our encouragement to you is, don't be the guy in the story. Be willing to follow the evidence wherever it leads.

Clever Solutions

THE QUESTION of human origins is also, of course, a question of biological origins generally. Organic life must overcome many thorny problems, both to be alive and to reproduce. While the laws of physics and chemistry are precisely tuned to permit life, they are incapable of causing it, and of course have no way to care whether life exists or not.

And the matter calls for considerable care. Life depends on a delicate balance of forces, arranged with precision. As Richard Dawkins famously put it, "However many ways there may be of being alive, it is certain there are vastly more ways of being dead, or rather not alive."[2] Life's margin of error is small. But as we'll show, jump-starting, sustaining, and reproducing life are enormously hard problems to solve. How is it possible to get so much right, to land within the margin of error again and again and again?

Hard problems require ingenious solutions. Fortunately for us, ingenious solutions are everywhere in biology—and nowhere more so than in the human body.

Virtually every one of the body's ingenious solutions involves one or more systems (1) composed of various parts that (2) work together to achieve a function that none of the parts can perform on its own, (3) all of which are correctly arranged, assembled, and integrated, with (4) exactly the needed range of capacities, while (5) operating within tight tolerances and under tight deadlines. Most of us know from firsthand experience that when any one of these systems breaks down, bad things happen.

Producing a next generation is even trickier. If something goes wrong, even something seemingly modest—and early in embryonic development, particularly—the result is that life simply ceases.

Life never exists as a formless blob, but instead always exists in an architecturally complex form. Nor, of course, does life exist in the often-fertile imaginations of materialist scientists. Life is found in the real world, and reality has a way of humbling theories that are not grounded in the nitty-gritty details of what life requires.

Coherent Interdependent Systems—Do or Die

PHYSICIANS DON'T get to make stuff up. They don't have the luxury to merely observe how life looks or theorize about its superficial qualities. They need to know how the body really works, how the parts affect each other, and what it takes in practical terms to keep it all working over a (hopefully) long lifetime.

Physicians know that every human body must do all the following, all the time:

- *The body must follow the rules.* The forces of physics and chemistry will not be ignored. So, for example, because chemical diffusion will lead to death, the body must work actively (and usually very hard) to counteract the force of diffusion. No exceptions.

- *The body must take control.* The only way to manage a separate equilibrium, and thereby stay alive, is to effectively control each of the thousands of required quantities and processes. When there is too much salt in the body, or not enough, the body must realize this and take the actions needed to correct it. Failure means death.

- *The body must possess exactly the right functional capacities.* The heart and lungs must have exactly the right capacities to deliver oxygen throughout the body, at levels appropriate to a wide range of activity levels. Every bone and muscle must be able to support exactly the needed weights and stresses, each the right size, strength, and flexibility for its particular tasks.
- *The body must be finely tuned.* It must manage all these things within remarkably tight tolerances. Failing to do so in any of the dozens of life-critical parameters or across thousands of control processes can lead to death.

Medical science obviously has much to teach us about such questions, but so too does engineering, since regardless of the origins story one prefers for the human body, the thing is an engineering marvel. An engineering perspective, then, should shed important light on how it works.

Though their mistakes sometimes take longer to discover than those of physicians, engineers also must live in the real world. Engineers design, build, deploy, and operate complex systems that do real work in the real world. And it takes yet more work to keep these systems from failing, which is pretty much guaranteed to happen at the least opportune times.

Engineers know that all the following are required to make systems that work:

- *Systems require many parts.* The parts are usually specialized to perform certain tasks under certain conditions. Systems are typically composed of other systems, constituting a hierarchy of systems—a *system of systems.*
- *Systems must be coherent.* A system's parts must be precisely coordinated. They must fit together correctly, with the right

interfaces and integrations for *functional coherence*. And they must be carefully orchestrated over time to achieve their overall function(s), for *process coherence*. Failure at either will prevent the system from working.

- *Systems of systems usually exhibit complex interdependencies.* Individual systems or subsystems often require other working subsystems in order to function. Many times, these dependencies go both ways. For example, your car's engine won't start without a charged battery, but the battery won't charge unless the engine runs.

For human engineers it takes a lot of ingenuity, hard work, and perseverance to achieve such things, typically including many iterations of the classic *design-build-test* cycle. Engineers know that working systems are never an accident. So if someone suggests that a coherent, interdependent system of systems (like the human body) arose by chance, they'll need to back that up with a detailed engineering analysis.

Asking Better Questions

Life is difficult to achieve. The world is not kind to partial experiments. Failure in any of a thousand processes means death. And yet the world is filled with an immense variety of living forms—flowers, trees, sponges, mollusks, birds, fish, and the great variety of mammals, from the tiniest rodent to whales and humans—not to mention all the bizarre creatures in the fossil record. We stand amazed at the intricate details turning up in molecular biology, including new discoveries from DNA sequencing. But if life is so tenuous, and the body so finely tuned, how could these things come to be?

It's quite a quandary. Life requires massive capabilities (coherent interdependent systems), which only work when adjusted to extremely fine tolerances. These are hard engineering problems to overcome, and the fact that they've not only been solved, but solved in so many different ways, by so many different plants and animals, is mind-boggling.

Moreover, living things must have solutions to all these problems, at all times, if they are to remain alive. How did life get it right in the first place?

If we hope to find honest answers, we need to learn to ask better questions—questions based on an understanding of real functions in real systems, with real complexity.

How many generations would be needed to gradually build all the required parts, assemble them, and optimize their performance? Could these systems be assembled gradually if death resulted from getting just one crucial thing wrong? How did the many control systems get their start? Where did the parts come from? How were all the parts properly assembled? Where did the assembly instructions come from? How was the whole finely tuned for just the right capabilities with just the right capacities? How did the amazing process of reproduction come about? If a particular system is necessary for survival, how could an organism build it when it requires that system just to be alive? For example, if it's necessary to control oxygen to be alive, but oxygen controls require many parts, how could the parts be gradually generated and assembled if there was no way to control oxygen in the meantime?

These are not trivial questions. The causal challenges are profound. It's our hope that this book will help you ask better questions and be less satisfied with simplistic answers.

When confronted with a proposed explanation for a given biological part or system, we should ask whether a causal mechanism is invoked in the explanation, or if once the verbal smoke and mirrors are removed, the explanation boils down to "it just happened that way because the system is helpful."

Neither physicians nor engineers are allowed to invoke magic in their work. Neither should biologists.

Can Design Be Accidental?

IN 1859, Charles Darwin titled his book *On the Origin of Species by Means of Natural Selection*, where he purported to explain how new species can arise without the benefit of a designer or engineer. Though he offered a simple, elegant theory, the intuitive *appearance* of design in biology has always presented a stumbling block for those considering his theory.

Few deny that living things appear designed. Dawkins, a leading evolutionist and apologist for atheism, famously said, "Biology is the study of complicated things that give the appearance of having been designed for a purpose."[3] Of course, Dawkins agrees with Darwin that this appearance is an illusion, achieved by the purposeless forces of nature over vast periods of time.

If it's an illusion, it's a persistent one. The "illusion" is now so pervasive that biologists regularly use engineering language to describe the things they see in living systems. Evolutionary biologists describe what they see as "natural genetic engineering." And talk of an "appearance of design" has morphed into saying that the design is real but was caused without purpose or intent (specifically, by the wonder-working powers of mindless natural selection or other evolutionary processes).

But regardless of labels, the basic question remains: Could the apparent design in living systems have happened by accident, or did it require an actual designer? Could any series of unguided errors, over any period of time, achieve the wonders of the human body?

Not all causes are created equal. Different causal forces do different kinds of work and have different limitations. While we'll examine these questions further late in the book, for now it's enough to note that there are two jointly exhaustive classes of causal forces: purely material causes and intelligent causes. In the end, then, the human body must have come about by some combination of forces from either or both these two classes.

Purely material causes work by the physical regularities of the universe, as described by the laws of mathematics and the laws and constants of physics and chemistry.[4] Material causes are repeatable. The same inputs produce the same results. Their repeatability makes experimental science effective. But physical laws can't desire that something be true.

They are incapable of intent or foresight, which limits their creative powers. No one would posit that a fully fueled, launch-ready Atlas rocket was generated by purely mindless material forces.

Purely material processes also encompass random events, such as random mutations to an organism's genetic information. Random events lack desire, intent, and foresight. At the same time, some random mutations may be heritable, so they may be passed on to the organism's offspring.

Unlike random mutations and other purely material processes, intelligent causes act with intention—they perform actions and build artifacts to achieve intended goals and purposes. Intelligent agents visualize an outcome, plan how to achieve it, and execute that plan to make the vision reality. They make specific choices to achieve the desired outcome, guiding the construction, assembly, and activation of the end product. Intelligent agents generate information and give it meaning. They design systems that harness the laws of nature to perform tasks that nature could never otherwise do—to channel the material forces of nature to achieve specific goals. Intelligent agents are able, using forethought and the hard work of design, to build large and coherent systems of systems.

Natural causes can do none of this. They must rely on blind trial and error, with lots and lots of luck. As we'll show, achieving any coherent outcome is profoundly improbable, and achieving all the coherent outcomes required for a human body, in any timeframe, is even more unlikely.

Another distinction is that material causes work mainly from *necessity*. When a set of conditions are present, the outcome will necessarily occur, every time. In contrast, intelligent causes are mainly *contingent*, guided by the choices of an intelligent agent. Contingency is an essential feature of information. Think about a manual for assembling your new lawnmower. No law-like algorithm can generate content of this kind. Rather, the information must be generated by an agent who is free to choose just the letters, words, and diagram options needed to create a meaningful, useful set of instructions—instructions that achieve a specific purpose, the assembly of a complex machine.

This insight is relevant to the question of human origins because information (including assembly instructions) underlies all of life—in DNA, RNA, and epigenetic repositories. Your body is coursing with biological information. Where did that information come from?

Intent is crucial to the creative process, but it's not enough. In a material world, intention must be converted into action, action to rearrange matter and energy to achieve the intended outcome(s). Intent springs from intelligence, and action from agency. Intelligent agents use these two capabilities to reconfigure the natural world to achieve specific desired outcomes. For example, with just a few thousand engineers, matter can be rearranged to make an Atlas rocket, set it on a launch pad, and fuel it, ready to launch a cargo into space. This takes two kinds of activities: *design* (intention) and *fabrication and assembly* (action).

We will make the case that, in the same way, the systems in the human body could only have been achieved through intentional acts.

Natural events may sometimes seem random, and in such cases may be considered contingent—like the actions of a designer—though it is usually more accurate to understand these random natural events as unpredictable rather than truly random. And in fact, where we have enough information about the conditions of a possible random event, we can predict its probability. The outcome of a single die toss is random in the sense of unpredictable, but law-like processes undergird the tumbling of the die, so we can predict that in a million die tosses, a two will come up about one-sixth of the time. This frequency occurs of necessity.

But random events cannot generate any significant amount of new information or functional form, such as we find in the human body. Monkeys randomly banging away on typewriters will never create a lawnmower assembly manual. What they will generate, given enough time, is a bunch of broken typewriters.

No combination of purely material forces can provide either intention or action as defined above. The closest thing is natural selection, in the place of intent, and random mutation, in the place of action. But as we intend to show, this duo is a weak substitute even at its best.

A Third Way?

To THEIR credit, many materialist scientists now openly acknowledge that current material explanations for the origin and diversification of life are insufficient. But so far, most of them have been unwilling to abandon the causal limitations of their deeply cherished materialist assumptions. This puts them in a quandary. The first class of causation (material causes) is insufficient, and the second class of causation (intelligent causes) is unacceptable.

This quandary has spawned a growing movement in biology, known as the "third way," whose proponents seek alternative explanations for the origin of complex biological features. But despite their persuasive arguments against all current forms of Darwinism, they've so far been unable to offer any new explanations that are causally sufficient and able to gain traction in the research community. We suggest that this is because they are searching for an unknown third class of causal force—one able to perform intentional acts, without meaning to.

We wonder whether, and when, they will expand their causal search into the second class of causal force, intentional action, a class of cause with the demonstrated capacity for sophisticated design.

Experiments, Inferences, and Worldviews

HERE WE should address a couple of potential stumbling blocks to fairly considering the evidence and arguments of this book.

First, one might dismiss the design inference when considering the origin of the human body, or the origin of other biological forms, on the grounds that the hypothetical cause can't be reproduced experimentally in a lab. But this is a category error. Because natural causes mainly work from necessity, they often yield well to exploration via *experimental sci-*

ence. Intelligent causes mainly work from contingency (non-necessary causes) and are not generally repeatable,[5] so they yield much better to *inferential science.*

Another class of events that yields less well to laboratory observation is that of non-repeatable past events. Sciences that deal with such past causes—like archaeology, forensics, and anthropology—are inferential because the contingent nature of history necessitates that we infer the timing and causes of events in the past, events we weren't present to see, and that cannot be reproduced in the lab.

Sciences that focus on identifying the causes of past events are called historical sciences, and scientists in these fields regularly make inferences they believe best explain the available data. Historical sciences are just as much science as any other scientific discipline, but they use certain distinct investigative tools and reasoning.

All sciences that focus on events in the past are inferential, and of course this includes the science of biological origins. Living systems arose by way of non-repeatable events in the distant past, so historical biologists are forced to sift through clues, weigh competing explanations, and seek out the explanation that they consider the best. Here we employ precisely this mode of scientific reasoning to infer that some form of intentional action was required for the origin of the human body.

A second stumbling block to fairly considering the argument we lay out here involves worldviews. A worldview is a set of core beliefs, or presuppositions, about the big questions in life—like *What's the nature of the world* or *What's my place in it?* These core beliefs define how we understand what we see and experience, what we believe about ourselves and others, and how we view foundational ideas like truth. It's important to build at least a rudimentary understanding of worldviews before we begin our explorations of the human body, because your worldview will play a critical role in how you view our evidence and reasoning.

Two worldviews vying for dominance in our society take more or less opposite positions on the big questions in life, and lead to more or less opposite outcomes.[6]

The first worldview is materialism, or naturalism.[7] The materialist worldview says that the material universe (i.e., nature) is all that exists. In particular, no force exists outside the universe that is capable of intentionally making a universe or affecting anything "inside" the universe. Since the material stuff of the universe is all that exists, the appearance of something being non-material, like the human mind or the concept of beauty, is an illusion caused by some (perhaps as-yet undiscovered or unexplained) material properties of the universe.

On this view, since the material is the only thing that's real, and science is the study of the material universe, the materialist generally views science as the best (and only true) path to knowledge. Materialism tends to promote science to something like a religion (scientism) and to demote traditional religions to a subfield of anthropology. Materialism also has little room for intentional causation in the natural sciences, and certainly not if the intelligent actor might turn out to be a transcendent God.

So, on this view, life and the vast diversity of life must have been generated by the laws and constants of nature, directly or indirectly, even if we currently have no causally adequate explanation along these lines.

Materialists trust that because science has discovered material causes for many hitherto mysterious things in nature, it will eventually do so for such stubborn mysteries as the origin of the first life, and that even if science doesn't unravel the mystery, we can and should remain confident that the cause was purely material. Materialism also tends to see human free will as illusory. According to materialism, we are the slaves of our environment, our genes, or some combination of the two. Materialism's rise in modern times has been fueled largely by Darwin's theory of evolution, in its original and updated forms.

The second view is theism. Theism holds that a powerful being exists in and through, but also outside, our universe—a being eternal and powerful beyond our imagination. Theism further holds that this being is the creative source of our universe, and that there is ample evidence within the universe that this transcendent being has acted within our universe, performing specific actions in specific places at specific times in our space-time continuum.

Such a being could generate life as we know it and direct the origins of the vast array of living organisms, both extant and extinct. Such a being could easily generate the information contained in DNA, RNA, and epigenetic repositories. Such a being could also create the human person—a creature with an immaterial soul along with free will and moral responsibility. And, notably, to do such things this being must be a designer-engineer on a level that we cannot begin to fathom.

It's hard to imagine any two views further apart. In the materialist view, the material universe generated life. In the theistic view, an immaterial life, God, generated the universe. Materialism says life came from a long and extraordinarily lucky, yet purposeless, series of cosmic accidents. Theism anticipates intention and purpose in life, even as it also makes room for degradation. In the materialist view, all immaterial properties, like the human mind or love, are (rather nice) illusions that must ultimately be reduced to material forces and, in the Darwinian formulation, explained by the struggle for survival. Love is reduced to a survival technique, so survival is the point of love. In the theistic view, love is the point of survival.

In materialism, the universe generates the mind and intelligence (or at least the appearance thereof). In theism, a mind generates the universe. In materialism, life must have occurred as the result of strictly materialistic (and therefore purposeless) processes. Since such processes cannot act with purpose or meaning, their outcomes cannot have purpose or meaning. Given the amount of raw organizational work that's required for life, it's probabilistically impossible that such things could have occurred all at once, so materialist explanations inevitably turn to gradual evolutionary processes. And for the materialist the only causal force able to produce contingency is similarly purposeless: random events like gamma rays hitting a molecule, or a copying error in a nascent information-bearing molecule.

In contrast, theism isn't at all surprised to see that numerous parts must be present all at once, and carefully orchestrated, for various living systems to function at all—that gradualism is not only unnecessary, but also extraordinarily unlikely. Theism expects to see purpose, coordination, optimality, and beauty, because this is the way skilled designers design.

Overall, the theistic view is much less constrained—it is open to both material and intelligent causal forces, so it is free to follow the evidence wherever it goes.

In the question of origins, then, we have an unavoidable worldview collision. Which of these stances is most likely to be true?

We hope to help answer this question by exploring the amazing design of the human body, getting past the surface explanations and the "just-so" stories about human origins to gain a realistic understanding of what it actually takes to be alive—including how the parts work together and the extraordinary depth and breadth of fine tuning in the body.

Only then can we ask realistic questions about how such things came to be.

PART ONE: LIFE

Equilibrium with the environment equals death. Maintaining an internal equilibrium that's different from the surrounding environment involves overcoming a host of challenges. So being alive means solving hard problems, and solving them all the time. Human engineers stand in awe of the capabilities that the human body, and its cells, deploy to be alive.

In this first section we will begin looking at ways nature provides both the potential for life as we know it, and the constraints that make life hard—constraints that are, in effect, trying to kill it.

As with Dorothy on the yellow brick road, it's best to start at the beginning. How does life work in the very small—in microscopic terms, at the level of atoms and molecules? Then, how does a large body, like the human body, build on that foundation? Most of what we do wouldn't be possible if we were just an amorphous blob of thirty trillion cells. What's needed is architecture. And lots of structure.

1. Being Alive

Nature, in order to carry out the marvellous operations in animals and plants, has been pleased to construct their organized bodies with a very large number of machines.... Machines will be eventually found not only unknown to us but also unimaginable by our mind.

—Marcello Malpighi, 1697[1]

I (Steve) was still mostly a youth myself, yet there I was, waiting for my first daughter to come into the world. It was a long night of painful labor, but around seven in the morning, after much weeping and gnashing of teeth (mostly by me), out poked a little head and a new life entered the world.

It's wonderful to witness such a thing—a new human leaving the warmth and nurture of mother and beginning a new life of exploration and discovery. A miracle of life.

Only many years later, after a couple more births, did I begin to explore just how special a new life is, and exactly how challenging life is from an engineering perspective.

We're surrounded by living things. Life flourishes almost everywhere we look here on planet Earth, even in remarkably inhospitable places. Perhaps because life is so common in our world, it's easy to lose sight of how tenuous—in a sense, how unnatural—it is.

The Greatest Discontinuity

Some scientists believe there must be a gradual continuum from non-living to "fully alive," but this is a presupposition starving for evidence. No one has ever seen something that was only partly alive. Alive, but dying, yes. Partly alive, no. Far from a continuum from non-life to life, everything we observe about life tells us life and non-life are not merely quantitatively different, but qualitatively distinct. As biologist Michael Denton so keenly points out, "Between a living cell and the most highly ordered non-biological system... there is a chasm as vast and absolute as it is possible to conceive."[2] Or, as he likes to say in his live presentations, "Life is the greatest discontinuity in the universe."[3]

In our experience, life always comes from life—never from non-life. No laboratory has observed life emerging from non-life, by any gradual or other process, and no one has any idea how to make something alive, even if all the parts are in place. (Dr. Frankenstein apparently had it figured out, but sadly, his notebooks were lost in the fire.)

Defining what life is proves challenging. Is it a substance? A quantity? A process? A force? An idea? Something altogether indefinable, and possibly unknowable? It turns out that life, like so much of what we experience, is easier to describe than to define or explain. But this isn't a total loss. Descriptions of life are themselves fascinating. Life has many curious properties, some of which we'll explore in this book.

Life is set apart from non-life in a host of dramatic ways. For example, all living organisms, from the simplest bacteria to humans, must maintain an internal equilibrium that is different from the surrounding environment. This involves chemical makeup, physical organization, energy production and consumption, and many other properties. This is obviously a taller order for humans (with more interesting solutions) than it is for bacteria, but the essential problems are the same.

The fancy word for this property is homeostasis, which means "staying the same." Every living organism must maintain its separate equilibrium. If it can't, it dies. Equilibrium with the surrounding environment equals death.

For humans, homeostasis involves thousands of activities to maintain precise balances across dozens of chemicals (like water, oxygen, carbon dioxide, sugar, sodium, potassium, calcium, iron, copper, and manganese) across hundreds of processes to control energy, temperature, blood pressure, and many other life-critical factors.

The laws of physics and chemistry drive everything unrelentingly toward equilibrium with the environment. In contrast, life insists upon a separate and distinct equilibrium. This requires continuous energy and precise regulation in a complex and coherent choreography. Life must control its own outcomes in the face of forces working constantly to destroy it.

Life has another extraordinary capability. It can reproduce itself. Living things make copies of themselves that can make copies of themselves, and they do this from the inside (though sometimes with outside help, as from their mother). The copies must then become self-sufficient to the point that they, too, can reproduce. The number of physical problems that must be overcome to make this happen are far beyond what science currently understands, though we'll explore certain parts of the process in Part Five.

No non-living object in the known universe can achieve both homeostasis and reproduction, and, notably, this includes anything designed and engineered by even the best human engineers.

The evidence tells us that these capabilities are required for life. They are *prerequisites* for life, not *outcomes* of it. There is no way for a creature to become alive first, then find a way to solve these problems. Without solutions to all these problems, life cannot exist.

At the Center of Life: The Cell

YOUR BODY is made of systems of systems of systems. At the foundational level are the trillions of cells that make up a human body. Each cell must follow the rules imposed on it by the laws of nature.

In Darwin's day, a cell was thought to be a mere bag of chemicals with unknown function.[4] Since then, science has shown that the cell is an extraordinarily complex factory—with its own information storage and processing facilities, energy production plants, and manufacturing plants for the thousands of structures and molecular-sized machines

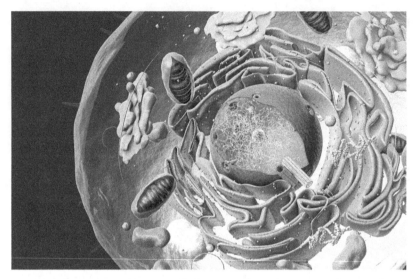

Figure 1.1. A typical human cell, showing cell membrane, cytoplasm, and organelles. As complex as the illustration appears, it is a vastly simplified representation. For a cell to be alive, it must solve numerous problems, and to do so it must contain an enormously complex, finely tuned factory.

that perform the functions needed for life. Every cell must have all of the following:

Containment

Each human cell is enclosed by a thin, double-layer wall called the cell membrane, which defines the boundaries of the cell, separating it from other cells and the outside world. It keeps what's needed inside and what's harmful outside. Obviously, the various chemicals and structures of the cell wouldn't be of much use if they could randomly wander off.

Specialized Gates

But a simple wall isn't enough. Just as a car needs gas and has to get rid of exhaust, each cell must bring in new supplies of the materials it needs, like oxygen, water, and sugar, and get rid of the toxic byproducts of its chemical reactions, like carbon dioxide and ammonia. So the cell wall incorporates gates that are tuned to allow just the needed raw materials to enter the cell, and the toxic waste materials to be purged. These gates can be either active (like pumps) or passive (like pipes, typically with valves to control flow). The gates also must be specific enough to prevent the wrong materials from passing in either direction. In addition, some chemicals, like water, can easily pass through the cell membrane, but again, these are only the ones needed for cellular viability.

The space within the cell membrane is filled with a fluid called cytoplasm, made up of water with chemicals like sodium and potassium dissolved in it.

The volume of water inside the cell applies pressure against the cell membrane, just like the air in a balloon. The more water in the cell, the higher the volume and the more pressure it applies. And just like a balloon, if there's too much water in the cell, the membrane will tear, killing the cell.

The water outside the cell, which surrounds and bathes it, contains many of the same chemicals, though most are at different concentrations from what's needed inside the cell. For example, the potassium level in the cytoplasm is much higher than in the water outside the cell, and the sodium level in the cytoplasm is much lower than in the water outside the cell. Maintaining this (and many other differences) at all times is critical to life.

Chemical Controls

Internal chemical balances must be maintained at all times, so the cell needs ways to control its internal levels of water, oxygen, carbon dioxide, glucose, hydrogen ions, sodium, and potassium, as well as other compounds for manufacturing amino acids, which are in turn necessary for DNA, RNAs, and the various cellular machinery. The right balances are critical and must be maintained within tight tolerances, regardless of the concentrations outside the cell.

Because concentrations inside and outside the cell are different, the cell works against natural forces like diffusion and osmosis to maintain the correct balances.

This is a complicated problem. The cell has to control both its water content and chemical concentrations, but these affect each other. So the cell has to coordinate these controls to work together to maintain the right balances.

Structure

Merely having a cell wall doesn't ensure a useable shape, so the cell also needs internal framing. Just as your body has a bony skeleton to support its organs, your cells have something called a cytoskeleton, made up of intermediate filaments, microfilaments, and microtubules that together provide the structural parts inside the cell to support its shape. Interestingly, they also provide pathways for specialized transport proteins to travel along, sort of like railroad tracks.

Modular Subunits

Compartmentalized subunits called organelles are suspended within the cytoplasm. The organelles house factories filled with molecular machinery to harvest and process raw materials, break down complex molecules into their parts, and build up other complex molecules from the raw materials.

A Transportation System

A human cell is large compared to its many millions of molecular parts, so it's necessary to actively move materials from place to place within the cell. Materials simply floating from place to place would be too slow and inefficient.

Much like cargo loaded into containers and trucked across town or shipped across the ocean, materials are loaded into sacs called vesicles, which are matched to motor proteins headed in the right direction. Motor proteins are specialized for about forty different types of cargo. Some motor proteins (kinesins) travel one way along the cytoskeleton, while others (dyneins) travel in the opposite direction, so the cell matches the right motor proteins for each payload and target destination.

In a meticulously choreographed operation, an organelle dumps outbound materials into a vesicle; then a motor protein picks it up and pulls it to its destination, where the target organelle membrane merges with the vesicle, in effect opening the cargo container and absorbing its contents.

How the cell knows what materials to carry where and when remains a mystery. But it's a good thing it works as well as it does, or you wouldn't be here to read about it.

Energy Production

Cells work hard, and that takes lots of energy. Energy-bearing chemicals must be converted to usable energy packets, which must then be consumed to perform the many tasks of maintaining life.

The mitochondria are the factories where your cells generate energy. In a process called cellular respiration, they use a series of specialized proteins to break down an energy-rich sugar, glucose, in the presence of oxygen, to release and harness that energy. This involves *catabolism*, the breaking of complex molecules into simpler ones. (And, of course, each molecular machine must have the right machinery to consume the available energy.)

Materials Production

If the cell had to rely on its environment for all the chemicals and complex molecules it needs, it wouldn't last long. Given the complex molecular machines that are essential to its life, the cell must have a way to convert the simpler chemicals it can get from the environment into the more complex chemical building blocks it needs to sustain life. The process of building up complex molecules from simpler ones is called anabolism.

Information

The production of virtually everything in the cell is based on digital information, encoded in DNA and other complex molecules such as various RNAs.

The nucleus holds this information and is the "brains" of the cell. The nucleus of each of your cells contains twenty-three pairs of chromosomes, each made up of long DNA molecules. Each DNA molecule consists of two separate strands of chemicals bonded together that spiral into a double helix shape. Inside the DNA molecules are the genes which contain much of the information for life—including the specifications for the complex molecules and molecular machinery the cell needs.

Information Processing

Information is no good unless it can be accurately decoded and processed. And this takes a lot of specialized molecular machinery, working in a precise choreography.

To get the information to make a protein or a duplicate copy of itself, the DNA molecule has to be "unzipped." Special enzymes called helicases break the hydrogen bonds that hold the double helix together, allowing the DNA molecule to unwind.

If the cell is making a protein, an enzyme called RNA polymerase jumps in to join amino acids together to form something called messenger RNA (mRNA), which is a copy of the specification in the DNA. mRNA is transported from the nucleus (where the DNA is located), through the nuclear membrane, to a ribosome where other enzymes are used to assemble the protein.

In a separate process, when the cell needs to make an identical copy of the DNA molecule, it uses DNA polymerase and two other enzymes.

Proteins as the Cell's Workhorses

MUCH AS cells are the core elements of the body, proteins are the core elements of the cell. Proteins are amazing, molecular-scale machines that construct, assemble, disassemble, join, cut, paste, copy, catalyze, enclose, and transport other molecules. Some proteins are essential for making energy. Others consume energy. Some do both. In fact, proteins do almost all the work in your cells.

In the "standard genetic code" they are made from an "alphabet" of twenty different amino acid "letters." Each letter is a complex molecule made of hydrogen, oxygen, carbon, and nitrogen (and in two cases, sulfur), and each is in a unique physical configuration, with unique chemical and electrical properties. (A twenty-first amino acid contains selenium, but it involves different coding and translation mechanisms and is beyond our scope.)

A protein is made of a string of these amino acid "letters," linked together in a specified order unique to that particular protein. Like functional software code, just any order of letters and symbols won't do; rather, a precise order is needed. Amino acids are connected end to end, like a chain, where the length of chain varies from one peptide or protein type to the next, from three (for glutathione, the smallest known functional chain, which is technically called a peptide rather than a protein) to 34,350 (for titin, which is the longest known protein chain in the body). Human proteins average around 480 amino acids in length.

The precise order of amino acids in a protein is substantially determined in the DNA—in the gene that codes for that particular protein. DNA uses a four-character alphabet, with values represented by the letters T, C, A, and G. These letters are arranged to form three-letter words. These three-letter words are called codons and specify to the translation machinery the type of amino acid to add. This set of rules is termed the genetic code. All but one of the amino acids are specified by at least two different codons, and there are also three-letter words/codons that mean "start" and "stop." As the DNA is processed linearly, the "start" and "stop" codons tell the translation machinery where to begin and end the linear chain of amino acids.[5]

When the specific order of a string of amino acids is just right, the chemical properties (primarily hydrophobic interactions) and locations of the amino acids enable the protein to spontaneously fold (much of the time) into a stable three-dimensional shape. Sometimes proteins need help folding, and this job is facilitated by a special protein called a chaperone. The protein's three-dimensional shape, together with the relative locations of its various bumps, notches, crevasses, and electro-chemical attractions, determines the functions that the particular protein can perform.

It's been shown experimentally that functional protein shapes are extremely rare among the set of all possible amino acid sequences. The overwhelming majority of possible sequences will not fold into a stable protein shape, and therefore are unlikely to provide a useful function.[6] And, of all the sequences that do fold into a stable shape, only a very few will perform a task that's useful to a given organism.

Illustrating this reality is the fact that while the potential medical benefits of designing new proteins are immensely attractive and therefore have attracted considerable funding and research efforts, progress in designing proteins that are both new and useful has nevertheless been extraordinarily difficult. The design challenge is daunting. Because the sequence space is very large and the number of stable folds (possible solutions) very small, and because the complexity of the physical, chemical, and electrical "shape" of the fold renders it difficult to calculate, this problem is enormously computation intensive. In effect, it's an immensely large search and optimization problem, which grows exponentially as the length of the amino acid sequence increases.[7]

Inventing a useful new fold is a bit like finding a molecule-sized needle in a galaxy-sized haystack.

The obvious question, then, is this: If it's so hard to intentionally design a protein, how could any non-intentional cause overcome the combinatorial search space for even one large protein, in the entire history of the universe, much less for all the proteins in the human body (or in all the other living organisms we see)?

Enzyme Cascades

MOST OF the chemicals the body needs are fairly stable. They don't break down or interact with other chemicals well, or quickly. If you put them in a test tube and swirl them around, very little of interest will happen.

This presents a problem for life, because almost all of life's essential processes require rapid changes in a variety of chemicals.

Some of the chemicals must be broken apart (catabolism). Others must be assembled (anabolism). Without help, such reactions would take days, years, or might never happen.

For example, a glucose molecule contains high-energy bonds, but these bonds are stable and are not readily released under normal circumstances. The glucose molecule must be broken apart step by step to release its embedded energy. No cell could survive long without a substantial supply of energy, so this reaction must happen quickly and predictably.

The energy in glucose is stored in stable molecular bonds so it doesn't get randomly released into the bodily environment, or even into the gastrointestinal tract (to be assaulted by acids). Instead, it stays intact until exactly where and when it's needed—when it gets to the energy factory in an individual cell, which has exactly the needed machinery to release (and put to good use) the glucose molecule's energy.

Enzymes are a special class of proteins that come to the rescue. They greatly speed up (catalyze) certain reactions, which is what the cell needs for pretty much all its internal activities. Specific enzymes catalyze specific reactions, so the cell needs a lot of different enzyme types. For example, in human cells, processing glucose to release and use its energy involves three major parts: glycolysis, the citric acid (Krebs) cycle, and the electron transport chain. Each part involves specific enzymes, many of which are tissue specific. It takes more than twenty-three distinct enzymes (for which there are often tissue-specific versions) working cooperatively to process glucose. The molecule that results from the first catalyzed reaction becomes the input for the second, and so on to the final result.

An enzyme cascade is a bit like an assembly line where each worker has a specialized skill for his particular step in the assembly process. That worker and no other can perform that step. Switch the workers around and the assembly process grinds to a halt. Only when each step happens correctly, and in the right order, does the final product roll off the line.

Further complicating matters for glucose, each of the three major processes for extracting its energy happens in a different place in the cell, so transport is needed to move intermediate products between locations. Notably, some of the intermediate molecules are toxic, so the whole process must be tightly controlled to prevent toxic chemicals from building up and killing the cell.

Several of the best known (and most toxic) human poisons work by interrupting a part of this central energy process. For example, cyanide blocks just a single enzyme in the chain, while arsenic blocks multiple enzymes in the chain. These poisons are especially nasty because every cell in the body uses this same process, so they will kill any cell they come in contact with. And when the cascade is interrupted at any point in the process, energy production fails and the cell dies. When enough cells die, the body dies.

We'll explore another example of an enzyme cascade in the chapter on blood clotting.

The Cell's Protein Machinery

Human cells can make numerous different proteins. While it's believed that about 20,000 human genes code for proteins, in many cases a single gene can generate a potentially large number of different proteins, so no one really knows how many different proteins are in the body. Estimates range from a few tens of thousands to several million.[8]

But all these proteins are not needed in every cell at all times, so the cell uses internal controls to determine whether and when to build each of these proteins. Simply put, each cell determines when a particular protein is needed, and makes more of it, as needed. If this weren't the case, the cell would expend virtually all its energy and raw materials generating proteins that aren't needed.

The specific shape of a folded protein will expose some of its amino acids to nearby molecules. The specific mechanical and electro-chemical properties of the protein provide a precise key-in-lock fit with one or more other specific molecules, such as molecular oxygen (O_2), glucose, an amino acid, or another complex protein shape like a hormone or neurohormone. This points to thousands of chicken-or-egg problems evolutionists must confront. So, for example, which came first, the neurohormone or the neurohormone receptor?

> Almost all the sensing and signaling in the body is based on the hand-in-glove fit of various molecules to protein active sites. It's essential for every control system in the body—from controlling respiration and blood pressure, to controlling the sugar and salt content of the blood. The total number of these specific sensor-receptors is unknown, but this book will touch on dozens of them.

Often proteins are composed of multiple units (multimers). The final structure might be an assemblage of four peptide chains (two from one gene and two from another gene, what biologists call a dimer of dimers). In other cases, unique proteins may be near other unique proteins to create complexes. Though a detailed discussion of multimers and complexes is beyond the scope of this book, much of the molecular machinery we discuss in these pages, including below, are multimers or part of a macromolecular complex. For an example of a multimer (dimer of dimers), see the discussion of hemoglobin in Chapter 6.

Now let's look at three of the cell's many thousands of specialized protein machines—specifically, three of the most interesting and best understood in the human body. These examples should give at least a taste of how astonishing the human cell is when its thousands of different molecular machines are considered together.

ATP Synthase

As NOTED above, the cell uses numerous distinct enzymes to release the energy from a glucose molecule. The final enzyme in this chain is ATP synthase. It's this final step that captures most of the energy that was stored in the original glucose molecule.

ATP synthase is an astoundingly complex, life-critical molecular machine that looks and works like a turbine. It's attached to the inner membrane of the mitochondrion and has all the parts of a human-designed rotary motor, including a rotor, stator, and camshaft. Protons flowing into a mitochondrion have to pass through intricate channels in the ATP synthase, which causes it to spin. Below the motor are six large subunits. As the driveshaft spins, a bump on the camshaft causes these lower subunits to open and expose a specially shaped and charged crevice, which allows a molecule called adenosine diphosphate (ADP) to enter. As the shaft rotates, the protein causes an additional phosphate group (PO_4) to attach to the ADP, turning it into adenosine triphosphate (ATP), the primary energy molecule in the cell. As the shaft continues to rotate, the ATP molecule is ejected from the protein for use in one of the other molecular machines in the cell.

A static illustration of ATP synthase can't possibly do it justice. To grasp the exquisite design of this machine, watch one or more animated online videos featuring this molecular wonder. Our favorite as of this writing is at YouTube under the title "Molecular Machines–ATP Synthase: The Power Plant of the Cell."[9]

Each molecular machine that uses energy must incorporate a special ATPase domain, which extracts the energy from the third phosphate bond in ATP, converting it back into ADP, its lower energy form.

Here's how it works: Each cell has about a million sodium/potassium pumps embedded in its cell membrane. These tiny molecular machines must work really hard, all the time, to keep the cell alive. Since the water inside the cell has a high concentration of potassium ions (K^+) and a low concentration of sodium ions (Na^+), and the water outside the cell has a low concentration of K^+ ions and a high concentration of Na^+ ions, diffusion makes these ions move across the cell membrane in the opposite directions—K^+ ions out of the cell, Na^+ ions into the cell—to try to equalize the concentrations on either side.[10] In addition, the fluid inside the cell contains a high concentration of protein compared to the fluid outside the cell, so water must move into the cell by osmosis to equalize the total concentrations of chemicals on either side of the membrane. Due to this rapid movement of water into the cell and long before equilibration of the ions can take place, the cell will literally die by "explosion."[11] To prevent this, the cell uses a Na/K pump which contains an ATPase domain (consuming the energy from ATP) to constantly force Na^+ ions out of the cell and bring K^+ ions back in—against their natural tendency to go in the opposite direction.[12] This maintains both the proper chemical balance and the water content (volume).

> One machine turns ADP into ATP; another turns ATP back into ADP—a complete energy cycle. One system infuses ADP with energy; another, encoded separately in the DNA, uses that energy. This cycle can ramp up production quickly, as needed, since nothing new needs to be manufactured—only rapidly recycled.
>
> Notice, too, that it takes two machines working together to achieve function. Neither would be useful without the other.
>
> If that's not challenge enough for any causal theory of origins, here's another: some of the enzymes needed to extract ATP from glucose must consume energy (in the form of ATP) to perform the chemical change at their step in the process. Thus, to generate ATP, ATP is required. There is no other way known to make ATP except by consuming ATP, and this presents a causal quandary known as causal circularity. The product of the reaction is required to start the reaction itself. So where do you get the ATP required to make the first ATP? There are many similar examples in biology.

Figure 1.2. Kinesin motor protein.

In fact, when you're at rest, about one-quarter of your body's energy needs are taken up by these hard-working pumps. Each of your cells has about a million of these pumps, and you have about 30 trillion or more cells, all trying to maintain their chemical balance. That's 30,000,000, 000,000,000,000 (3 x 10^{19}) sodium-potassium pumps working, even when you're sleeping.

Kinesin

ANOTHER OF the hardest-working proteins in the body is a cute little guy called kinesin. Kinesin is a motor protein that transports cargo along microtubules from one place in the cell to another.

In a way reminiscent of a person walking, kinesin has two "legs" that attach to the microtubules in the cell. (See Figure 1.2.) One leg detaches, swings forward, and then reattaches. Then the other leg detaches and swings forward, et cetera. Kinesin contains an ATPase domain, so it consumes ATP to power this walking motion.

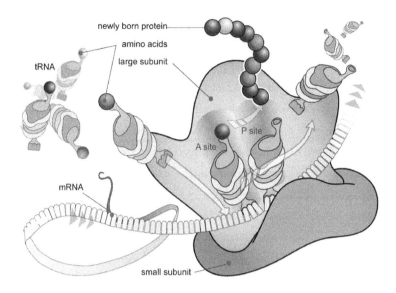

newly born protein
amino acids
tRNA
large subunit
P site
A site
mRNA
small subunit

Figure 1.3. A ribosome, showing the input string (mRNA) and the output string, a newly born protein.

The "body" of the kinesin has a specialized molecular clamp that attaches to a vesicle. As the kinesin walks down the microtubule, it pulls the much larger vesicle with its cargo inside to its proper destination. It's amazing to watch an animation of the kinesin in action.[13] Human cells build around forty different types of kinesin, with most of the differences in the types of clamps, or adapters, that attach to different types of cargo. In nerve cells kinesins transport mitochondria and vesicles containing neurotransmitters from the cell body along the axon to the synapse. Somehow, kinesins know exactly what they're supposed to do: pick up the right cargo from the right source, take it to the right destination, and drop it off.

Ribosomes

THE RIBOSOME is a large molecular machine made of over 300 proteins and rRNA. It's a critical part of the cell's information processing, making up the last step in converting the information encoded in the DNA into proteins (see Figure 1.3).

Messenger RNA (mRNA) is a copy of the nucleotide sequence in the DNA. The mRNA molecule is transported out of the cell nucleus (through the nuclear membrane) to a ribosome. The ribosome pulls in the mRNA, reading its linear sequence of codons. As it comes through, each codon is paired with an appropriate transfer RNA (tRNA), which carries the associated amino acid. The ribosome pulls the amino acid off the tRNA and attaches it to the previous one, thus stringing the amino acids together into a protein chain, in the exact sequence specified in the DNA. Once again, an animation of the process is helpful for understanding how this amazing machine works.[14] How many different actions must be properly orchestrated for this to work?

A typical human cell contains around 10 million ribosomes.

DNA contains large amounts of information, information essential for life. But as with any information source, the information is useless without a means of decoding and processing it. The ribosome serves this role, but the ribosome is itself made up mainly of proteins, which can only be produced by a ribosome. So the information-processing machinery cannot be constructed without the information that it must process itself.

Here, then, is yet another chicken-or-egg problem. Which came first: the information or the ribosome? How could the information originate when it has no value without the processing machinery? And how could the processing machinery originate when there's no information to build it? This is another case of causal circularity. As with all biological systems, the human body contains many such causal circularities.

Many human-made systems have similar chicken-or-egg problems, which is why engineers usually build in a separate subsystem to jump-start their systems. The "jump-starter" sets up the initial conditions needed to launch the system. This is exactly how a gas-powered car uses the battery and starter motor to start its engine.

Engineering Hurdles

To be alive, each cell must perform thousands of complicated tasks, with both functional and process coherence. This includes all the capabilities discussed earlier in this chapter: containment, special-purpose gates, chemical sensing and controls (for many different chemicals), supply chain and transport, energy production and use, materials production, and information and information processing.

What does it take to make these work? Designing solutions to problems like this is hard, especially given two additional requirements.

The first, *orchestration*, means the cell has to get all the right things done in the right order at the right times. The activities of millions of parts must be coordinated. To this end, the cell actively sequences activities, signals various parts about what to do, starts and stops various machinery, and monitors progress.

The second requirement is *reproduction*. As if being alive weren't difficult enough, some of the body's cells must be able to generate new cells. This imposes a daunting set of additional design problems. Each new cell needs a high-fidelity copy of the parent cell's internal information, all the molecular machines needed for life, and a copy of the cell's structure, including the organelles and microtubules. And it needs to know which internal operating system it should use. Once these are all in place, the cell walls must constrict to complete the enclosure for the new cell, without allowing the internals to spill out.

Somehow cells solve all these problems. Each cell is a vast system of systems, with millions of components, machines, and processes, which are coherent, interdependent, tightly coordinated, and precisely tuned— all essential characteristics of the cell if it's to be alive rather than dead.

To better grasp the engineering sophistication of human cells, we encourage you to watch a four-minute online video by the Human Protein Atlas titled "The Human Cell."[15] (At some point this video will be superseded by a new and improved video on the subject, so interested readers are also encouraged to research on the web for newer resources.)

There remains no plausible, causally adequate hypothesis for how any series of accidents, no matter how lucky and no matter how much time is given, could accomplish such things. Presently it even lies beyond the reach of our brightest human designers to create them. Human engineers have no idea how to match the scope, precision, and efficiencies of even a single such cell, much less organisms composed of many cellular systems of systems, each system composed of millions or billions of cells.

When Darwin first espoused his theory, none of the cell's complexity was known, so the idea of making a cell seemed simple. If the cell merely contains "jelly-like protoplasm"—well, how hard can it be to make that? Science and medicine (and engineering) have exploded that simplistic view of the cell. We can now better assess the causal challenges imposed by cellular function. With this more realistic view of what it takes for a cell to live and work properly, we can ask harder questions and demand more rigor from those who would explain its origin.

2. TRILLIONS OF CELLS WORKING TOGETHER: THE BODY

Life is not found in atoms or molecules or genes as such, but in the organization, not in symbiosis but in synthesis.
—EDWIN CONKLIN[1]

IN MY FIRST RESEARCH JOB, I (STEVE) WORKED ON A TEAM TASKED with automating sawmill machinery. Aside from the research work, I enjoyed hanging out in the organized chaos that was a factory floor. There's just something about the constant activity, noise, and sawdust flying everywhere. Saws of all shapes and sizes, slicing, shaping, chopping. Conveyor belts crisscrossing everywhere, carrying logs, lumber, and scraps from one machine to another. Sawdust collected by huge suction pumps and blown through big metal pipes to other machines for processing. Electricity for running the motors, water for cooling the blades, steam for heating the kilns, and computers for keeping track of everything. Somehow, through it all, logs went in on one side and green lumber came out the other, to go to the kilns for drying, then to the planers for final shaping, then to shipping and on to the lumber store. To build a home for a family somewhere.

To make the decisions and to keep it all running, there were sawyers and machine operators; millwrights, electricians, pipefitters, and tinbenders; packing and shipping crews; forklift and sorter drivers; cleanup crews; foremen, shift supervisors, and plant managers. To make it possible, there were also foresters, loggers, truck drivers, train operators, utility companies, property managers, and investors.

There was a certain ingenuity and elegance to the operation. Every part and every person had a defined set of jobs to do, and when each one was doing the right things in the right ways at the right times, the plant operated smoothly, turning raw materials into quality products quickly and efficiently.

It's a well-established principle that diversification of skills and tasks is essential for running a large and complex organization, or to efficiently achieve any large and complex task.

This is just as true for large multi-cellular organisms. So, just as a sawmill works only when all the workers and machines perform their specialized tasks in a timely and skillful manner, your body needs its trillions of cells doing their varied tasks correctly and on time.

Hard Problems on Top of Hard Problems

As we saw in the previous chapter, to be alive every cell needs solutions to a complicated set of problems—containment, gates, controls, structure, transport, energy, information, and reproduction. Zooming out from a single cell, the human body as a whole is made up of around thirty trillion cells (a figure that varies widely with an individual's size). It needs to solve all the same kinds of problems that a cell does, plus quite a few more. And it needs new ways to solve old problems, ways completely different from how the same problems were solved at the cellular level.

For example, a single-celled organism is like a microscopic island of life. The cell gets what it needs and gets rid of what it doesn't need from its surrounding environment. In contrast, a large multi-cellular organism (like you) is more like a continent with a deep and dark interior. Most of the cells reside deep in the interior with no direct access to the body's surrounding environment. For a multicellular organism, then, harvesting the raw materials its cells need and getting rid of toxic byproducts becomes a major logistical problem.

Several hundred such problems must be solved for a complex body to be alive. And many of the solutions to these basic problems generate new problems that must also be solved, or that constrain other solutions in critical ways. The result is that for a complex body to be alive, thousands of deeply interconnected problems must be solved, and many of them solved at all times, or life will fail.

Additionally, many of the problems the body faces are much more complex than those solved in any individual cell. For example, while it takes impressive engineering for cells to sense their environment (a process not well understood), sensing poses a considerably greater engineering challenge for a human body, since it involves much more sophisticated forms of sensing—like vision, hearing, taste, smell, and the fine-touch sensing in your hands.

The bottom line is that, as hard as it is for a cell to maintain life, it's much harder for an organism with a complex body plan like yours.

Hard Problems Take Clever Solutions

TOGETHER, THE many thousands of problems the body must solve for survival and reproduction require many thousands of ingenious solutions. Most of these solutions need special-purpose equipment across all levels of the body plan, from specifically adapted molecular machinery (like hemoglobin molecules) to specialized cells (like red blood cells) to tissues (like bone marrow) to whole body systems (like the cardiovascular system). This may involve hundreds of thousands of parts, replicated in millions of places.

Solutions to this class of problems always exhibit four interesting characteristics:

Specialization

It takes the right parts to make a working whole. Each part must perform a function with respect to the larger system. Each part must be made of the right materials, fine tuned to precise tolerances, and equipped with suitable interfaces with the other parts. This is a design principle known as separation of concerns. Virtually every designed object in human experience is based on this design strategy. And this appears to be equally true in biological systems, including virtually every capability in the human body.

Organization

The parts must be in the right places, arranged and interconnected to enable the function of the whole. Each part must work with the other parts in an integrated way. The parts are often made of different materials, where a material is chosen for how its particular properties support the specific needs of that particular part and how it must function in light of the whole. This is a design principle known as the rule of composition. It counterbalances the separation of concerns principle. Separation of concerns breaks large problems into subproblems that are (slightly) easier to solve, while the rule of composition puts the solutions to the subproblems (the parts) together such that the function of the whole is achieved.

Integration

The parts must have exactly those interfaces that enable the parts to work together. With bones, this obviously involves their shapes, especially at their connection and articulation points (the joints). For other body systems this can involve structural support, alignment, shock absorption, gating and transport systems, electrical signaling, chemical signaling, exchange of complex information, and integrated logic.

Coordination

The parts must be coordinated such that each performs its respective function or functions at the right time. This usually requires one or more control systems, either active or passive, and usually some form of sensing and communication between the parts and the controls. This property is achieved by orchestration or choreography, which differ in the ways the controls are achieved, the former by a more centralized approach and the latter by a more distributed approach. In an old Chevy pickup, this function for the engine is achieved by a camshaft. In ATP Synthase, this is also achieved by a camshaft.

Because human engineers like to be efficient, they often design generic parts that can be reused across a wide variety of systems, like nuts and bolts in mechanical systems, or shared libraries of subroutines in software engineering. This idea is also seen in some of the body's systems, especially at the lower levels of the design hierarchy, which is also where it is most often seen in human-engineered systems.

In designing a complex system, all four of the above factors must be considered across the whole when designing each of the parts.

When a system has all the right parts, in all the right places, made of the right materials, with the right specifications, doing their respective functions, at all the right times, to achieve an overall, system-level function that none of the parts can do on its own, you have what is known as a coherent system. Coherence, in this sense, is a functional requirement for all non-trivial systems. Moreover, in life the systems are never standalone—there are always interdependencies between and among the various component systems and parts. The human body is composed of coherent, interdependent systems.

Of course, each part in a larger system may be a system itself, composed of specialized parts, which may also be systems composed of specialized parts, and so on, forming a hierarchy of design. As with most human-designed artifacts, living systems consist of layers of systems and subsystems—a system of systems. This is exemplified in the human body. (See Figure 2.1.)

The Scope of the Body's Solutions

It takes a lot of work to keep a sawmill running. Logs need to be obtained, sorted, and brought in. Cut lumber needs to be taken away for further processing. The motors need electricity. The saw blades need to be changed out and sharpened. The workers need coffee. Lots of coffee. All these require various systems within the larger system.

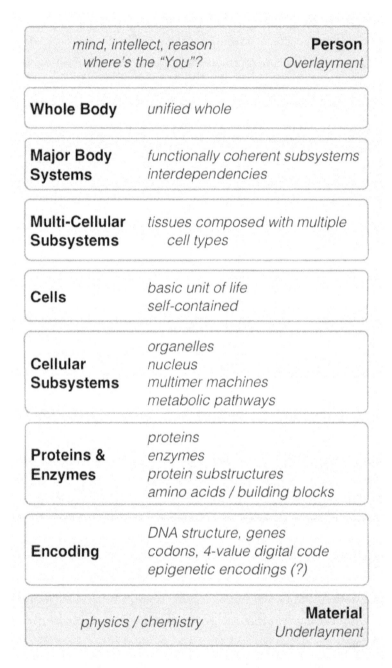

Figure 2.1. Hierarchical layers of the human body.

Similarly, to keep your cells alive and working properly, your body requires eleven major organ systems[2] to distribute, dispose, defend, generate energy, and perform other crucial tasks. The systems and their roles:

- The respiratory system takes in the oxygen (O_2) your cells need and gets rid of excess carbon dioxide (CO_2).

- The gastrointestinal (digestive) system takes in the water, sugar, fat, protein, salt, vitamins, and minerals your cells need.

- The renal/urinary system rids your body of excess nitrogen (ammonia, urea) and helps maintain your blood pressure and control your body's water and salt content.

- The cardiovascular system pumps blood throughout your body to provide "just in time" delivery of supplies to every organ no matter what you're doing. It's also critical for managing temperature, dissipating excess heat, and distributing chemical signals throughout the body.

- The integumentary system (skin) protects your body from the outside world while helping control your temperature through sweating. It continually replenishes itself from the inside out and is remarkably good at repairing itself when it gets cut or scraped.

- The skeletal system (bones) provides support and protection for many of your vital organs (like your brain, spinal cord, lungs, and heart) and is the framework for the muscles. Its structures, organization, and proportions enable an amazing range of movement and activity.

- The motor system (muscles) allows the body to move around, stay balanced, and handle things. It's capable of a wide range of strength demands yet possesses extraordinarily fine controls.

- The nervous system (nerves and brain) allows the body to sense your surroundings, maintain your body's vital functions, and control your activities. It also allows you to be awake and aware—to think, communicate, imagine, and create.

- The immune/lymphatic system protects you from invading pathogens.
- The endocrine system sends out hormones to regulate things like your metabolism and growth.
- The reproductive system, male and female, enables new human life.

Each of these is a specialized subsystem in the body. The body needs all of them, organized properly, and coordinated to remarkably fine tolerances. In turn, each of these subsystems is a complete system, itself composed of many specialized subsystems and parts, organized in specific ways, and precisely coordinated.

Working Tissues

TISSUES ARE the next level down in the body's hierarchical design. Tissues are groups of cells that come in different varieties with different functions. Many tissues are made up of multiple types of cells interwoven or interlaced in interesting ways to achieve an overall function.

There are four basic types of tissues in your body. Most organ systems are made up of a combination of these tissues: epithelial tissue, connective tissue, muscle tissue, and nerve tissue.

Epithelial tissue is what separates you from your surroundings. It's the top layer of your skin and forms most of the barrier walls, or containers, in the body. It lines your respiratory, gastrointestinal, and genitourinary tracts. It also makes up the glands in your body. The epithelial cells that line your blood vessels are called endothelial cells.

Connective tissue provides the structure and support to stabilize the body's parts and hold them in place. Bones, blood, cartilage, tendons, ligaments, fat layers, and an array of interwoven fibers that hold organs and other tissues in place are all connective tissues.

Muscle tissue works by contracting. Your heart and skeletal muscles pump blood and let you move around and handle things. Smooth muscles surround your blood vessels, respiratory, gastrointestinal, and genitourinary tracts, and help them perform their functions.

Nerve tissue transmits electrical signals. It makes up the brain, spinal cord, and the millions of nerves that interconnect the body's systems and provide communication and signaling throughout the body.

As with the major body systems, tissues exhibit the same core design principles. Specialized cells are organized into functional groupings (tissues) coordinated in specific ways to work together.

Specialized Cells

NEITHER THE body's major systems nor its tissues would be of much use without the extreme specialization, organization, and coordination of individual cells. The human body has around 200–300 types of specialized cells we know about, and it's believed there are hundreds more yet to be identified. Some of the cell types have different shapes, necessary for their specific functions (see Figure 2.2), while many other cell types look similar but seem to be running different internal logic. Recent studies indicate that the immune system alone may have a couple hundred different cell types, the retina a hundred different kinds of nerve cells, and the brain possibly five hundred or more different types of specialized nerve cells.

Each of these cell types has just the right capabilities to do one or more specific tasks, and in most cases, to do them near-optimally. The process of generating these various specialized cells during the body's development is known as differentiation.

The following is an abbreviated list of known cell types in the body, and their general functions:

- Many types of epidermal and dermal cells make up your skin.
- Many types of squamous cells line and protect your respiratory, gastrointestinal, and genitourinary tracts and help them function.
- Squamous endothelial cells line and protect your blood vessels.
- Many types of exocrine gland cells make things like mucus, sweat, tears, saliva, and digestive enzymes.

- Many types of endocrine gland cells make hormones like insulin, thyroid hormone, estrogen, and testosterone, which help control your body's metabolism and functional development.
- Many types of fibroblasts make various types of collagen, the main supporting protein in the connective tissue.
- Osteoblasts, osteoclasts, and osteocytes make up your bones and manage your body's calcium.
- Skeletal muscle cells, attached by tendons, move your bones.
- Cardiac muscle cells pump blood throughout your body.
- Smooth muscle cells control your blood vessels, gut, and genitourinary systems.
- Sensory, motor, and autonomic nerve cells do the work of the nervous system.
- Red blood cells make hemoglobin, which allows them to carry O_2 in the blood.
- White blood cells like neutrophils and lymphocytes help your body fight infection.
- Platelets in your blood work to prevent bleeding.
- Fat cells store energy and provide insulation and cushioning.
- Many different types of cells in your kidneys work to control various chemicals in your body.
- Liver cells do about five hundred different jobs for your body.
- Many different types of cells in your eyes work together to let you see. Dozens of specialized tasks are required for sight, like those performed by the rod photoreceptor cell.
- Sperm cells in men make it possible for new life.
- Egg cells in women make it possible for new life.

Not only do the body's cells take many different shapes and sizes, but their internal structures also differ profoundly. A red blood cell, for example, uses a highly coordinated process to eject its nucleus before en-

A Few Cell Types

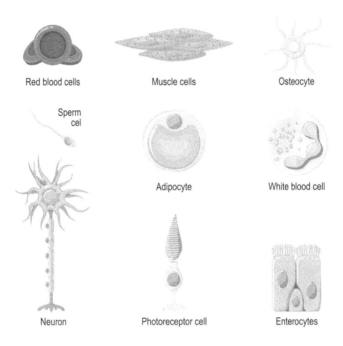

Figure 2.2. Just a few of the hundreds of cell types in the human body, a variety required for the body to function. Note that each drawing here is a vastly simplified representation of a far more complex cellular form.

tering the bloodstream. Only with its nucleus gone can the cell squeeze through the narrowest capillaries.

However, since DNA is necessary for making new proteins, this process can only occur after a red blood cell has generated all the hemoglobin proteins it will need during its life. Eject the nucleus too soon and there's no DNA for making hemoglobin, and the blood cell is useless. Eject it too late, and the red blood cell gets stuck in a capillary somewhere and cuts off essential circulation. As we'll see again and again, the body only works when the orchestration of the parts within each system is exactly right.

Specialized cells also have specialized internal machinery. While specifications for every protein machine in the body are present in the DNA of most of your cells, only certain cells need certain specific proteins, so each cell type has just the internal controls and processing machinery to "turn on" the genes that are needed, exactly when they're needed, and to "turn off" the genes that aren't needed. The technical term for this is "expressing" the genes. Certain types of cells express certain genes, while other cell types don't.

Different types of cells also respond differently to different signals in the body. Some signals are only meaningful for specific types of cells, and then sometimes only in specific locations within the cell and at specific times. Each cell must participate flawlessly in this complex choreography.

Each differentiated cell type is, in effect, running a different software program specially tuned for that cell's job. This program knows what kind of cell it is and uses its internal logic to perform the actions needed for its function.

How does cell differentiation cause certain cells to run these different programs? How does the body know which cells need which proteins? Where do these programs come from, and where (and how) are they encoded? Remember that we're talking about controlling tens of thousands of different proteins. How could such programming come to be? The level of control is off the charts, especially given that these systems have complex interdependencies.

Making It So

WHILE SPECIALIZATION, organization, integration, and coordination are essential, they are no good by themselves. Each part, and the whole, must be built. Then they have to run in order to perform their functions, and persist in the face of internal errors and external threats. At least four types of processes are needed for success:

Fabrication

Each of the parts must be generated. The body must have a way to make new cells of each of its hundreds of cell types, using the right materials to make the right shapes with the right internal composition, the right proteins, the right properties, and the right programming.

Assembly

The parts must be assembled according to the organizational design of the whole. The right parts must be in the right places and connected in the right ways. And as with most complicated devices, assembly must be done according to a specific order of assembly.

Operation

Once assembled, the whole must be initialized, launched, and run. Each of these is a different kind of process, and almost always non-trivial. Initializing sets up initial conditions. Launching jump-starts the potentially many interacting processes. This can be difficult, especially when the process involves complex chemical reactions, as almost all biological systems do. The run phase controls those processes and their many potential interactions over time, maintains stability of the overall system, and varies processes based on changing conditions. For example, when the body detects a drop in available glucose, its favored source of energy, it shifts to backup metabolic processes that can use other energy-packed molecules. But these processes require a different chain of metabolic proteins, so the body switches on the production of the other proteins needed for the backup metabolic processes. In other words, it adapts as conditions change.

Failure Prevention

The human body has something else, a property that's quite rare in human-engineered systems, though much desired. It's a property extremely difficult to engineer: the ability to keep working even when failures or errors occur, or when the system is under attack. This capability normally involves monitoring the system's various activities, detecting when something is amiss, and taking action to fix the error or counter the threat. Failure prevention requires anticipating the failure modes and designing systems to counter them before they are experienced.

Any of these four capabilities would be impressive by itself, but the human body has all four. How do you fabricate a bone of just the right size, strength, and shape for its particular task? How do you place that bone in just the right place, with the right orientation, within a developing body? How do you ensure that it's symmetrical with the corresponding bone on the other side of the body? How do you attach all the right muscle tendons and ligaments to where they need to be so the joints work correctly? How do you keep it working when there is blow to the body that tears a ligament or cracks a bone?

Asking Good Questions

MANAGING ALL these systems and capabilities is extraordinary. Just getting all the requisite parts in place is daunting enough. But as any engineer can tell you, having all the parts lying around doesn't magically make them come together into a working system. And any physician can tell you that having one or more working organ systems in your body doesn't magically make them perform fast enough or well enough to maintain control of the many necessary chemical and physiological parameters.

If you were tasked with designing a body, how would you get from none of the body's essential capabilities to all of them? If you started with a single living cell, what would you need to do to generate all the cell types in the human body? If you started with the capabilities of the cell, what would be needed for a large, multicellular organism like the human body? Remember that the body must be alive and functional at each step along the way, and this requires solutions to every one of life's thorny problems at every step along the way.

If this seems like a hard thing to do, that's because it is. Even the best human engineers have no idea how to achieve even a small portion of the body's capabilities.

Each of the systems and capabilities described in this chapter re-quires distinct information and logic. So in an evolutionary scenario, how many changes would be needed to generate a new system, or a new cell type?

Or, thinking about this from the other direction, how many systems or subsystems or specialized cell types in the body can be removed, or substantially modified, without causing the body as a whole to fail? In addition to coherence, interdependence, and dynamic capacity manage-ment, there's a level of irreducibility here that amplifies the challenges facing any attempt to explain the origin of these features of the human body.[3]

These are real questions, which demand real answers. They pose formidable obstacles to any proposed cause for the origin of the human body. And we have only scratched the surface.

3. STRUCTURE AND SUPPORT

Your bones and your skeleton are truly amazing…. they grow,
repair themselves and keep your entire body positioned as you
move through your life.

—KIM STEARNS[1]

PHYSICIANS COME TO APPRECIATE THE CRUCIAL ROLE VARIOUS
parts of the human body play by observing cases in which one of
those parts is faulty. In the same way that a production line of even top-
class cars will occasionally turn out a car with a crucial part that is defective, so too the human body occasionally gets produced with a faulty
part, and in both scenarios when this happens, the owner quickly develops a keen appreciation for the value of having that part in place and
working properly.

When I (Howard Glicksman) met Sam, she was the primary care-
giver for her grandfather. She would often tell me of her interest in judo
and once showed me pictures of her performing in historical fighting
scenes in the local "Medieval Days" pageant. Unfortunately, she was
prone to injury, which often sidelined her from these activities. One day
she showed me why.

While standing and facing me, with her knees locked, she twisted
her body almost 180 degrees around. Then she hyperextended her elbows and thumbs. As she went to dislocate her shoulder, I told her I had
seen enough; she didn't need to do that, too. I was impressed.

She told me she was thinking of being checked out for Ehlers-Danlos syndrome, a condition involving defective connective tissue. I told
her that based on what I'd seen, I was pretty sure she had it. She was

concerned because she knew that in addition to causing musculoskeletal problems, this syndrome can also affect the major organs. It can even lead to death.

Think of a car. What's needed for it to work properly? An engine, fuel, exhaust, transmission, drive train, axles, wheels, tires, oil, radiator, springs, hoses, brakes, steering wheel, and a seat to sit on. That's a good start, but you also need the chassis, clamps, nuts, and bolts—a structural framework to hold the many parts in the right positions for their functions. Without this, a car could never stand up to the forces exerted on it, like gravity, acceleration, deceleration, and centrifugal force.

In the same way, your body needs an underlying framework. All the systems, tissues, and cells need to be in the right places, and they need to stay there. Your body needs bones and other connective tissues to hold its trillions of parts in place—to position and support them, bind them together, and separate and lubricate them.

Connective tissues provide this structure—they act as the chassis for the body, within which the other tissues are bound. Connective tissues can be divided into ordinary connective tissues (like tendons and ligaments) and special connective tissues, like bone and cartilage, which need ordinary connective tissue to function properly. Without the connective tissues, other types of tissues (including muscle tissue, nervous tissue, and epithelial tissue) would lack structure and be prone to fail. The opposite is also true. Without the other types of tissue, the connective tissues would fail. You'd be little more than a bag of bones, and indeed, even the bag—your skin—would be missing.

Skin and More

LET'S START with epithelial tissue, and once we've done a quick survey of its many vital functions, we'll look at how connective tissues provide it indispensable structural support. As we sweep through this quick survey, try to think in engineering terms. If you prefer, set aside for the moment the question of how these systems came to be. Just pay attention to all the engineering challenges and engineering solutions involved.

Epithelial tissue covers the external and internal surfaces of your body. It sits directly between you and your environment, separating what's inside you from what's outside. The most obvious epithelial tissue is your skin. Other epithelial tissue lines your respiratory, gastrointestinal, and genitourinary tracts. It also lines the inner aspect of your blood vessels, though there it's called endothelium. All the glandular tissue in your body, both exocrine (like sweat glands) and endocrine (like the thyroid gland), including your pancreas, liver, and kidneys, consists of epithelial tissue.

This tissue is made up of cells closely joined together in one or more rows like a phalanx of shield-wielding soldiers. They are glued together by chemicals that connect the cell membranes of each neighbor, leaving minimal space and fluid between them. Along the epithelial surface are intermittent openings where an in-folding of cells forms a passageway leading to a gland. Glands send out fluid containing chemicals to help the organ system or the body as a whole.

The epithelial layer of your skin is called the epidermis. Its primary job is to protect your body from the forces of nature like trauma, friction, ultraviolet light, chemicals, and microbes. The epidermis consists of plate-like (squamous) cells called keratinocytes, which make a firm protein called keratin. As they mature and die, the keratinocytes move to the surface of the skin where they provide protection until sloughed off. Along the epidermis are openings to sweat glands below, which produce sweat to help your body regulate your core temperature. There are also sebaceous glands associated with hair follicles, which send out an oily, waxy substance called sebum that helps lubricate and waterproof your skin.

The epithelial tissue of the conductive portion of your respiratory system runs from your nose and mouth through your pharynx and larynx (voice box) into your trachea, bronchi, and bronchioles. It provides a pathway for air to go in and out of your lungs, warming and humidifying it on the way. It mainly consists of column-shaped (columnar) cells

TYPES OF EPITHELIUM

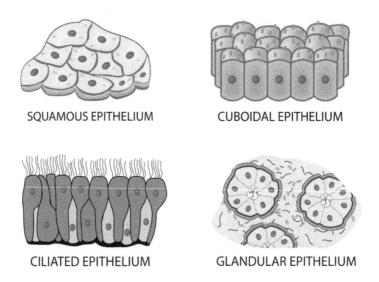

SQUAMOUS EPITHELIUM

CUBOIDAL EPITHELIUM

CILIATED EPITHELIUM

GLANDULAR EPITHELIUM

Figure 3.1. Sampling of various epithelial tissues. Epithelial tissue does most of the work in your respiratory system, gastrointestinal tract, and skin.

with goblet-shaped cells in between that send out mucus to the surface to entrap dust, bacteria, and other foreign matter. This is then swept out of the lung by cilia, little hair-like strands projecting from the columnar cells. The cilia move rhythmically in a wave-like motion upwards, toward the exit of the respiratory system, where the mucus (sputum/phlegm) can be spit out or swallowed.

The gas exchange portion of your respiratory system is made of tiny, thin-walled air sacs called alveoli. To help diffuse oxygen (O_2) from the air into the blood, and carbon dioxide (CO_2) from the blood into the air, the alveoli are lined with a single layer of squamous cells. Due to the alveoli's minuscule size and the surface tension of water, the linings of your alveoli are always at risk of sticking together after you breathe out. If this should happen, the alveoli would collapse and the exchange of gases would be impossible. Scattered between these squamous cells are cube-shaped (cuboidal) cells that send out a fatty chemical called pulmonary surfactant. This enters the thin fluid that lines the inside of the alveolus and, like detergent, reduces its surface tension to prevent the walls from sticking together and collapsing.

The epithelial tissue that lines the inner surface of the gastrointestinal system is called the mucous membrane (mucosa), which emits a layer of slimy fluid called mucus. In the esophagus it consists of squamous cells that protect it from any harmful chemicals that may be ingested, as well as from extremely hot or cold foods. This layer also sends out mucus to help the food move from the pharynx down to the stomach. In the stomach the epithelial tissue is mainly columnar cells that send out mucus to protect it from the process of digestion. The stomach's epithelial tissue has ducts for special glands to inject enzymes and hydrochloric acid to help with digestion. The intestine's epithelial tissue consists of columnar cells that send out mucus and other fluids containing chemicals that aid in digestion, protect the mucous membrane, and absorb the nutrients your body needs to live.

But epithelial cells are made mostly of water; and water, being a liquid, can't provide much structure or support. So, the epithelial tissue needs something to hold it in place. That's where ordinary connective tissue fits into the plan.

> The various types of "skin" (epithelial tissues) are specialized and fine tuned for their many and very distinct functions in the body. Each has just the right kind of cells in the right structures and shapes, with just the right glands, to inject exactly the right chemicals into the right locations to make the major body systems function properly. Even plain old skin is highly specialized to serve crucial roles.

Ordinary Connective Tissue

IN CONTRAST to epithelial tissue, which is mostly made of cells packed tightly together, connective tissue consists of sparsely scattered cells embedded in a matrix of fibers and surrounded by *ground substance*, a clear, colorless, gel-like material made of water with dissolved proteins and sugars.

Most of the cells in ordinary connective tissue are what are known as fibroblasts. These are flat or spindle-shaped cells that produce the ground substance and secrete the fibers that crisscross the connective tissue. Together, the ground substance and fibers make up the extracellular matrix (ECM), which binds the fibroblasts and other tissue cells within it.

In addition to providing structure and support for epithelial tissue, ground substance is also critical in transport. All capillaries are embedded in the extracellular matrix. The only cells that obtain the O_2 and nutrients they need directly from the blood are the endothelial cells that line the capillaries. All other cells get their O_2 and other nutrients by diffusion, transported through the ground substance, from the capillaries to the outer wall of the cells.

> How do you deliver the materials essential for life to every one of the thirty trillion cells in your body? This is the last step in the body's transport system. In the telecommunications industry this is known as the "last mile"—the final step in which services are delivered to a specific end customer. In the supply chain industry this is the delivery guy who drops the package off at your door. The body solves this challenge with a variety of supply chain solutions, ones we will explore in later chapters.

Thus, without the extracellular matrix around the capillaries surrounding the alveoli, your lungs could not absorb oxygen or expel carbon dioxide, and you'd die from oxygen deficiency or carbon dioxide poisoning. Without the extracellular matrix around the capillaries servicing the epithelial cells of the intestine, your body couldn't absorb water or the basic nutrients essential to sustain basic metabolism, and you'd die from dehydration or malnutrition. And without the extracellular matrix in your skin, your body couldn't control its core temperature and you'd die of hyperthermia.

The extracellular matrix's protein fibers consist of different types of collagens and elastins combined in different ways to provide different types of support, for different uses. Like steel-reinforced concrete or web-like lattice networks, different combinations add different qualities of structure, strength, and flexibility to the semi-fluid ground substance.

There are about sixteen different types of collagen. Type I collagen fibers are long, thick, and strong. They provide tensile strength, the ability to withstand being pulled without bending or breaking. Reticular fibers are made up of type III collagen fibers, which are shorter and thinner than type I collagen fibers and branch out to make delicate networks. Elastic fibers are long and thin and made of elastin, more flexible than collagen. They can stretch and recoil to reassume their previous shape.

All the different collagens and elastins are produced by fibroblasts. Although the fibroblasts in different tissues produce different types of fibers, under the microscope the fibroblasts all look the same. Also, fibroblasts seem to be able to change the quality of the fibers they produce depending on what's going on in the tissues around them. Fibroblasts in different tissues express different genes to produce different fibers, which may mean that although all the fibroblasts look the same and do similar things, they may actually be different types of cells.

Why is this important? For starters, without the extracellular matrix's ability to manufacture these different kinds of support, your body would either be a rock, or more likely, a blob of jelly lying on the floor. Plus, you'd be dead.

But there's more to it.

Dense or Loose

THE SUPPORT mechanisms in your car do different jobs, so they need different properties. To hold the engine and transmission in place, the frame and various brackets must be solid and immovable against the tremendous forces of torque and heat, while still damping vibrations. The springs in the suspension must be solid too, but also able to flex and recoil as the car moves. The hoses bringing air to the engine need flexibility, yet without collapsing.

In a similar way, the different organ systems need connective tissues with different physical properties, and this requires differences in the amount and types of protein fibers within their ground substance. By varying the blend of the collagens and elastins, the body can achieve different biomechanical properties in the extracellular matrix, qualities such as tensile strength, hardness, and elasticity.

With more collagen fibers and less ground substance and reticular fibers, ordinary connective tissue has higher tensile strength and is called *dense connective tissue*. It is found in the dermis, which supports the epidermis of your skin, and in the capsules around your joints. It also makes up the ligaments that join bone to bone at the joints and the tendons that join muscles to bones across joints.

In contrast, connective tissue with less collagen fibers and more ground substance and reticular fibers is more delicate and works like a net. This is called *loose connective tissue*. It's the most abundant connective tissue in your body and is roughly akin to bubble wrap or packaging material. It provides support for most of your organs, undergirds the lining of almost every passageway, and is found below the skin in the subcutaneous tissue. It also makes up the mesentery, the connective tissue that attaches the intestines to the abdominal wall, within which the blood vessels and nerves are embedded.

Elastic fibers can be found in varying quantities in all ordinary connective tissue. They are most plentiful in ligaments and tendons, skin, blood vessels, and the airways of the lungs.

Through different combinations of collagens and elastins, the fibroblasts are able to make an enormous array of different structures, each with different finely tuned mechanical properties. Further, it seems that each structure is produced in exactly the place(s) where it's needed and optimized for its specific use in that location.

Without these, your spleen would end up in your feet after you ran a 10K, and your stomach would impinge on your heart every time you lay down. Of course, if you didn't have these tissues, you wouldn't be able to run a 10K, or even a lap around the track. And if you lay down, you wouldn't be able to get up again.

Human engineers have thus far been utterly stymied in their attempts to mimic the astounding capabilities of the extracellular matrix's structures, even though there's a serious fortune awaiting anyone who can figure out how to do similar things at the same scales in human-made materials.

More Connective Tissue Jobs

CONNECTIVE TISSUES play several other critical roles in the body. These include promoting growth and repair, regulating energy and temperature, and producing blood cells.

But ordinary connective tissue also poses a problem for the body. While this tissue is perfect for transporting nutrients to the body's cells, it also presents an ideal location for microorganisms to invade and proliferate. Whereas the dense cellular structure of the other three types of tissue is more resistant and less attractive to invaders, the ordinary connective tissue offers a treasure trove of oxygen, water, and other nutrients, all in a warm and roomy environment—perfect for an invader.

To counter this, ordinary connective tissue is peppered with stationary immune cells called macrophages and mast cells. These detect and fight invading microorganisms. Other immune cells called lymphocytes pass through the ground substance on the prowl for invaders as well.

When they find an invader, they signal other immune cells (neutrophils) and antibody proteins to join the fight. The ensuing reaction in the tissue is called inflammation, which ultimately works to kill the enemy.

> The same properties that make ordinary connective tissue ideal for transporting nutrients to the body's trillions of cells make it equally attractive for invaders to set up camp. This kind of thing is common in engineering: the perfect solution to one problem often creates another problem, which requires yet another solution. Here, offering a banquet for the body's cells offers the same banquet for harmful invading organisms. So, it will take additional mechanisms, ones able to give the right cells a pass while fending off the wrong ones. Once again, the engineering challenge is met, with the body fielding an army of macrophages, mast cells, lymphocytes, and other combatants to answer the threat.

Ordinary connective tissue is also key to healing. Once a fibrous clot stops the bleeding at the site of an injury, fibroblasts move in, forming new scaffolding for the epithelium to grow on and depositing collagen to form a scar.

Some types of ordinary connective tissue also contain adipocytes, or fat cells. From a mechanical perspective these cells serve as cushioning to prevent damage when pressure is applied. But they also insulate against extremes in temperature and can release the energy in their fat for heat and fuel when needed.

Finally, connective tissue also serves in the formation of blood cells (red and white blood cells and platelets). This happens mainly in the bone marrow, housed in the special connective tissue called bone.

Bone and Cartilage

LIKE ALL other connective tissue, bone is made up of cells that live within the ground substance and crisscrossing protein fibers the cells secrete (the extracellular matrix). The cell that secretes the matrix for bone formation is called an osteoblast. It produces an extracellular matrix called osteoid, which contains ground substance and type I collagen fibers.

What sets bone apart from other connective tissue is that the osteoblast also deposits calcium crystals into the osteoid to form a solid and rigid structure.

There are over two hundred bones in the adult human body. These provide support and protect from external injury. The skull protects your brain, the vertebrae protect your spinal cord, and your ribs and breastbone protect your heart and lungs. Many of the bones have internal cavities that house marrow.

The bones also act as a calcium reservoir for your body. Calcium is deposited or withdrawn from the bones as needed to maintain the precise level of calcium required for proper nerve, heart, and skeletal muscle function.

Each of your bones is precisely shaped for its specific function in the body, and each must fit exactly with the other bones it connects to. The bones are attached to each other by ligaments to form the body's joints. Your upper body has shoulders, elbows, wrists, and finger joints. Your lower body has hips, knees, ankles, and toe joints.

Skeletal muscles are attached to the bones by tendons. Muscles span the joints so that when the muscle contracts, the relative positions of the bones change, generally rotating around the joint. This is how you move around and handle things.

There are also joints between the vertebrae in your spinal column; at both ends of your ribs; and between your jaw and temporal bone, which allows you to open your mouth to talk and chew. Finally, there are three tiny but very special bones (ossicles) in each ear, which allow you to hear.

Bones are an especially intriguing part of the body's exquisite makeup. Each bone must have a specific and precise shape, especially anywhere it must intersect with other bones or connective tissues.

For example, each of the twenty-four vertebrae in your spine (not counting the sacrum and coccyx) is an irregularly but symmetrically

shaped bone with projections for attaching muscles and retaining alignment during movement, and each has a central hole on its vertical axis
for the spinal cord to pass through. Each is different, yet each is precisely
shaped to fit with the vertebra above and below it. If any of these is mis-
shapen, it could pinch or cut the spinal cord, which would be debilitating
at best.

What does it take to build a bone? Where are the shapes for
these bones specified?

Since bones are made by many individual (and independent)
bone cells, building a bone is an inherently distributed problem.
How do the individual bone cells know where to be, and where
and how much calcium to deposit? How is this managed over
the body's development cycle, as the sizes and shapes of many
of the bones grow and change? Surely the specifications for the
shapes, their manufacturing and assembly instructions, and
their growth patterns must be encoded somewhere. There must
also be a three-dimensional coordinate system for the instructions to make sense.

Is the information located in each bone cell, or centrally located
and each individual bone cell receives instructions? If each bone
cell contains the instructions for the whole, how does it know
where it is in the overall scheme? How do all those bone cells
coordinate their actions to work together rather than at odds
with each other?

As yet, no one has answers to these questions. One thing we can
expect, though: whoever solves these mysteries will likely win a
Nobel Prize—which invites a question: If it takes someone of
Nobel-caliber brilliance to answer such questions, why wouldn't
it have taken similar or greater intelligence to engineer it in the
first place?[2]

There's one other special connective tissue that's associated mostly with bone. It's called cartilage and covers the surfaces where the bones in your joints come together. This includes your ribs and the joints between the bones of your spine. Cartilage is also present in the ear, nose, larynx, trachea, and large bronchi.

Cartilage is a flexible connective tissue made by special cells called chondrocytes. There are different types of cartilage. The ground substance for each contains different amounts of type II collagen and elastin. This results in their extracellular matrix having different qualities. Some are sturdier while others are more flexible.

Cartilage provides support for the respiratory tract, reduces friction within the joints, and acts as a shock absorber for weight-bearing joints in the spine and lower extremities. It also makes up the "bones" of the embryo. As the child develops, especially after birth, the osteoblasts deposit calcium within this cartilage to make it hard and rigid bone.

Sam's Concerns Confirmed

THINK BACK to the beginning of this chapter and the contortions Sam could do. She could win a flexibility contest, but her condition compromised her health and could even prove deadly. The name for her condition, Ehlers-Danlos syndrome, refers to a group of inherited disorders of the connective tissue. Caused by one or more genetic defects, it can affect not only the joints, but also the skin, blood vessels, heart, and other internal organs.

The defect usually involves the processing of collagen or its structure. Connective tissue supports the skin, so a person with this syndrome will often bruise easily and have overly stretchy skin that, when damaged, doesn't heal well.

Sam possessed the classic sign—generalized joint hypermobility (GJH). Since collagen is essential to the function of the joints (including the joint capsule, ligaments, and tendons), it's not surprising a defect in the collagen would result in overly flexible joints.

Easily placing your hands on the floor without bending your knees, bending your thumb back to touch your forearm, and easily doing the splits are all signs of GJH and possibly Ehlers-Danlos syndrome too. Unfortunately, even though such maneuvers can impress your friends, having joints, ligaments, and tendons without the necessary stability and strength can lead to serious and recurrent injuries, resulting in chronic arthritis and debility, as Sam was learning.

When you run and suddenly stop, jump down from a height, or twist your body in all sorts of directions, you may take for granted that your musculoskeletal system is up to the task of keeping you stable. But if the connective tissue that's supposed to stabilize your joints isn't strong enough, you may find yourself on the ground with an injury. In fact, just rolling over in bed can be high risk for someone with a serious case of Ehlers-Danlos syndrome.

Sam had already had several injuries involving her shoulders, elbows, wrists, fingers, hips, knees, and ankles. With her weakened joints she was also accident prone, often dropping things for no apparent reason.

But what she most worried about were the other ways this syndrome can affect the body. A deformity of the connective tissue anywhere along the spine from top to bottom can result in significant neurological malfunction and even death. The heart valves are mainly made up of, and stabilized by, connective tissue, so defects there can lead to serious heart conditions and death. And since blood vessels are made up of and supported by connective tissue, the vascular form of this syndrome can cause a lethal arterial rupture, spontaneous rupture of the intestine or colon, or even a rupture of the uterus during pregnancy.

The bottom line: your connective tissues are indispensable.

Rodney Dangerfield, an iconic comedian in the latter part of the twentieth century, made a career out of complaining that he didn't "get no respect." If your connective tissue had a voice, it would say the same thing. The epithelial, muscle, and nerve tissues certainly have major roles to play in your survival. They're like the stars and co-stars of a movie. But the connective tissue is the supporting "cast of thousands" that makes it all possible.

Medical science currently knows of at least twenty different genetic defects that cause Ehlers-Danlos syndrome. So we know there are at least twenty things that have to all be right for proper function of the connective tissue.

The actual number is bound to be much higher. The various connective tissues need to be blended in just the right ways for the body's structure to work. The bones have to be shaped just so. And without the cartilage between them at the joints, even basic motion would be painful or impossible.

What does it take to get everything right? How much information, how many assembly steps, how many connections (with the right ligaments), how many specialized cells and proteins? For example, the three bones (ossicles) in your inner ear must have very precise shapes to produce hearing. How many ways could these bones be built wrong—either in size, shape, or connection—such that hearing would be impossible?

We must wrestle with such questions if we hope to understand the requirements for life. Only by understanding the true requirements for these things to work properly can we hope to accurately assess the relative abilities of our two classes of causal forces to create them.

PART TWO: HOMEOSTASIS

Whether it's a single-celled amoeba or an organism like you with thirty trillion or more cells, all living things must maintain a stable, consistent internal equilibrium, different from that of their surrounding environment. The word for this is homeostasis.

Your body must strictly manage thousands of quantities, including its supply of such essential materials as oxygen, sugar, and calcium, as well as numerous critical physiological parameters, including respiratory and heart rates, blood pressure, and core temperature. Each of these needs to stay in its narrow range or else bad things happen (like debility and death).

The urge to breathe, and the thirst and hunger you feel, are triggered by your body's homeostatic mechanisms. In some cases, it's up to you how to respond. But most of the systems in your body respond to homeostatic needs subconsciously. To achieve this, the body employs three main tool types:

- *Controls.* The body uses an array of interconnected control systems. Each control system must have at least three key parts—one to detect what needs to be controlled, a second to apply decision logic, and a third to change the thing being controlled. Without all three, control would fail and the life that depends on it would cease.

- *Signaling.* The body uses many different types of signaling systems. Each one has a sender, a communication medium, and a receiver.

- *Metabolic Processes.* The body uses many metabolic (from the Greek word for "change") chemical reactions to stay alive. Some break large molecules into smaller ones, and others build larger molecules from smaller ones.

It's intriguing that, at the core of all life, homeostasis (not changing) could not happen without active metabolism (changing). Surely this has some deeper philosophical meaning, but we'll leave that for others to ponder.

4. The Respiratory System

Behold, I will cause breath to enter you, and you will live.
—Ezekiel[1]

My (Howard's) son and his wife had just been blessed with the birth of their daughter Celina. We were especially excited because my son worked in Rome. We're Catholic, and Celina was to be baptized in St. Peter's Basilica. Family had flown in from the United States for the celebration, and the house was filled with excitement and joy.

But within a few days of her birth, Celina began to cough, wheeze, and breathe faster than normal. My son and his wife quickly realized that Celina's condition was life-threatening. The joyful mood quickly gave way to fear. What was Celina's condition, and how was it threatening her life?

I had encountered such moments countless times in my profession, but now I was facing it in an all-too-personal way: a physical breakdown underscoring just how delicately balanced the human body's sophisticated system of systems must remain in order to maintain function.

Invisible, Indispensable

At just two weeks old, Celina had come down with bronchiolitis, an infantile viral infection that constricted her airways and left her tiny body starving for oxygen. She was having so much trouble breathing that she was hospitalized and switched from room air, which contains about 21 percent oxygen, to air with a higher concentration of oxygen (around 28 percent).

Your body is made up mainly of carbon (C), hydrogen (H), nitrogen (N), and oxygen (O). These four elements combine in various arrangements to form many different types of molecules. Some of the more important molecules your body needs are molecular oxygen (O_2), water (H_2O), a sugar called glucose ($C_6H_{12}O_6$), and proteins made up of nitrogen along with the same atoms that make up sugars.

The chemical formula for cellular respiration is straightforward:

$$C_6H_{12}O_6 + 6\,O_2 \rightarrow 6\,CO_2 + 6\,H_2O + \text{energy} + \text{heat.}$$

The process itself is complex, deploying twenty-three special enzymes in a precise series that converts one glucose molecule and six oxygen molecules into six carbon dioxide molecules and six water molecules. This process is known as aerobic respiration, meaning it uses oxygen as an input. The process releases the energy stored in the glucose molecule: 40 percent of the energy is captured by converting thirty-six low-energy adenosine diphosphate molecules (ADP) into thirty-six high-energy adenosine triphosphate (ATP) molecules. The remaining 60 percent of the energy is released as heat. (This will be important in Chapter 9 when we look at how the body controls its core temperature.)

Your body consists of trillions of cells, and each must have enough energy to work properly, or it will malfunction and die. Cells get this energy from a process called *cellular respiration*, which breaks the chemical bonds between the atoms of the glucose molecule, releasing energy. As we saw earlier, the cell captures this energy in the ATP molecule, energy it uses to power virtually all the cell's machinery.

The chemistry of this process requires six O_2 molecules as input, so cellular respiration cannot occur unless O_2 is present. The reaction also produces carbon dioxide gas (CO_2) as a byproduct. CO_2 is toxic if allowed to build up in the body. These two chemicals must be controlled within narrow tolerances at all times, regardless of how quickly the body

The Respiratory System

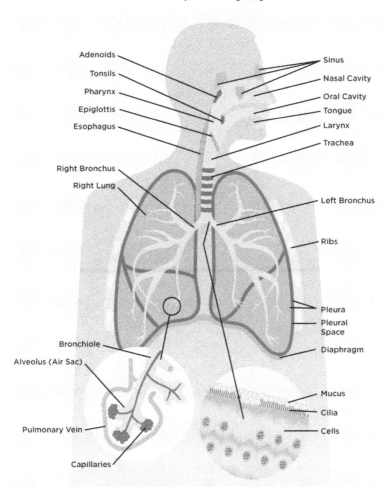

Figure 4.1. A simplified schematic of the human respiratory system.

may change its activity level, which requires equally rapid changes in the supply of O_2 and a corresponding need to rapidly remove more CO_2.

So, to stay alive your body faces a challenge. It must ensure it always has enough O_2 to meet the energy needs of its trillions of cells. And it can't allow too much CO_2 to build up.

ALVEOLUS GAS EXCHANGE

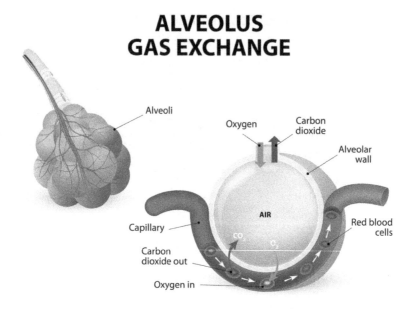

Figure 4.2. Gas is exchanged in the alveoli, where red blood cells take on oxygen from the air and offload carbon dioxide to the air. Your lungs contain some 300-million alveoli.

My granddaughter Celina was at risk because her bronchiolitis was preventing her from bringing in enough O_2 and getting rid of enough CO_2 to stay alive.

The Respiratory System

YOUR BODY is equipped with two lungs, placed within the chest cavity, which is bounded by the ribs and other bones to provide protection and support.

Your urge to breathe is generated by the cells in the respiratory center in the medulla, a part of your brainstem. The nerve messages to breathe travel through the spinal cord to the muscles of respiration—in particular, the diaphragm and the intercostal muscles between your ribs. When they contract, your chest cavity expands and the resulting negative pressure sucks air (like a vacuum) into your lungs through your nose and mouth.

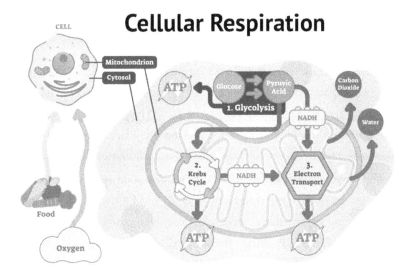

Figure 4.3. Cellular Respiration.

The air you breathe in is about 21 percent O_2 and 0.04 percent CO_2. As you inhale, it travels through the airways, deep into the lungs, until it reaches the 300-million grapelike sacs called the alveoli. Each alveolus is surrounded by several hundred small blood vessels called capillaries. The vital exchange of gases occurs here. O_2 enters the blood from the inhaled air, and CO_2 leaves the blood and goes into the air to be exhaled. Because of this exchange, the air you exhale only has about 16 percent O_2, but it has a 100-fold increase in CO_2, now around 4 percent.

Control Systems at the Core of Life

THE RESPIRATORY system is how your body brings in essential O_2 and offloads CO_2. But the mere presence of your respiratory system doesn't explain how your body knows to take on the right amount of O_2 and shed the right amount of CO_2. To begin to appreciate how it manages this trick, consider what happens when you hold your breath. Your body has sensors in the main arteries leading to your brain that detect the levels of O_2 and CO_2 in your blood. The CO_2 level directly affects the

H^+ ion (acid) level in the blood,[2] which is sensed in the brainstem. All this information is sent to the respiratory center in your brain, which analyzes it.

When you hold your breath, the amount of O_2 in your blood drops below normal because your cells keep using it for their energy needs even though no new O_2 is coming in. At the same time, the CO_2 level rises above normal because your cells are continually producing it, but it has nowhere to go.

The urge you feel to breathe comes from your respiratory center when it learns of this situation from your O_2 and CO_2 (and H^+ ion) sensors. It's trying to get you to correct the problem as soon as possible. The longer you ignore this warning, the lower your O_2 drops and the higher your CO_2 rises, and the stronger the urge to give in and breathe to stay alive.

At rest the average body needs 250 mL/min of O_2. With maximum activity, as in a fight-or-flight situation, it needs upwards of 3,500 mL/min. Most adults with normal lung function breathe in 350 mL of air to their alveoli at complete rest, about twelve times a minute (4,200 mL/min). During maximum activity, they breathe in about 60,000 mL per minute. Air contains 21 percent O_2, and the alveoli manage to extract about 30 percent of the O_2 sent to them:

Complete rest: 4,200 mL/min x 0.21 x 0.3 = 265 mL/min (250+).
Survival mode: 60,000 mL/min x 0.21 x 0.3 = 3,780 mL/min (3,500+).

So we see that the respiratory system is fine tuned to supply exactly what the body needs, both at rest and during extreme exertion.

So how does this signaling system work? The body employs a triple-input control system to manage respiration. It's triggered by very low O_2

levels, or by high CO_2 or H^+ ion levels. During intense activity, the respiratory center also receives information from your muscles about their activity level and metabolism, along with insight from the higher centers of the brain about its plans. Based on all this information, the respiratory center generates the signals that tell the body how hard and fast to breathe. And it does this without any conscious effort from you.

What's required of such control systems? Even the simplest control system needs several different parts working together to achieve and maintain control. Every control system, whether in a biological or a human-engineered system, must include some means to achieve each of the following:

Sensing

If you can't detect what needs to be controlled, control is impossible. Sensors must be in the right places, with the right capacity and sensitivity to detect what needs to be controlled. The O_2 and CO_2 sensors are in the main arteries leading to the brain, not in, say, the spleen, where they would be of little use. And they detect what needs detecting—the blood levels of O_2 and CO_2 rather than, say, blood flow or temperature or any of a thousand other things.

Control

Control is impossible without a way to make decisions about what to do. Data from a sensor must be received, integrated with information coming in from other sensors, and interpreted. The controller must apply its internal control logic to decide what to do, and then send the right signals to the right places to adjust levels as needed. The O_2 and CO_2 sensors send their information to the respiratory center in the brainstem, where the information is needed, rather to any of a thousand other possible sites (for example, the visual or auditory cortex). The respiratory center analyzes this information and sends orders through the nerves to change the body's breathing pattern.

Effectuation

Obviously, no control is possible without some way to change what must be controlled—some organ, tissue, or other body subsystem. Control decisions are sent from the controller to the effector, where they must be received, properly interpreted, and applied. Effectors need to have the sensitivity and capacity to respond quickly enough to maintain controls within proper levels at all times. The respiratory center sends orders to the muscles of respiration, not to any of a thousand other places in the body, telling these muscles how hard and fast to breathe, which they immediately do to maintain the current level of activity.

Signaling

All control systems need some kind of signaling infrastructure to carry signals from the sensors to the controller, and from the controller to the effectors. Signals must carry the correct information, be directed to the right components, and arrive soon enough. Signaling takes many different forms in the human body. (We'll see more examples in upcoming chapters.)

Dynamics

The system must respond quickly enough to maintain the tight tolerances needed in the timeframes needed. For example, it just wouldn't do for the oxygen control system to take ten minutes to increase oxygen levels if your body needs more oxygen right now for you to escape a raging wildfire. In the respiratory system, not only are the capacities just right, but so are the dynamics.

Harvesting and Garbage Removal

FINALLY, FOR many factors that the body must control (like O_2 and CO_2), there are two additional functions required, harvesting and garbage collection.

When a control system needs to add more of some chemical to the body, it must be able to harvest the needed raw materials from the environment—in the right amounts and at the right times—and convert them as needed for a particular use.

And when a control system needs to remove a chemical from the body, it must be able to gather that chemical and expel it into the environment—again, in the right amounts and at the right times. Any chemical, if allowed to build up in the body, will become toxic in sufficient quantities, including O_2.

Consider a home furnace. Most are fairly simple, using a single sensor (a heat sensitive coil or a semi-conductor heat sensor) designed to monitor room temperature. The control logic consists of a simple on-off switch connected to the heat sensor, which can be adjusted to the desired room temperature (what engineers call a setpoint). The effector is the furnace, which converts chemical energy (from natural gas, for example) into warm air, which is pushed into the room by a fan. When the room heats sufficiently, the sensor tells the switch logic, which turns the furnace off until the room cools and the switch logic again reactivates the furnace.

In most furnace systems, the signaling infrastructure consists of copper wires that carry the switch's status (either on or off) via a low electrical voltage to the furnace. The furnace has harvesters for both its natural gas fuel and an outside oxygen source, and a "garbage collection" subsystem to expel exhaust to the outside air.

Even the simplest furnace system has all the parts of a control system, and if you want to spend more money, an engineer can design a heating system with many more sensors, more effectors, and much more complex control logic, like you'd see in a large office building. Yet even these massive heating systems are simple compared to the controls needed for the complex distribution of O_2 and CO_2 in the human body.

From the respiratory control center in your brainstem and the bones that make up your chest cavity to your muscles of respiration, your lungs, their alveoli, the capillaries surrounding them, and the nervous system that carries these signals, it takes a lot of parts to make respiration work.

But just having the parts is not enough. The respiratory system has to be assembled, with each part in the right place, performing the right function at the right time, with the right signaling and responses in the right quantities and in the right timeframes. Otherwise, the body will go into respiratory failure, and we know what happens then.

The human body isn't immune to death and disease, but it often proves amazingly resilient. This was the case with my granddaughter, Celina. When bronchiolitis compromised her respiration, her O_2 and CO_2 sensors informed her respiratory center of the problem, triggering it to send signals to her muscles of respiration, instructing them to try to correct the situation by breathing harder and faster. This enabled her body to compensate until she could obtain medical attention. After a few weeks in the hospital, Celina improved enough to go home. Her respiratory system continued to recover, and she's been a healthy little girl ever since.

The Explanatory Burden

Though we've omitted most of the complicated details, our description of respiration is medically and scientifically accurate. The facts are uncontested. Similarly, the basic engineering required to make it work is uncontroversial.

Modern science, in both biology and medicine, is pretty good at discovering and describing the body's parts, their interactions, and their processes. But it falls short in explaining how these things could have come into existence.

What, exactly, does it take to engineer all this stuff, and more importantly, to make it all work? Current explanations from evolutionists consist largely of imaginative storytelling, usually with a lot of hand-waving around the details. For instance, you might be told that as life moved from the water onto the land, the water creatures' gills evolved into the land creatures' lungs because that's what they needed to obtain oxygen from the air. That's pretty vague, and it fails to answer any of the salient questions posed by a detailed analysis of the respiratory system.

How could any unintentional evolutionary processes build the systems just described? Where did all the parts of the control systems come from? How was the orchestration for all those systems programmed? How did it manage all the engineering details we left out (which would fill several volumes)? And how could any creature survive while these things were being gradually assembled over thousands or millions of generations?

There may be answers to these questions, but none have been offered so far.

5. The Cardiovascular System

> At the moment that my first husband died in May 1999, I was by his bedside and had my hand on his chest just over his heart. I felt its last rhythmic beatings, and then—nothing. It's the nothing that gets you pondering the mystery of the something. That is to say, it isn't amazing that a heart should stop beating; rather, it's amazing that it keeps beating.
>
> —Andrée Seu Peterson[1]

JERRY WAS QUITE A CHARACTER. I (HOWARD) MET HIM THROUGH MY medical practice. The man seldom came to my office, but he often called to try to get prescriptions based on what he thought was wrong with him. Early one Friday afternoon he called and told my secretary he felt dizzy and wanted me to call in a prescription for vertigo medication. When she gave me the message, I told her to tell him that if he's dizzy, he'd better come see me before we decide on a treatment.

Much to my surprise Jerry showed up at my office. But true to form, he tried to get a prescription without sitting down for an exam. Finally, he relented, and as I walked in I could see he was upset about having to be there. I asked him what was going on and he said under his breath, "Sometimes when I stand up, I feel a bit dizzy, sort of light-headed." Then he added, "But Doc, it's different than when I get vertigo. And the last few days I've been tired and short of breath, so I haven't been able to get things done."

With that, I shot out of my chair to listen to his heart and count how fast it was going. Then I measured his blood pressure. His heart

Anatomy of the Human Heart

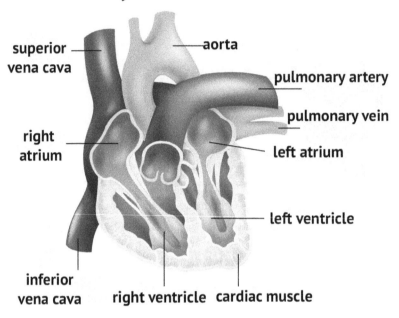

Figure 5.1. A simplified illustration of the human heart.

rate and blood pressure were both much lower than normal. I knew right away Jerry had a serious cardiovascular problem that needed immediate action.

As if to underscore the point, a moment later, as he tried to stand, he passed out. I gently lowered him to the ground and called an ambulance. Something in Jerry's body was illustrating in dramatic fashion a reality many physicians encounter every day—that the human body is a hive of interdependent and essential subsystems, such that if just one of them malfunctions, death is right around the corner. Such appeared to be the case with Jerry. Something indispensable in his body had broken down.

Generating Blood Flow

YOUR BODY is specially tuned to bring in exactly the amounts of O_2 it needs and put it into your blood. This oxygen-enriched blood then needs to get to all your thirty trillion cells. That's no simple task. It involves pumping blood throughout your body by way of about 60,000 miles of pipe called blood vessels. And just as it takes energy to roll a ball up a hill (against gravity) or push a chair across the floor (against friction) or accelerate a car (against inertia), the body must constantly use energy to work against all these forces to move blood through the blood vessels.

The heart is a muscular pump divided into right and left sides. Each side has a thin-walled upper chamber called an atrium, which acts like a holding area for incoming blood, and a more muscular lower chamber called a ventricle, which does the pumping. Between the atria and the ventricles, and the ventricles and their outflow tracts, v-shaped one-way valves point in the direction of blood flow. When the valves open, they let the blood move forward in the direction it's supposed to go. And when they close, they prevent the blood from going back to where it came from.

The left ventricle pumps blood through the aortic valve into the aorta and the systemic arteries. The blood travels through progressively smaller arteries to the arterioles, and from there into the microscopic capillaries where chemicals like O_2 are offloaded to the tissues and CO_2 is taken on board. The blood then moves into the venules and through progressively larger veins on its return to the heart through the superior and inferior vena cava.

On arrival the blood enters the heart's right atrium and moves into the right ventricle. From there it's pumped through the pulmonary valve into the pulmonary arteries on its way to the lungs. In the lungs the blood goes through a similar series of ever smaller arteries and arterioles to the millions of capillaries surrounding the alveoli, where it offloads the CO_2 it picked up in the tissues and picks up a fresh supply of O_2. Then it goes back to the left side of the heart through the pulmonary veins. Here it enters the left atrium, goes through the mitral valve into the left ventricle, and is again pumped into the systemic arteries.

And so continues this vital lifelong cycle: blood coming from the lungs goes to the body, while blood coming from the body goes to the lungs. Think of it as a sort of figure-eight circulatory pattern, with the heart in the center.

> The cardiovascular system (CVS) is a closed system composed of two circular pathways, or circuits. As the blood transits a complete route, it's pumped twice by the heart, once to drive it to the lungs to pick up oxygen, and a second time to drive the oxygenated blood throughout the body. Because the blood flows continuously around this closed system, O_2 delivery to the body can be adjusted simply by varying the rate the blood is pumped. It doesn't need to create more blood every time the body demands more oxygen, which is a good thing, as that would take much too long.

Balancing the Flow—Cardiovascular Control

IT'S NOT enough to merely move blood around the body. The cardiovascular system must adjust blood flow as the body moves and changes position. For example, after doing work at ground level for a while, when you stand up quickly the reduction in blood flowing back to your heart and from there to your brain (mainly due to gravity) can cause you to feel dizzy or even make you pass out. So your body has to act fast to ensure that your brain gets the O_2 it needs.

Blood flow throughout the body depends mostly on the blood pressure in the systemic arteries. Blood pressure is the force the blood applies against the walls of your large arteries as it flows through them. The higher the blood pressure, the greater the blood flow. Lower blood pressure means less blood flow.

Blood pressure is mainly controlled by two factors: cardiac output and vascular resistance. Cardiac output is the amount of blood the heart pumps into the arteries. When the heart pumps faster and harder, the cardiac output increases and so does the blood pressure. Slower pumping with less force decreases cardiac output and blood pressure.

Capillaries

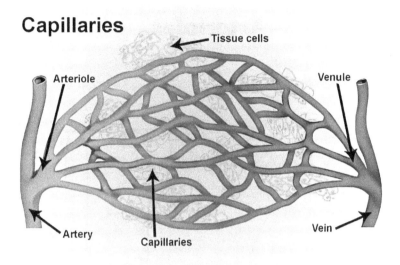

Figure 5.2. An arteriole branching into capillaries.

Vascular resistance determines how much blood leaves the arteries. The arterioles are the key to vascular resistance. Arterioles are small blood vessels branching out from the arteries, eventually themselves branching into capillaries. Most arterioles are wrapped in a layer of smooth muscle (in contrast to striated skeletal muscle), which contracts or relaxes to change the vascular resistance and thereby control how much blood flows through into the tissues. When the arteriole muscles contract, making these blood vessels get smaller, the vascular resistance rises, less blood goes through to the tissues, and more stays in the arteries, which increases blood pressure. When the arterioles relax (contract less), these blood vessels get larger, vascular resistance drops, more blood goes through to the tissues, and less stays in the arteries, which decreases blood pressure.

Maintaining adequate blood flow to the tissues means balancing output against resistance. If either fails, major problems occur, as Jerry learned.

Arterioles

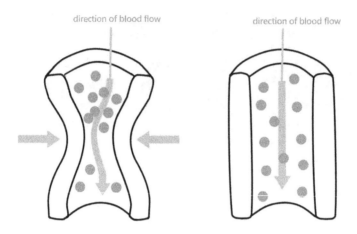

Figure 5.3. Constricted arteriole (left) vs. relaxed arteriole (right). The degree of contraction applied by the smooth muscle surrounding the arteriole determines its diameter, and with it, the rate and amount of blood flow to the tissue it supplies.

Controlling Cardiac Output

THE FIRST step in balancing blood pressure is managing the inflow of blood to the arteries, and, as with most things required for life, this takes specialized systems.

The heart is a specialized muscle that works differently from the skeletal muscle attached to your bones. Skeletal muscle only contracts after being told to do so by the nervous system. The heart is unique in that it has a clump of cells in the right atrium called the sinoatrial node that automatically sends electrical signals to the rest of the heart. As the heart's natural pacemaker, the sinoatrial node triggers the atria to contract. From there the electrical signal travels along a conduction system that triggers the ventricles to contract and pump blood into the arteries.

The sinoatrial node is what usually sets your heart rate, and the conduction system passes these signals to the various muscles in the heart. While this system defines the precise sequencing of the heart's rhythm, the sinoatrial node also needs to know how much blood the body requires at any given time, and for this it needs some help.

> Your heart has built-in programs that generate exactly the right sequence of heart muscle contractions required for proper function. You may be familiar with the characteristic graphic electrical signature (the EKG) of a heartbeat in normal sinus rhythm. The highs and lows of this pattern show the electrical activity resulting in the coordinated contraction of the atria and ventricles in their characteristic (and essential) sequence. Almost any other heart rhythm would make survival more difficult or impossible—a fact well known to cardiologists.

The autonomic nervous system, which provides involuntary control of many body processes, tells your heart how fast and hard to beat to match the body's changing energy needs. Sensors in your muscles inform your brain about their movement and metabolic activity. The higher brain centers also send information about plans for upcoming activity. The autonomic nervous system analyzes all this information and sends out signals (at one-third the speed of sound!) that reach the heart and the rest of the cardiovascular system in about a hundredth of a second.

When the body is at rest, the autonomic nervous system sends signals along specific nerves to release a neurohormone called acetylcholine. Acetylcholine attaches to special receptors in the sinoatrial node, the conduction tissue, and the heart muscle. When these receptors detect acetylcholine, they reduce the heart rate and force of contraction. That's why your pulse at rest is relatively slow and not very strong.

As your body becomes more active, the autonomic nervous system gradually turns off the acetylcholine-producing signals and turns on other ones that cause a neurohormone called norepinephrine to be released. The autonomic nervous system also signals the adrenal glands to send out a hormone called epinephrine. By attaching to specific receptors in the sinoatrial node and heart muscle, these two chemical messengers tell the heart to pump harder and faster. That's why your heart beats harder and faster when you get more active.

So, the sinoatrial node and the conduction system control the sequencing and rhythm of the heart's action, while the autonomic nervous system determines how fast and hard the heart should pump. Together they control cardiac output.

> It takes two independent systems to control cardiac output. If either were absent or defective, you'd either have difficulty returning to rest after being active or be unable to become active after resting. This is another instance of the push-pull principle in the human body: two separate systems are required to achieve even the most basic coherent functions. One to ramp things up, another to ramp things down. One to start, another to stop. One to send, another to receive. One to push, another to pull. Watch for many more examples in other chapters.

The Brain Drain—A Quick Test

OFTEN, WHEN we stand up too quickly, we feel dizzy for a second or two. Have you ever wondered why?

Like all fluids (which, like solids, have mass), blood wants to flow downhill (due to gravity); so when we stand, the blood tends to pool in our lower extremities. Less blood returns to the heart and consequently less flows to the brain. When your brain doesn't get enough blood, it warns you by making you dizzy. Obviously, this needs to be corrected quickly or you'll find yourself on the ground, like Jerry did. But the problem usually goes away in a second or two.

How? Sensors in the main arteries leading to your brain monitor how much the arterial wall distends (due to blood pressure) and sends this information to the brain. When the blood pressure drops too low, the brain reacts by telling the autonomic nervous system to send more norepinephrine to increase both cardiac output and vascular resistance. This quickly raises your blood pressure to overcome the negative effects of gravity and increase blood flow to the brain. And, voilà, within a couple seconds, the dizziness subsides.

My patient Jerry passed out because something had gone wrong with his body's ability to control his blood pressure. It couldn't react quickly enough to overcome the force of gravity, and he needed help.

> Changes in the body's position require precise adjustments in the body's dynamic plumbing, and these must occur in a second or two. This is not some "nice to have" feature. It's necessary for basic survival. And it requires multiple clever mechanisms, each with many parts orchestrated by complicated control logic and signaling.

Directing the Flow—Vascular Controls

BUT THERE'S another do-or-die level of control required of your cardiovascular system. All the tissues and organs of your body need exactly enough blood flow to meet their energy needs no matter what you're doing. This is a profoundly difficult engineering problem. Different parts of the body have different needs for different activities. Blood must be directed in exactly the needed quantities, to exactly the right places, at exactly the needed times. And the flows must adapt just as quickly as the body and its organs require.

Since the heart is a single pumping system that affects the whole body, and the arterioles are localized to specific places in the body, it makes sense that arterioles are the key to distributing the blood. To control vascular resistance, the autonomic nervous system only uses the nerves that send out norepinephrine and the ones that tell the adrenal glands to send out epinephrine. Your body is set up so the muscles surrounding the arterioles supplying blood to different organs and tissues respond differently to these chemical messengers. To do this it uses two different types of receptors for the same hormone signals.

The first type, alpha receptors, cause the muscles around the arterioles to contract, which reduces blood flow through those arterioles. The second type, beta receptors, cause the muscles around the arterioles to relax, which increases blood flow. The alpha and beta receptors respond inversely to the same hormone signals.

For example, the muscles surrounding the arterioles in your gastrointestinal system have mostly alpha receptors, so with more of these hormones they contract more to reduce blood flow. In contrast, the muscles surrounding the arterioles in your heart and skeletal muscles have mostly beta receptors, so the same neurohormones cause them to relax more, increasing blood flow.

Notice that the inverse logic of the alpha and beta receptors means the cardiovascular system can adjust blood flow to specific areas of the body with the same hormone signals. Once the balance is correctly set up, the entire system can be adjusted with a single hormone signal. To accomplish this, the numbers and placement of the receptors must be exactly right. You wouldn't be alive if your alpha and beta receptors got switched around, were located on the wrong arterioles, or were missing altogether.

At rest, the autonomic nervous system sends out a basal amount of norepinephrine, which ensures that all your organs and tissues get the blood flow they need to do their jobs. With increased activity, more norepinephrine and epinephrine are released, causing the muscles surrounding the arterioles throughout your body to either contract or relax more, as noted above. The result is that with increased activity, all your organs and tissues get the blood flow they need to do their jobs.

When you're highly active, you need five times more cardiac output than when you're at rest. And almost all that five-fold increase needs to go to your heart and skeletal muscles, the parts doing the extra work. This is where the increase in norepinephrine and epinephrine works its magic, reducing blood flow to the gastrointestinal system and increasing it to the heart and skeletal muscles—effecting a sort of body-wide balancing act. Most animals need this ability and need to be able to invoke it in an instant. It can mean the difference between eating and being eaten.

Of course, not all muscles are involved in all activities, so the cardiovascular system needs finer-grained flow controls to give more blood to specific muscles based on their individual needs. It turns out that increased metabolic activity causes certain chemicals like carbon dioxide, nitric oxide, and lactic acid to build up. Lactic acid builds up in your muscles when they're not getting enough O_2, causing the burning soreness you feel in your muscles during vigorous exercise. The arteriolar muscles in the immediate area detect this buildup and respond by relaxing even more, allowing still more blood into those specific muscles.

This adds another mechanism for getting exactly the right amount of blood to exactly the muscles that need it, exactly when they need it—a sort of demand-based power boost localized to specific muscles. This gives the body extremely fine-grained controls over blood flow to specific tissues. Once again, the exact parts and systems are exactly where they're needed.

Jerry's Problem Solved

IT TURNS out Jerry's problem was that his sinoatrial node wasn't working right and hadn't been for a while. That's why his blood pressure and heart rate were low. Remember, blood pressure depends on cardiac output, which depends on heart rate. Jerry's autonomic nervous system worked fine, but his natural pacemaker wasn't responding properly. It had served him well for decades, but it had begun to malfunction (as do all machine parts, given enough time and wear). Any time he tried to be more active, his heart wouldn't speed up enough to give him the blood flow he needed. When he passed out in my office, his sinoatrial node had quit working altogether; so when he tried to stand up, his heart didn't respond adequately, his cardiac output didn't increase, and he ended up on the floor.

As soon as Jerry's medical team saw his EKG, they realized the problem. He was whisked into an operating room to have an artificial pacemaker implanted.

But why didn't Jerry die as soon as his sinoatrial node bit the dust? How was he able to slog along as long as he did? It turns out that the conduction tissue and muscle in the heart have the potential to be natural pacemakers. The sinoatrial node dominates because it's set at the highest rate (60–100 bpm), so it electrically triggers the others before they can do it themselves. But when the sinoatrial node is broken, the conduction system (set at 40–60 bpm) or the ventricles (set at 20–40 bpm) will take over. When Jerry's doctors looked at his EKG, they would have seen that the sinoatrial node wasn't working and that one of these others was picking up the slack.

The heart thus incorporates a built-in series of fallback controllers. If the first fails, the second picks up the slack (though at a reduced heart rate), and if that one fails the third will go to work. In engineering this is called functional redundancy. This is a highly desirable design pattern, but there's a trade-off because the redundancies can lead to resource inefficiencies; so functional redundancy is not always possible or advisable. Sadly, trade-offs are present in all engineered systems. Since the fetal heart starts to pump at three weeks but the sinoatrial node seems not to start working until a few weeks later, one has to wonder if the fallback controllers have a role to play during this early period.[2]

For Jerry, these built-in compensating mechanisms bought him some time and gave him the impetus to seek medical attention just in the nick of time.

Pressurized Hydraulic Controls

FLUIDS UNDER pressure follow the path of least resistance. The arteriolar muscles adjust the effective diameter of the blood's pipes (the blood vessels), making them work like valves. When one valve closes partially, more blood flows to areas with wide-open valves. This is an ingenious system for directing flow to needed locations in plenty of time to be effective.

The cardiovascular system is a complex system with many parts that together achieve fine-grained control of blood flow:

- It has a pump and dual closed-circuit pathways to move blood around in a circle (two circles, actually). And this must happen continuously from about three weeks after conception until the moment you die.

- It uses special unidirectional valves in the heart to prevent backflow and force the blood to always move in the right direction. When the blood pressure on the upstream side is higher than on the downstream side, the valve opens and allows blood to flow through. When the pressure reverses, the valve closes and prevents blood from flowing in the wrong direction. These valves must have precisely the right shapes and strengths for this purpose, and point in the right direction.

- It uses multiple control systems to achieve the fine-grained flow adjustments needed to direct blood in the right quantities to exactly the right areas at the right times. The systems include adjustable pressure, individually adjustable valves, and controls localized to specific muscle groups.

- It uses multiple signaling pathways to pass requisite information across all the varied pieces and parts scattered throughout the body.

- It's able to react to the body's changing needs for oxygen, usually even faster than the body's needs change.

The cardiovascular system works a bit like a pipe organ, in which a single pump generates air pressure and the many pipes each have a valve. When the organist presses combinations of keys on the keyboard, the valves at specific pipes are opened (some more, some less) to achieve the correct timbre, and music happens.

The plumbing architecture for the cardiovascular system is ingenious. Closest to the heart the arteries are larger, with less resistance, the better to handle higher and faster flows; and closest to the heart the arteries have thicker walls to handle the higher pressures. This distributes oxygenated blood to remote areas of the body swiftly. The arteries branch and become progressively smaller the closer they get to their destination. As the pipes get smaller, their resistance increases, and the blood pressure and rate of flow decreases. With lower blood pressure, the vessel walls can be thinner.

When the blood gets to the capillaries, where the exchange of O_2 and CO_2 occurs, the vessel walls are extremely thin and the blood has slowed to a crawl. Here the blood vessels are so small that individual red blood cells can only pass through one at a time, and then only by being squeezed as they pass through. The squeezing action deforms and elongates the red blood cells,[3] increasing the contact area between the blood cell and the extremely thin vessel walls. The thinner capillary walls, the slow blood flow, and the red blood cell deformation caused by the narrow capillary diameter all combine to maximize the efficiency of the exchange of O_2, CO_2, and pretty much everything else the cells need.

The Challenge of Building the Cardiovascular System

THE CARDIOVASCULAR system is a wonder. It is an extraordinarily complex system of systems in which each part must be present, all the parts must be properly connected, and each part must function correctly—with precise timing, precise signaling, precise controls, and precise plumbing—to solve the set of difficult problems imposed on the body by the laws of physics and chemistry.

To work, the cardiovascular system must be more than complex; it must be coherent. All must be just right or else the system doesn't work, and when the system doesn't work, the body doesn't work. Moreover, all the orchestrated precision that causes the system to work happens subconsciously, so we don't have to spend all day thinking about how to balance our blood flow.

As a whole, and in each of the parts, the cardiovascular system presents an enormous explanatory challenge to any theory purporting to explain its origin.

6. HEMOGLOBIN

The elegance of the way the hemoglobin system functions is simply astounding, and a source of wonder to everyone who is familiar with its intricate ingenuity.

—MICHAEL DENTON[1]

FRANK IS A MIDDLE-AGED CONSTRUCTION WORKER WHO HAS AL-ways been active and healthy, a non-smoker with no history of lung or heart disease. But this morning as he walks from his truck to the foreman's office, he becomes so short of breath that his co-workers sit him down on the ground and call an ambulance. Soon he is at the ER.

As he lies on the stretcher in his sweaty cement-powdered overalls, he looks anxious. The attending physician notices that his heart rate is quick but not overly so, and he wonders if Frank's problem is anxiety. But then why would his shortness of breath mainly happen when he is exerting himself at work?

His oxygen saturation, chest x-ray, and EKG are all normal. But lung and heart problems aren't the only reasons someone can be short of breath. The physician orders some lab work, and based on the results, he admits Frank to the hospital and gives him four units of packed red blood cells the next day. The reason he does this is that Frank is anemic. But what does anemia have to do with being short of breath?

Frank is a composite character, but I (Howard) have seen many like him in my years practicing medicine. Cases like his stem from iron's crucial role in the functioning of an essential molecule—hemoglobin.

Hemoglobin

YOUR RESPIRATORY system brings in life-essential O_2 and infuses it into your blood, but with this mission accomplished, your body faces another problem: O_2 doesn't dissolve well in blood's watery matrix, called plasma.

One liter of blood can only hold about three milliliters of O_2 in solution. At rest your body needs 250 mL/min of O_2, and to be active enough for survival mode, it needs 3,500 mL/min. (By survival mode we mean active enough for our primitive ancestors to survive—i.e., eating rather than being eaten.)

At rest, your heart pumps about five liters of blood per minute. If the only way your body could send O_2 to its cells was by dissolving it in blood plasma, it could only send 15 mL/min (3 x 5) of oxygen, or 6 percent of the 250 mL/min it needs at rest.

For survival mode activity, involving vigorous activity, it only gets worse. The maximum cardiac output for a non-athlete is about 25 liters of blood per minute. So, if being dissolved in blood plasma were the only way your body could send O_2 to its cells, then it could only provide 75 mL/min (3 x 25), or just 2 percent of the roughly 3,500 mL/min it needs when highly active.

So your body faces yet another do-or-die challenge. It needs a better way to get O_2 into the blood or you won't last more than a few minutes at rest, much less while fighting for survival.

And, once again, the body has an ingenious (and complicated) solution. To solve this problem, your red blood cells make a clever, special-purpose protein (multimer) called hemoglobin.[2] As new red blood cells develop in the bone marrow, they begin to produce hemoglobin. Once the red blood cells mature, they're sent into the blood, which is circulated throughout your body by your cardiovascular system.

Only red blood cells generate hemoglobin, which makes sense as it's only useful in the blood. While the genetic instructions to make hemoglobin are present in all your body's cells, they're only activated (expressed) in red blood cells, and then only until their nucleus is ejected.

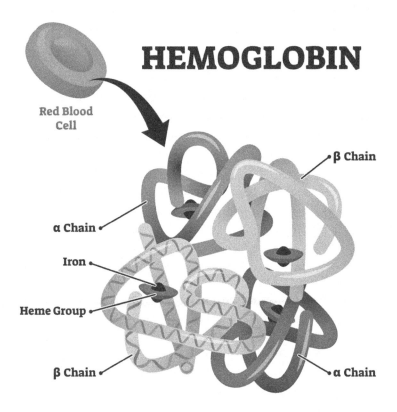

HEMOGLOBIN

Red Blood Cell

β Chain

α Chain

Iron

Heme Group

β Chain

α Chain

Figure 6.1. The structure of the hemoglobin multimer.

So some kind of underlying programming tells the red blood cells—and only the red blood cells—to make hemoglobin. How and when this is activated is not well understood, but it seems to occur in conjunction with the cell differentiation process.

The Problem of Iron

EACH MOLECULE of hemoglobin carries four atoms of iron, which O_2 readily attaches to. When the iron in your hemoglobin is fully loaded with O_2, it's red. That's why arterial blood is red. After it gives some of its O_2 to the tissues and heads back toward the heart through the veins, it takes on a bluish tinge. Look at the blood vessels on the back of your hands. Do you think they are arteries or veins? Their purple-blue color indicates they are veins.

Hemoglobin's iron atoms aren't a nice-to-have frill or some mere optimization detail. Without the iron, O_2 wouldn't stick to hemoglobin, rendering the hemoglobin useless, and your tissues wouldn't get the oxygen they need. So the body needs to get iron from the environment and transport it to the bone marrow where it can be used to make hemoglobin in the red blood cells.

> To have enough oxygen to survive, the body needs to manufacture that ingenious molecule, hemoglobin. But to make the hemoglobin, the body needs iron. This is a problem, and the solution requires yet another supply chain. It's like manufacturing cars. Each car gets an engine, but where do the engines come from? They come from an engine assembly plant, but each of these needs an engine block, so where do the engine blocks come from? An engine block fabrication plant uses steel to build them, so where does the steel come from? And so on.
>
> What we see is a cascading series of problems. Each solution presents new problems, which in turn need new solutions. All these problems must be solved for the system as a whole to work. If any of these subproblems goes unsolved, the whole system fails.

But to get iron to your bone marrow, your body faces yet another problem: free iron in solution is toxic. To solve this problem, your liver makes a transport protein called transferrin, specific for iron. When iron enters the blood from your gastrointestinal system, it attaches to transferrin so it can be sent to your bone marrow. The stem cells in the bone marrow (that develop into red blood cells) have specific transferrin receptors on their cell membranes. Transferrin and its iron cargo lock onto the receptor, and the iron is deposited into the cell. Compared to the other cells in your body, the developing red blood cells in your bone marrow have a much higher concentration of transferrin receptors, so they take in most of the iron that's continuously available from your blood.

This is a good thing, because each of the estimated twenty trillion or more red blood cells[3] in your body lives for only about four months. Your body loses about two hundred billion red blood cells a day, so to maintain your oxygen-carrying capacity, your bone marrow must receive enough iron to supply two hundred billion new red blood cells a day, about two million every second.

In a healthy human, this runs like clockwork. Frank's problem is that he doesn't have enough red blood cells and hemoglobin, meaning his blood doesn't have enough oxygen-carrying capacity, leaving him short of breath.

Hemoglobin Control

JUST DESCRIBING where red blood cells come from and noting their ability to produce hemoglobin isn't sufficient to explain how your body can transport enough O_2 to your cells. Given that the bone marrow must make two million new red blood cells every second, a next question is, how does the body control this process?

Your body uses specialized kidney cells to help control production of red blood cells and hemoglobin. These cells have sensors thought to detect the O_2 content of your blood, which provides a sense of your red blood cell mass and hemoglobin content. The specialized kidney cells send out a hormone called erythropoietin (EPO), which boosts red blood cell production. As O_2 levels drop, these specialized kidney cells send out more EPO. As O_2 levels rise, they send out less. This is another perfect solution to a difficult control problem.

The EPO boosts hemoglobin by traveling in the blood to the bone marrow, where it attaches to specific EPO receptors on certain immature stem cells. (Stem cells are cells that have not yet differentiated into specific types of cells with specific roles). The EPO then tells the stem cells to develop into red blood cells, which will produce hemoglobin.

Controls are necessary for every function needed to sustain life. To control the respiratory and cardiovascular systems, your body uses nerves and neurohormones. Hemoglobin control (like many other metabolic processes) uses gland cells and a hormone that travels in the blood. Though the way they work is different, all the basic control components of a sensor, integrator, and effector are here.

Iron Control

IF FRANK had a kidney problem, his EPO level might have been too low, causing his red blood cells and hemoglobin to be depleted. If Frank had chronic unseen bleeding, say from his stomach, that could cause an iron shortage, which in turn would leave him without enough hemoglobin. While the body can store iron in various places (mainly the liver and bone marrow) and draw on those sources as needed, chronic bleeding can quickly burn through those reserves.

When it comes to how much iron you have in your body, the adage "everything in moderation" applies. When lack of iron slows hemoglobin production, you can end up like Frank. But having too much iron isn't good either, because if it builds up in your major organs, it can lead to debility and death (in a disease called hemochromatosis). So the body must maintain tight control of its iron. Only in the last few years has medical science begun unraveling how some of this works.

Besides producing transferrin, the liver also plays a major role in controlling how much iron the body brings in through the gastrointestinal (GI) system. Liver cells store the most iron in the body. As we've said, iron in solution is toxic; but just as the liver cells make transferrin to carry iron safely in the blood, they also make and use a special protein, called ferritin, so they can safely store iron. In general, the liver cells send out varying amounts of a hormone called hepcidin based on how much ferritin the liver cells have. Hepcidin tells the intestine how much iron to bring in.

Iron enters the cells in the intestinal wall, but it doesn't automatically move from there into the blood, the way water does. To go into the blood, it must pass through a membrane-based protein called ferroportin, which acts like a gate. These ports are controlled by hepcidin, which attaches to the ferroportin proteins on the intestinal cells, to close them and prevent iron from exiting into the blood. If iron isn't needed, the sequestered iron then leaves the body when the intestinal cell is shed a few days later.

So when iron storage increases in the liver cells, they emit more hepcidin into the blood, which slows iron's absorption into the body. Lower ferritin levels have the opposite effect, causing more iron to be absorbed. Here we see yet another exquisite control system for staying in yet another crucial Goldilocks zone.

Functional Capacity

WE'VE JUST described how your liver controls the intake and transport of iron to the bone marrow and how your kidneys control the production of red blood cells and hemoglobin.

So, how much O_2 can hemoglobin carry, and is it enough to do the job? A healthy body at rest removes about 25 percent of the available O_2, and with high levels of activity this peaks at about 70–80 percent. Each gram (gm) of hemoglobin can carry 1.34 mL of O_2, and the average man has 150 gm of it in each liter of his blood (15.0 gm/dL). This means that rather than carrying just 3 mL of O_2 per liter of blood based on O_2's solubility in blood plasma, with the help of hemoglobin, each liter of blood can carry 200 mL of O_2 (1.34 x 150).

For survival mode activity, the body needs 3,500 mL/min of O_2. With 200 mL of O_2 per liter of blood and a high-activity cardiac output of 25 L/min, the blood can carry 5,000 mL/min (200 x 25) of O_2 to the tissues. But the tissues can only remove 70–80 percent of the available O_2—3,500–4,000 mL/min. That's exactly what is needed!

What about our composite patient, Frank? The lab results said his hemoglobin was only 5.0 mg/dL (one-third of normal), but also that he had normal kidney function and normal iron levels, so he doesn't have chronic gastrointestinal bleeding. What he has is aplastic anemia, a disease where the bone marrow can't make enough red blood cells. This is diagnosed by looking at a sample of the patient's bone marrow under a microscope. The disease means Frank only gets enough O_2 to keep him alive at rest. No wonder he can't even walk without getting badly winded; a body subsystem that most of us aren't even aware of went offline, which threatens his entire system.

Why highlight a scenario of this sort in a book about the exquisite interdependent functionality of the human body's systems of systems? Again, the story of Frank, like the other health crises described in this book, underscores what we tend to take for granted: while a healthy human body typically lasts far longer than the best mass-produced automobiles and is a marvel of multifaceted capabilities, all that comes at a price. Our bodies require all manner of functioning systems within functioning systems for the overall system to work, and this poses a steep causal challenge—a point we will explore in greater detail deeper in the book.

Chemical Signaling

IN THE previous chapter we looked at communication over a distance via electrical impulses in the nervous system. Here we see another type of signaling based on special-purpose chemicals (EPO and hepcidin) entering the blood and flowing through the body via the cardiovascular system. Since these chemicals are sent through the circulatory system via the blood, it would be possible, in principle, for their signals to be received by almost anything, almost anywhere in the body. But the signals are read precisely where they need to be read, with only the correct body subsystems having the appropriate receptors to properly receive and act on these signals.

To make matters still more interesting, the chemical signals described in this chapter consist of complex protein molecules with specific shapes and chemical properties. Not only does the geometry (bumps and crevices) have to be complementary, but so do the surface chemical attractions and repulsions (such as oily patches and electrical charges). To receive this kind of signal, the receiving cell must have a receptor specially fitted to the shape of that particular protein molecule—like a key just right for a particular lock. Additionally, the receptor must be connected to the right effector to perform the right task in the right quantity, which in some cases requires additional molecular signaling.

Finally, for all this to work, the system requires the correct processing logic. As the level of iron (stored as ferritin) in your liver goes up, your liver sends out more hepcidin to reduce iron intake. This is *direct* logic. In contrast, your kidneys use *inverse* logic to determine how much erythropoietin (EPO) to push into the blood—with less O_2 and red blood cell mass, they increase their output of EPO. In both cases the setpoints (the triggers that tell whether, when, and how much to send) must be just right.

If any of this processing fails to work correctly, your life is in danger.

A Supply Chain for Iron

Since hemoglobin cannot work without iron, the body needs a complete supply chain solution to get iron from the environment to exactly where it's needed, in the right amounts, at the right times.

Engineering a solution to this challenge involves a cascade of problems, and each problem has a unique, complex solution. We find these solutions in the gastrointestinal and cardiovascular systems, including in the liver, kidneys, bone marrow, and blood, and in special-purpose protein molecules and equally special-purpose protein receptors. Each of the parts must be present, working correctly, and controlled within narrow tolerances.

Each problem must be solved within tight constraints, and each solution leads to additional problems that must be solved. In some cases this involves a causal circle, in which the solution to problem A requires a solution to problem B, but the solution to problem B requires the solution to problem A. So, for example, you can't get O_2 to the tissues without hemoglobin, but hemoglobin requires iron, and you can't get iron to the bone marrow (to make hemoglobin) without the cardiovascular system delivering O_2 to the bone marrow so that the developing red blood cells can survive long enough to make hemoglobin.

Information

THE AMOUNT of information the body needs to fabricate, assemble, and operate all this is overwhelming:

- Information to construct red blood cells with the right size, shape, and flexibility.
- Information and sequencing for the red blood cells to dump their nuclei and other organelles so they can squeeze through the capillaries.
- Information to fabricate hemoglobin (with its iron atoms as payload).
- Information to fabricate transferrin in the liver.
- Information to fabricate transferrin receptors on the membranes of developing red blood cells.
- Information to fabricate O_2 sensors on kidney cells.
- Information to fabricate erythropoietin in the kidneys.
- Information to fabricate erythropoietin receptors on the surface of stem cells in the bone marrow.
- Information to fabricate ferroportin (gates) on intestinal cell membranes.
- Information to fabricate hepcidin in the liver.
- Information to fabricate hepcidin receptors on ferroportin.
- Setpoints and thresholds for all the above controls, which must be precisely tuned to the required Goldilocks values.
- Processing logic for hemoglobin controls.
- Processing logic for iron controls.
- All the information required to generate the host tissues and organs, including the liver, kidneys, lungs, GI tract, cardiovascular system, bones, and bone marrow.

That's a lot of information, all for a molecule to boost oxygen delivery. Even without going into the details about where the information is located or how it's encoded, decoded, and copied, we can see that a great deal of information is needed for these systems to work.

The case of hemoglobin, moreover, is not the exception to the rule but an illustration of it: even the simpler functions in the body are not so simple.

7. GETTING THE RAW MATERIALS FOR LIFE

To eat is human, to digest is divine!
—*THE NETTLETON COOKBOOK*[1]

I (HOWARD) MET LUCY (NOT HER REAL NAME) WHEN SHE CAME ON hospice with liver failure. She had been drinking alcohol heavily every day since she was a teenager. Interestingly, long before her liver problem became life threatening, for a time she had suffered from malnutrition, despite eating well. Most people know that alcohol can damage the liver and nervous system, but how could it lead to malnutrition in a person who is eating all the right foods? To understand this, it's necessary to see how the body gets essential nutrients.

We've looked at how your body gets oxygen (O_2), but what about all the other chemicals it needs? These come in through the gastrointestinal system. Your cells and the blood in your circulation need water (H_2O) and chemicals like sodium (Na) and potassium (K). Your bones need minerals like calcium (Ca), and you need iron (Fe) to make hemoglobin. All sorts of vitamins are needed for the chemical reactions that drive your body's metabolism. Not least, your body needs lots of nutrients—carbohydrates, fats, and proteins.

Carbohydrates include single-sugar molecules like glucose as well as groupings of two or more sugar molecules joined together by chemical bonds. Much of our food contains molecules of two sugars joined together. These include sucrose (table sugar), which is made up of fructose and glucose, and lactose (milk sugar), made up of galactose and glucose.

But most of our carbohydrates are made up of long chains of hundreds to hundreds of thousands of glucose molecules joined together. These include the starch in wheat, rice, corn, and potatoes. Some of these sugar molecules, like glucose, are used to make ATP, the main molecule that stores and transfers energy within the cell. Some sugar molecules make up the structures of the complex DNA and RNA molecules. In addition, your body joins certain sugars and proteins together to make molecules that are part of your bones and connective tissue. And it also joins certain sugars and fats together to make molecules that are part of the tissue that insulates your nerves so they can work properly.

Fats are complex molecules made up of fatty acids and glycerol. Your body uses some of the molecules it gets from fats to provide the structure for the cell membranes of your trillions of cells. Your body also stores fat as an energy reserve, handy when food becomes scarce. Your body also uses fat molecules to make certain lipids and places them within a fatty layer in the skin to provide insulation, and over bony prominences for cushioning. Your body also uses some of the molecules it gets from fats to produce steroid hormones to control growth, development, and metabolism.

Proteins, as noted in Chapter 1, are mostly large molecules made up of sequences of amino acids joined together by chemical bonds into long strings and folded into various shapes. Your body breaks incoming proteins into small chunks no larger than tripeptides (composed of three amino acids), because the intestine can't absorb anything bigger, then converts those modular building blocks into the tens of thousands of specialized proteins it needs, exactly when and where it needs them. This includes hemoglobin, transport and chaperone proteins, molecular machines like kinesins and ribosomes, collagen and elastins, the many enzyme types, the structural parts of the cytoskeleton, the structures that enable your muscles to contract, your clotting factors, your antibodies, and your hormones. The human body is buzzing with many kinds of specialized proteins, and they do most of the body's work.

Demand and Supply

JUST AS your body uses up O_2, so too it uses up the sugar and other nutrients it gets from carbohydrates, fats, and proteins. These nutrients aren't always available like the air that surrounds us, so to stay alive your body must collect and store them when it can get extra, then release them as needed. There is nothing simple about either of these jobs. Supplying all these essential bodily nutrients requires, once again, solving a cascade of interrelated problems.

The food you ingest can't just float around randomly inside your body; it remains within an enclosed membranous tract. An added challenge is that most of the nutrients the body needs are present within large molecules, which don't easily pass through membranes. Together these two issues present a daunting problem. The body must find the right raw materials, ingest and place them in a separate membranous tract, break them down into their constituent parts, pass them through the membrane into the blood, and deliver them to the appropriate locations in the body. The molecules that pass through the membrane form the body's set of basic chemical building blocks. Or, viewed from the opposite perspective, the membrane must be able to absorb all the basic chemical building blocks the body needs. These must then be sent to the right locations in the body, where they're assembled into the specific, large molecules the body needs.

Now let's see how the body does all this.

The Gastrointestinal System

COLLECTIVELY THIS work is done by the Gastrointestinal System (GIS), shown in Figure 7.1. Your GIS consists of many different parts, including the mouth, tongue, teeth, salivary glands, pharynx, esophagus, stomach, small intestine, pancreas, liver, gall bladder, colon (i.e., large intestine), rectum, and anus. Each part plays an important role. All must work together in a precisely choreographed dance.

The first job of the GIS is to digest your food. Digestion is the process of breaking down the larger and more complex molecules to produce

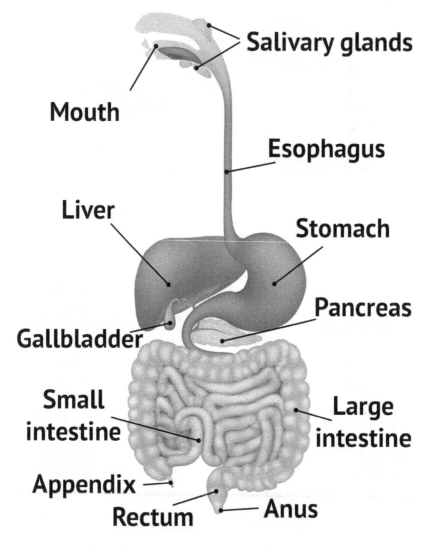

Figure 7.1. The gastrointestinal system, including the main parts involved in digestion and absorption.

smaller and simpler ones. Only then can the GIS perform its second job, the similarly complicated process of absorbing those simpler molecules into your blood.

The GIS works a bit like an automated car wash, which sprays water and soap through hoses as cars enter and move along a track, then turns on brushes to scrub them, and then performs more rinsing, a blow dry, and a wax job. It would be wasteful for the car wash to do all these tasks all the time, even when cars weren't present. In the same way, the GIS starts working only when you put food into it—when it has something to do. And each part of the process activates only when it's needed. The rest of the time it's mostly dormant.

The process begins when you feel hungry. Your body's hunger center is in the hypothalamus. There's also a satiety center nearby which tells you when to stop eating. Medical researchers have recently discovered a salt hunger center in the brain, which may increase your appetite for other foods as well. They're still trying to figure out how this works. But one thing they do know is that these centers constantly receive information from nerve and chemical messengers sent from the organs involved in getting, using, and storing these nutrients.

The first stage of digestion begins as soon as you take a bite of food. Its physical presence along with its taste and smell are detected by your nervous system, which triggers the release of saliva from the glands in your mouth. Saliva contains the enzymes amylase and lipase. Amylase breaks the chemical bonds between the sugar molecules within carbohydrate molecules like starch, and lipase breaks the chemical bonds between the fatty acids and glycerol that make up fats (lipids).

As you chew to break the solids into smaller, more manageable sizes and mix them with saliva, your tongue forms them into a small mushy lump called a bolus and moves them back toward your pharynx.

Up to this point, most of the actions have been voluntary. From here on the process is involuntary. The next step is getting the bolus from the pharynx into your esophagus without misrouting it to your windpipe and lungs. Sensors in the pharynx detect the bolus and send information to the brain, which initiates the swallow reflex. Swallowing involves the autonomic coordinated action of about fifty pairs of muscles working together with exquisite precision to propel the bolus down into your esophagus while protecting your airway. Once inside the esophagus the bolus moves by spiral muscle contraction into the stomach. This is called peristalsis and is how everything in the GIS moves.

Your stomach is activated when you smell, taste, and eat food. It sends out mucus, hydrochloric acid (HCl), and an inactive protein called pepsinogen. The mucus protects the stomach lining from the harsh chemicals needed for digestion. The HCl helps break down the food fibers, kills microbes, and converts pepsinogen into a powerful protease, an enzyme that breaks the chemical bonds between the amino acids that make up protein molecules.

The stomach churns and mixes the contents of the fluid, which speeds up the digestive process. It then releases a little at a time into the intestine to allow for more efficient digestion. This is an ingenious design. The longer the fluid stays in the stomach and the more gradually the fluid is sent into the intestine, the longer the stomach and intestine will have to work on the food and the more effectively the digestive tract can do its job.

> The digestive acids essential in the stomach become a problem in the next stage of digestion. If left alone, these will damage tissue further downstream, where the membrane walls get thin enough to allow chemicals to transit into the bloodstream. So the body must neutralize these acids as soon as they leave the stomach. Fortunately for us this occurs in just the right place, at just the right time. Here we see yet another instance of the solution to one problem creating a new problem, which needs yet a different solution, and so on. We get something like the following chain: problem → solution → problem → solution, et cetera. This is but one of many instances of this kind of problem-solution chain in the gastrointestinal system.

The fluid coming from the stomach pushes against the walls of the intestine, which triggers it to emit its own fluid and chemicals. This includes sodium bicarbonate ($NaHCO_3$), which begins to neutralize the acid from the stomach, and enzymes to break down certain molecules.

The intestine contains other enzymes for breaking various sugars down further, eventually to glucose. Certain cells in the intestine detect when the glucose and other small molecules, like fatty acids and amino acids, are being broken down from the larger ones in your diet. Those intestinal cells react by emitting hormones that signal your pancreas to send out fluid and chemicals. These include sodium bicarbonate, which helps to further neutralize the acid from your stomach. It also has all the other enzymes (in an inactive form) needed to complete the digestion of the carbohydrates, fats, and proteins in your diet. Further, these hormones trigger your gall bladder to send out bile, which helps the intestine digest fat.

Now that the smaller molecules have been released from your food by digestion, it's your intestine's job to absorb them. In addition to water, glucose, amino acids, cholesterol, and simple fats, the intestine also absorbs minerals like calcium and iron; electrolytes like Na^+, K^+, and Cl^- ions; and vitamins like A, C, D, E, K, and all the B vitamins, including B_{12}. To accomplish this feat the membrane of the intestinal cell has many different specific transporters which aid absorption, not only into the cell but also from there into the blood.

About 1.5 liters of fluid move daily from the small to large intestine, where mostly water and Na^+ and Cl^- ions are reabsorbed. The remaining one hundred or so grams of feces that daily exits your GIS through the anus usually is made up of about 70 percent water and 30 percent solids from undigested plant fibers like cellulose, bacteria, and cells shed from the GIS at the end of their lifespan (usually a few days to a week or two).

Poorly Designed?

WE SWALLOW about a thousand times a day. It's possible to choke on food, in rare cases to death, but this happens mainly to people who aren't exercising ordinary caution, or who through injury or disease have developed a functional defect. Choking is possible because our pharynx is the same pathway for breathing in air and for taking in food and drink.

Some evolutionists point to the pharynx and the rare risk of choking as an example of poor design, and as evidence that the pharynx arose from millions of years of happenstance and evolutionary dead ends. But the pharynx generally works beautifully, and there would be significant negative design trade-offs for the human anatomy if our breathing apparatus were separate from our eating/drinking apparatus. Rather than dive into the details of that matter here, though, we will address it in Chapter 23 along with the main variations on the "bad design" argument for unguided evolution.

When It Goes Wrong

Each day the healthy human pancreas produces ten to twenty ounces of a juice that contains digestive enzymes. But Lucy's pancreas was far from healthy. Her many years of heavy drinking had damaged her pancreas, resulting in chronic pancreatitis, a permanent condition that limited how well her pancreas could function. As a result, after eating, Lucy would have abdominal bloating and gas along with large, bulky, foul-smelling stools that she couldn't flush down the toilet. She was also losing weight.

A gastrointestinal specialist ran several tests to see what was wrong. A CT scan confirmed that Lucy's pancreas was shriveled up. Other tests showed that her stools were full of fat. Her pancreas wasn't making enough digestive enzymes to break down the carbohydrates, fats, and proteins in her diet, so many of these essential nutrients were passing right through her. Her body could not benefit from the foods she ate, and that's why, despite eating well, she suffered from malnutrition.

The gastrointestinal specialist put Lucy on digestive enzymes that she took every time she ate. They allowed her GIS to adequately digest her carbohydrates, fats, and proteins so it could absorb the vital nutrients her body needed.

Before the invention of enzyme supplements, chronic pancreatitis would have proven deadly, since it prevents the body from absorbing enough nutrients to supply its needs. This should lead us to wonder: if the pancreas originated by some gradual, unintentional evolutionary process, how did it acquire all its essential parts, with just the right capacity to make enough of just the right digestive enzymes? Remember that each enzyme type consists of numerous copies of an information-based specialized protein. In what order did the different types of enzymes come along? And how could any transitional organism that needed the same nutrients as we do survive without all those specialized enzymes already present?

Further, in the GIS you have two separate systems that must talk to each other to achieve function: the intestine, which sends out hormones when it detects glucose, and the pancreas, which responds to those hormones by sending inactive enzymes into the intestine, where they're activated. Which of these systems came first?

Thinking It Through

THE GASTROINTESTINAL system is a remarkable feat of engineering, one that effectively and efficiently solves a demanding set of design challenges. The GIS must break foods into their component building blocks, absorb the ones presently needed (or that will soon be needed), and slough off anything harmful or unneeded. This takes a lot of specialized parts working together in a complex choreography—hundreds or thousands of highly specialized mechanisms operating under precision controls using dozens of independent signaling systems (of which we've only covered a few).

The GIS protects the body's internals against both ordinary waste and the many crazy substances and hard objects that might be foolishly or inadvertently ingested. It also protects the body's internal systems from the nasty chemicals, like digestive acids and enzymes, required to break your food down into its component parts. These chemicals are just as capable of breaking down the flesh that makes up your body as they are of breaking down the flesh you eat, so they cannot be allowed to get loose inside the body.

Further, this system has amazingly helpful (but rather unpleasant) autonomous mechanisms for protecting itself against certain ingested toxins or poisons—vomiting, to eliminate things at the front end of the system, and diarrhea, to eliminate things that make it further in. Again, each of these involves numerous mechanisms to detect problems, determine the best course of action, and launch appropriate countermeasures. Also, the system usually warns us when this will happen, giving us time to get to a suitable location. And afterwards, the appendix, it would appear, repopulates the gut with the bacteria it needs to begin digesting foods again.

This separation of concerns makes digestion efficient while protecting the body's internal organs, but it means that all the body's nutrients must be absorbed through the walls of the GIS. The processes that make this possible are ingenious, both in their breadth (covering all the needed nutrients, minerals, and vitamins) and in their effectiveness.

Further, all these nutrients, minerals, and vitamins must be available at the times they're needed, which means that many of them must be stored somewhere and retrieved when needed. This usually takes two separate mechanisms—one for storing a chemical and a different one for retrieving it. Just imagine what would happen to your body if it could only do one or the other, but not both. For any given vital nutrient, such a scenario would either be highly debilitating, to the point that a person could not survive long-term without advanced medical care, or else lethal.

As an exercise for the reader, how many parts have we discussed in this chapter, even just at this high level, and how many control systems and communication pathways are involved? The answer—a lot.

The GIS, like most other systems in the body, features many ingenious, interconnected solutions to a cascade of hard design problems. The GIS is good at doing things that are simply hard to do, and all the harder to do at only the correct times and in only the correct places, which the GIS also manages to do.

A system like this takes many specialized parts—properly organized, integrated, and carefully coordinated to work together—to achieve even its most basic functions. Each part must be fabricated, the whole must be assembled, and then the system needs to be initialized and properly run. It needs the right capabilities with the right capacities, all at the right times.

The more we learn about how the body works, the more explaining is needed. Nothing about medical science's understanding of the body is getting simpler—only more complex, with each successive discovery revealing new levels of interdependent sophistication. Explanations that were weak (at best) in the past have only grown weaker. Many questions remain. How could this system of systems have come to be? Some series of real events occurred in the distant past resulting in this remarkably ingenious system. But what were they? What sort of causal forces and factors must have been involved?

8. SUGAR, WATER, AND OTHER KEY CHEMICAL SUBSTANCES

Life is water, dancing to the tune of macromolecules.
—COMMONLY ATTRIBUTED TO ALBERT SZENT-GYÖRGYI[1]

HUMANS ARE OMNIVORES, ABLE TO THRIVE ON AN ASTONISHING variety of diets found in cultures around the world. However, the explosion of Type II diabetes in recent decades makes it clear that humans are not optimized for a diet high in refined carbs and added sugar, typical of the modern Western diet. Bill could have been a poster child for this fact. As a diabetic, he had been on insulin for over ten years, but despite his diabetes, he often indulged in sweets and adjusted his dose of insulin as he saw fit. Due to this he had developed some of the telltale signs of poor diabetic control—blurry vision, tingling feet, and imbalance. It wasn't unusual for the ER to wake me (Howard) in the middle of the night to inform me that Bill had once again been brought in by ambulance. He was usually unconscious with a blood sugar that was either sky high or dangerously low, both of which are life threatening.

As we will see, Bill's case illustrates a central theme of this book, namely that it requires only a seemingly minor defect in the human body's delicately orchestrated system of systems to cause major problems.

Goldilocks Sweetness

YOUR CELLS, recall, get much of their energy by releasing it from glucose (sugar) with the help of O_2. While your body has no way to store O_2, it can store sugar in various organs and tissues. This is why you can only live a few minutes without breathing but can go days without eating. However, as Bill's condition demonstrates, storing sugar isn't enough. Your body must ensure that the blood always has the right amount of sugar—not too much and not too little.

The human body generally does an excellent job at this, but when abused with lots of sugar and refined carbs over many years, particularly when combined with a sedentary lifestyle and a genetic predisposition, this system can begin to break down, leading to diabetes mellitus.

Diabetics have difficulty controlling the amount of sugar in their blood. Too much sugar in the blood causes the cells and the kidneys to lose too much water, which exits the body as excessive quantities of urine. "Diabetes mellitus" refers to passing lots of sweet-smelling urine. This, in addition to a metabolic reaction that produces too much acid in the blood, can quickly lead to dehydration, coma, and death. Before insulin was discovered a century ago, most diabetics suffered this plight within just a few short weeks of developing symptoms.

Insulin treatments are a lifesaver for diabetics because they work to bring down dangerously high levels of blood sugar, but the treatments come with a risk. Too much insulin can leave too little sugar in the blood. When this happens, your cells, particularly the ones in your brain, can't generate enough energy, so they start to malfunction. If the medical warning signs aren't addressed quickly enough, you can die. That's why insulin treatments can't be administered indiscriminately, but must be tightly controlled and carefully monitored.

In a healthy body, the precise controls (and monitoring) of insulin levels are achieved through yet another sophisticated subsystem.

Sugar Control

EXOCRINE GLANDS such as your sweat and gastric glands secrete outwardly onto the external or internal surfaces of your body (like your skin and inside your stomach). In contrast, endocrine glands like your pituitary and adrenal glands secrete inwardly, sending hormones directly into your blood. These hormones work as signals between systems in different places in the body.

The pancreas is a two-way player. It's an exocrine gland, secreting fluids containing digestive enzymes into the gastrointestinal system. And it's an endocrine gland, secreting hormones into the blood. Two of these hormones are insulin and glucagon. Together they work to control your blood sugar.

After you eat, your blood sugar rises because your gastrointestinal system starts to break down and absorb the carbs in the meal. Beta cells in your pancreas have sensors that detect this rise in blood sugar and, in response, manufacture and send out more insulin. Insulin travels in the blood and, among other things, attaches to specific receptors on liver cells, triggering them to increase their intake of sugar molecules and join them together to form a large storage molecule called glycogen.

Normal blood sugar usually runs between 70–100 mg/dL (3.9 to 5.6 mmol/L).[2] But after you eat, as your gastrointestinal system brings in sugar, your blood sugar rises, usually peaking at about 120 mg/dL within a couple hours. Then, as your body continues to use sugar and the liver cells store some of it as glycogen, your blood sugar level drops back down. As the level drops into the normal range, the beta cells in the pancreas detect this and reduce their output of insulin to a basal (low) rate. When you are very active, your body may need to quickly use a lot of sugar. Or, when you go several hours without eating (like overnight), your blood sugar can drop. If it drops below 60 mg/dL it can cause brain malfunction. Your body, however, has a way of preventing this. As the blood sugar drops towards 70 mg/dL, the alpha cells in your pancreas sense this and respond by manufacturing and sending out glucagon.

Glucagon travels in the blood and attaches to specific receptors on the liver cells. This triggers them to break up glycogen and release the stored sugar into the blood. As the blood sugar rises back up over 70 mg/dL and beyond, the alpha cells detect this and reduce their output of glucagon to a basal rate.

> The body cannot manage its energy supply without both systems working properly. How might a dual system like this, with exquisite coordination, have evolved gradually, over many generations, when the whole is required in order to stay alive? This presents a quandary, to be sure. Effectively controlling blood sugar requires two systems—the insulin system and the glucagon system. Each has all the parts of a control system, with its own specialized pancreatic cells, blood sugar sensors, and logic. The setpoints, hormone signals, hormone sensors, and effectors are different for each system, but the two systems must work together to achieve the needed result.
>
> We wouldn't live long if we could only bring the blood sugar down when it's too high but couldn't bring it up when it's too low, or vice versa. Similarly, it would be no good for the same amount of both hormones to be produced at the same time. It takes both systems, with independent but perfectly coordinated setpoints, to control blood sugar in exactly the needed range. And, as with all the systems required for life, these must work in exactly the right capacities and in the right time frames (dynamics).
>
> This is yet another example of the push-pull principle—two separate control systems working in harmony to manage a single, life-essential process.

The way this works is complex, but the gist of it is that basal (low) levels of both insulin and glycogen are produced all the time, but when blood sugar levels are high, the beta cells increase insulin output, and the alpha cells reduce glycogen output. When blood sugar levels are low, the beta cells reduce insulin output, and the alpha cells increase glycogen output. It's the ratio of insulin to glucagon that mainly affects the blood sugar controls. Maintaining the proper balance between these two hormones is key to making this system work.

The Other Diabetes

BILL SUFFERED from diabetes mellitus. Another, less common type is diabetes insipidus, which involves passing lots of pale urine. Understanding this type of diabetes requires understanding how our kidneys work. No matter how much water you drink, your gastrointestinal system readily brings it into your body and puts it in your blood. So, unless you know how much water your body loses and can measure how much you take in, you'll need some other way to control it. For this your body has the renal system, and in particular, the kidneys.

Next to the brain and liver, the kidney is perhaps the most complex organ in the body. It performs several key functions. Earlier we talked about how it sends out a hormone called erythropoietin, which attaches to specific receptors on stem cells in the bone marrow to spur red blood cell development and hemoglobin production. It also helps control your blood pressure.

> The body has many nasty chemicals to get rid of, and other essential ones to keep. The solution? A complete, molecular-level water treatment plant to filter out the toxic stuff and retain the good—your kidneys. Imagine what would be needed to design and construct something like this!

The kidneys filter urea out of the blood. Urea is a nitrogen-containing molecule made in the liver from ammonia, a toxic by-product of protein metabolism. Either urea or ammonia, if allowed to build up in the body, can cause debility and death.

The kidney traps urea by passing blood through specialized capillaries that filter the water from your blood into microtubules. This filtered water, with urea and many other chemicals in solution, then moves through the kidney and comes out as urine. Along the way, the kidney retains the chemical substances, including water, that your body needs.

Water, Water Everywhere, and Just the Right Amount

BY WEIGHT, water makes up about 60 percent of your body. About two-thirds of that is inside your trillions of cells, and the rest is outside your cells. Of the water that's not in your cells, one-fifth makes up the fluid in your blood and the rest surrounds your cells.

Each cell must control its water volume. Just like air in a tire, it can't lose too much and go flat or gain too much and burst. Water also makes up the fluid content of your blood. This means that your body must control its total water content and, with it, your total blood volume. Too much will raise blood pressure, burst blood vessels, and flood the tissues. Too little will drop blood pressure, reduce blood flow, and starve the tissues. Neither scenario is compatible with life.

In the movie *The Good, the Bad, and the Ugly*, when the outlaw Tuko (played by Eli Wallach) forces Blondie (played by Clint Eastwood) to walk across the desert, we get to see what not having enough water looks like. He starts out with a swagger in his step but soon, after losing about 5 percent of his water content, he's tired and thirsty. Continuing to about 10 percent loss, he becomes sluggish and weak. With around 15 percent loss he has difficulty standing and even talking. At about 20 percent water loss he becomes lethargic and confused, barely able to stay awake, bordering on coma. By the time the circumstances change and Tuko decides he wants him to stay alive, Blondie can barely swallow.

Death usually takes place at around 25 percent total water loss. At this point the chemical concentrations in the cells have gotten so high that the cell membranes and basic metabolic processes no longer work properly. At the same time, blood volume has dropped dramatically, and blood pressure is so low that the cardiovascular system can't provide enough blood (with its oxygen and sugar) to the body's tissues.

So, just as with O_2 and sugar, having the right amount of water in the body is a matter of life and death. And the body's capacity to control the amount of water it has is constantly being put to the test. Your body is always losing water. You lose water when you breathe in and out. You lose water when you perspire. Your gastrointestinal system loses water. And what about all that urine you send out each day?

A drop in total water content makes all the cells shrink a bit. The hypothalamus has cells called osmoreceptors that can detect this shrinkage and react by stimulating your thirst center. It also stimulates the release of a hormone from the posterior pituitary gland called anti-diuretic hormone (ADH).

With more water loss you get thirstier and more ADH is released. ADH travels in the blood and attaches to specific receptors on specific microtubules in the kidneys. The increase in ADH tells the kidneys to retain more water from the urine in production, and so only a small amount of very concentrated urine is sent out.

When you get a little dehydrated and drink water to quench your thirst, the water is readily absorbed into the body by the gastrointestinal system and put into your blood, where it makes its way back to the cells. This reverses the shrinkage and plumps the cells up a little. The osmoreceptors in your hypothalamus detect this change, the amount of ADH is reduced, and your thirst goes away. Less ADH tells the kidneys to bring back less water into the body from the urine in production, so they send out large amounts of dilute urine.

The osmoreceptors in your hypothalamus are so sensitive that they react to just a 1 percent change in total body water. So, when your body loses about 400 mL (14 oz) of water, you start feeling thirsty and more ADH is sent out. These sensors act as an early warning system, so you have time to find water before you've lost anywhere close to 25 percent and are dead—at which point getting more water won't help much.

Your kidneys filter about 7.5 liters of water an hour (180 liters a day). If none of it were brought back into your body by the kidneys, you'd be dead in about an hour and a half. Fortunately, they're set up to automatically bring back about 90 percent of that water. But that still leaves 10 percent (about 18 liters a day in an average-size person). This is where ADH fits into the picture. It's the ADH that prevents most of these 18 liters a day from being lost. The additional effect of ADH tells the kidneys to bring back all but about 1 percent of the water. That's why you urinate only about 1.5 to 2 liters daily, and why you're still alive.

With diabetes insipidus, the body has an ADH deficiency. Either the pituitary gland isn't making enough ADH or the kidneys aren't responding well enough to the ADH. A person with this condition would be unable to retain much of the remaining 18 liters of water, and without intervention would die in about twelve hours. In a desperate attempt to survive, he could try to drink 750 mL (25 oz) of water, and pass the same amount of urine, every hour for the rest of his life—an unlikely prospect. Luckily for patients with this condition, modern medicine has developed desmopressin, a drug that can be inhaled, swallowed, or injected to provide enough ADH. With this treatment a person with diabetes insipidus has the means to control his body's water content.

While these modern medical interventions have been a blessing to many, the wonder in all this is that most people have no need for such heroic medical interventions, because their kidneys handle the demanding job of maintaining the body's total water content just fine.

A Pinch of This and a Pinch of That

So FAR in this chapter we've reviewed what can happen if your body can't control two of its most essential molecules, glucose ($C_6H_{12}O_6$) and water (H_2O), and two of its most toxic molecules, ammonia (NH_3) and urea (CH_4N_2O). Death.

But your body needs many other chemical substances to live, ones that have to be in exactly the right places, joined into the right molecules and, just like the others we've discussed, kept within tight tolerances.

The chemical formulas of the molecules noted above involve just four elements—carbon (C), oxygen (O), hydrogen (H), and nitrogen (N).

Add to them calcium (Ca) and phosphorus (P), mainly in your bones, and you've accounted for about 99 percent of all the atoms in your body.

Most of the remaining atoms are sodium (Na), potassium (K), chlorine (Cl), magnesium (Mg), and sulfur (S). Also needed are trace elements like iron (Fe), copper (Cu), zinc (Zn), iodine (I), fluorine (F), selenium (Se), chromium (Cr), lithium (Li), molybdenum (Mo), manganese (Mn), and cobalt (Co).

Though present in relatively small amounts, each of these trace elements plays a critical role in life. If any were missing, you wouldn't be alive. Let's look at just a few of them.

Salt

SODIUM, POTASSIUM, and chlorine make up the dietary salts sodium chloride (NaCl—table salt) and potassium chloride (KCl—salt substitute), both found in many foods. As your body takes in NaCl and KCl, they dissolve in the body's water. When dissolved in water, sodium and potassium each give up an electron to the chlorine atoms. This makes them positively charged sodium and potassium ions (Na^+ and K^+) and negatively charged chlorine ions (Cl^-).

Water passes freely through biological membranes. So how does your body make sure the right amount of water is present inside and outside your cells? As discussed in Chapter 1, the force of diffusion can alter the chemical concentration of your cells because it causes K^+ ions to leave and Na^+ ions to enter. In addition, as Na^+ ions enter the cell they bring water with them (by osmosis). Each cell has about a million sodium/potassium (Na^+/K^+ ion) pumps in its membrane that use energy from ATP to constantly pump Na^+ ions out and bring K^+ ions in to maintain their proper ion concentration. However, as the Na^+ ions are pumped out of the cell, some water goes out with them. A good rule of thumb regarding the body is wherever Na^+ ions go, water follows. Thus, the millions of Na^+/K^+ ion pumps in the membranes of your trillions of cells make sure that both the Na^+ and K^+ ion concentrations and the volume of water inside and outside of them remain relatively constant.

144 / Your Designed Body /

It's important to realize that having enough Na$^+$ ions outside your cells ensures you have enough water there too. And since the water outside your cells includes the water in your blood, your blood volume and blood pressure also depend on the amount of Na$^+$ ions outside your cells. So, no Na$^+$ ions would mean no water in your blood. No water in your blood means no blood volume, which means no blood pressure. And no you.

K$^+$ ions are the most abundant positively charged ions in your cells. Despite the action of the Na$^+$/K$^+$ pumps, more K$^+$ ions tend to leak out of your cells than Na$^+$ ions leak in. This net loss of positively charged ions makes the inside of the cell membrane negative and the outside positive. This is called the resting membrane potential (RMP).

Nerve and muscle cells, when stimulated, have a mechanism that lets Na$^+$ ions flood into the cell to reverse the polarity of the RMP, so the inside becomes positive and the outside negative. This is called depolarization and is essential for transmitting nerve impulses. If the concentration of K$^+$ ions outside your cells is too high or too low, this affects the RMP and interferes with depolarization, causing the nerve and muscle cells to malfunction. Of course, this includes brain and heart function, so when the balance of K$^+$ ions goes wonky, your entire body goes wonky. Fortunately, in most cases when this happens, the body is able to compensate long enough for you to get medical treatment.

The amount of Na$^+$ and K$^+$ ions in your body is controlled by an adrenal hormone called aldosterone. The adrenal glands seem to be able to sense the Na$^+$/K$^+$ ratio in your blood at any given moment and, in response, send out the right amount of aldosterone. Aldosterone secretion is also affected by other hormones.

Aldosterone travels in your blood and attaches to specific receptors in your kidneys, in effect telling them how much Na$^+$ to retain from the urine in production and, by association, how much K$^+$ to offload. When it comes to Na$^+$ and K$^+$ ions, aldosterone does for the body exactly the opposite of what the Na$^+$/K$^+$ ion pumps do for the cells.

Calcium

EVERYONE KNOWS calcium is needed for good bones. But the amount of calcium in your blood and in your cells plays an important role in nerve and muscle function. When calcium salts dissolve within the water in your body, they separate and the calcium gives up two electrons to become Ca^{2+} ions.

For your nerves and muscles to work properly, the concentration of Ca^{2+} ions outside your cells must be ten thousand times higher than it is inside your cells. To maintain this ratio, nerve and muscle cells have calcium pumps that push Ca^{2+} ions out of their cellular fluid. Additionally, for nerve and muscle cells to depolarize and work properly, the concentration of Ca^{2+} ions outside your cells must not rise or drop more than 50 percent beyond the normal range. So, too much or too little calcium in your blood means no proper nerve or muscle function. And no you.

Calcium levels in the blood are controlled by the parathyroid glands embedded in the four corners of the thyroid gland in your neck. They have calcium receptors to detect the level of calcium in the blood. In response to low calcium, these cells send out parathormone (PTH), which travels in the blood and attaches to specific PTH receptors that ultimately affect your bones, gastrointestinal system, and kidneys to keep blood calcium within range.

Trace Metals

TRACE METALS like iron (Fe), copper (Cu), and zinc (Zn) are present in thousands of proteins in your body. Chapter 6 explained how iron (Fe) is vital for transporting O_2 in the blood. Remember that O_2 attaches to the iron atoms in hemoglobin. So, without iron there's no hemoglobin. And without hemoglobin there's no O_2 transport, and no you.

Similarly, copper, zinc, and the other trace metals are critical, both to the structure of certain proteins and to how those proteins work.

But as is generally the case in engineering, the solution poses a new problem: trace metals readily interact with other molecules in the body to form toxic substances. To prevent this, the body deploys specialized transport proteins that bind and transport these metals. The transport proteins neutralize the reactive properties of the metal atoms by storing them in a special way that prevents unwanted reactions in the body. This allows them to safely transit through the body to the cells where they'll be used. Some well-known transport proteins your body makes are transferrin for iron, ceruloplasmin for copper, and albumin and alpha-2 macroglobulin for zinc.

Scientists are still studying how the body maintains the right level of trace elements like iron, copper, and zinc. What they do know is that the liver plays a major role and that having too much or too little of any of them results in debility or death.

> The human body needs many chemical substances that, if left to their own devices, would quickly kill the body. The body must do several things to address this problem. (1) It must know that these chemical substances are needed and have a way to harvest them in the right quantities from the environment. (2) The body must be able to transport each using an appropriate, specialized molecule that renders it incapable of interacting with the wrong chemical substances or being in the wrong places. (3) Then the body must transport the given chemical substance to the point of use, where it is unbound from the container. (4) Then the chemical substance must be fabricated into the specific protein that's needed for a particular use at a particular time and place.
>
> Said more simply, each of these chemical substances must be harvested and leveraged for their positive properties for life, without allowing their negative, death-dealing properties to damage or kill the body. Each stage of this process is a thorny engineering problem. Taken together, they form yet another daunting set of challenges for the body.

Insights

HUNDREDS OF other chemical substances, organic and inorganic, are also essential, and each requires the same kinds of functions as those we've discussed thus far: materials harvesting, precision controls, production and assembly, and runtime management.

But even in just this short chapter we have highlighted the importance of dozens of different kinds of molecules, trace elements, and organic compounds, each of which must be either harvested from outside the body or manufactured within, and in either case must be controlled for human life. This includes molecules like sugar, water, and salt; trace elements like iron, copper, and zinc; and organic molecules like insulin, glucagon, and aldosterone along with their specific receptors and the transport proteins.

To stay alive, the human body must continuously determine what materials it needs, harvest them from the environment, process them into their constituent chemical building blocks, possibly store them and later retrieve them from storage, process them into forms the body can use, transport them to the right locations, and use them in one of the processes of life. It must also collect any byproducts or "garbage" and either recycle or eliminate them from the system. That the body does much of this work at the molecular level is amazing.

How many different systems and components are required for the body to supply its material needs? Don't worry if you don't know. Neither does anyone else. It's literally more than we can count at this stage.

Have you ever heard a reasonably detailed description of how any of these chemical control systems and processes might have evolved through unintentional natural processes, especially given that a complex body like ours cannot exist without all of them? If you haven't, don't worry about this either. Nobody has. No such description exists, nor even a feeble initial outline of one. And the failure is not for lack of trying, or for lack of intellectual talent brought to bear on the question, or for lack of research funding.

9. Temperature

Goldilocks went inside. First she tasted the porridge of the great, huge bear, and that was far too hot for her. And then she tasted the porridge of the middle bear, and that was too cold for her. And then she went to the porridge of the little, small wee bear, and tasted that. And that was neither too hot nor too cold, but just right.

—"Goldilocks and the Three Bears"[1]

Consider the case of Julia. She and her best friend travel to Florida to play in a collegiate beach volleyball tournament, and while warming up on the beach, Julia notices she doesn't have her usual strength. The pair lose their first match badly and her friend scolds her for not playing up to her usual. So, in the next match Julia pulls out all the stops to make up for her previous poor performance. But suddenly she feels not just weak, but awful. The month before the tournament, Julia had some unintentional weight loss, a hand tremor, heart flutter, and excessive sweating, but she and her mother just chalked it up to nerves. Now she wonders if that was a mistake.

But she doesn't wonder long, for in the next moment she passes out on the sand. The medics arrive to find her unconscious body shaking and panting. They take her vitals and find that she has a high fever and a fast heart rate.

In the ER Julia is stabilized and sent to ICU. Without swift, skilled medical care, she will likely die. After further investigation the physicians learn that while this athletic young woman was in otherwise excellent health leading up to the tournament, a single system in her body had stopped working properly, and the problem was compounded by a separate short-term health challenge. The result was that her body lost control of its core temperature.

Here again we have a medical scenario illustrating just how much has to go right for the sophisticated system of systems that is the human body to survive and thrive.

Heat and Temperature

THE LAWS of physics apply to the human body just as they do to everything else made of matter. Touch a hot stove and the transfer of heat from the stove to your fingers will burn your skin. Grab an ice cube and the heat from your fingers will make the ice melt.

In Chapter 1 we saw how cellular respiration releases energy from glucose. This process also generates heat. The more work your body does, the more active your cellular respiration and the more heat it produces. However, most places on Earth are cooler than your body temperature, and most people spend most of their time in environments cooler than their body temperatures, so our bodies tend to lose heat to our surroundings. A body's core temperature results from how much heat it produces and how much heat it loses to (or sometimes gains from) its surroundings.

Just as a machine can malfunction if it's too hot or too cold, your cells can stop working if your internal temperature gets too hot or too cold. Most of the enzymes your body uses work best within a temperature range of 97° to 99°F (36° to 37°C).

As your core temperature rises above the normal range, the structural proteins and enzymes in your cells begin to malfunction. When it goes above 107°F (42°C) they break down, impairing cellular respiration and destabilizing cell membranes. This results in loss of temperature control, multi-organ failure, and death.

As your core temperature drops below the normal range, critical enzymes in your cells slow down. When it drops below 91°F (33°C) they stop working, impairing metabolic activity and decreasing energy production. This results in loss of temperature control and, unless quickly corrected, multi-organ failure and death.

As we saw in the story of Julia, keeping the human body at the right temperature is a matter of life and death. The body must be not too hot and not too cold. Goldilocks, again.

> Temperature is a measure of an object's internal energy. This temperature, or heat, is always seeking an equilibrium state. Put a warmer object (or substance) next to a colder object (or substance), and the warmer object will lose heat (energy) to the colder one while the colder one will gain heat from the warmer one. Before long they'll both be at the same temperature, somewhere in between the warm and the cold. This is known as heat transfer.
>
> When a machine uses energy to do work, it naturally gives off heat. In the same way, the body's metabolic activity releases heat, even when it's at rest. The body cannot allow its internal heat to build up indefinitely, so it must shed this heat to its surroundings. How can the body move that heat from where it's generated, especially from the cells at the body's core, to somewhere outside the body, and in a way that cools exactly the right places in the right amounts at the right times? This is yet another thorny problem the body must solve to stay alive.

Regulating Heat

WHEN YOUR body is at rest, the amount of energy it needs to maintain cellular integrity and organ function is called its basal metabolic rate (BMR). This is the minimal energy the body needs to consume to keep its organs working and to stay alive.

Your body's metabolism is a form of work, even when you're at rest, and work releases heat, so your BMR determines the minimum amount of heat your body produces. Any activity you do beyond total rest, including eating and drinking, makes your body work harder and generate more heat.

Just as heat radiates from the sun, much of the heat produced by your body is lost through your skin, at least when the air is cooler than your body. In most cases, this accounts for about half your body's heat loss. Your body also loses heat by conduction, usually aided by convection. This happens when you're in contact with a cool breeze that clears away the warmer air close to your skin. This accounts for about one-quarter of your body's heat loss.

Evaporation occurs when water on a surface absorbs heat from its surroundings and is released into the air as water vapor. Heat loss by evaporation takes place from your lungs, mouth, and perspiration on your skin. It accounts for about one-quarter of the total heat lost from your body.

Your body needs to keep its core temperature between 97° and 99°F, no matter where you are or what you're doing. In a process called thermoregulation, the body controls your metabolic rate and internal temperature by quickly adapting to changing conditions. This requires yet another control system that can quickly adapt to rapid changes in activity levels as well as to swings in the outside temperature and humidity, which affect the direction and rate of heat transfer with the environment.

This control system must be able to sense body temperature, apply appropriate decision logic, and invoke just the right changes in the body's internal temperature via body systems specialized to effectively distribute and discharge heat. This includes, notably, the circulatory system, which serves a secondary but critical role of evenly distributing heat throughout your body. Most often it will transfer heat from your body's core to your skin and lungs, from which the bulk of the heat will dissipate into the air.

As with all the control systems we've seen so far, heat regulation is do or die. In the story of Julia, she fell seriously ill on the sun-scorched beach because her body couldn't maintain its temperature within the range necessary to sustain life, and her body temperature spiked way above normal. The surrounding hot, humid environment would make it challenging for anyone to shed enough heat, particularly if the person chose to ignore the body's warning signs and persisted in exercising vigorously in the full sun, as Julia and the other intrepid beach volleyball players did. But additionally, our unlucky heroine is experiencing a chemical imbalance that increased how much heat her body produces.

BMR Control

THE HORMONE that affects almost every chemical reaction in every cell of your body, and therefore your metabolic rate, is thyroid hormone. This complex chemical is produced in the thyroid gland in your neck. Thyroid hormone binds to a specific receptor in the nucleus of your cells

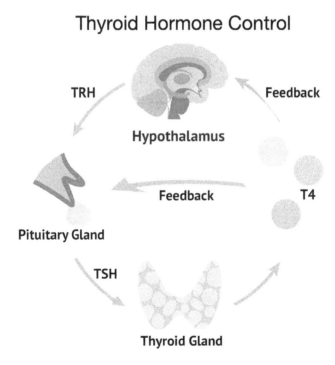

Figure 9.1. The hypothalamus-pituitary-thyroid axis.

and stimulates protein synthesis and cellular respiration. This causes an increase in your body's O_2 consumption (metabolism) and thus in its heat production. Since thyroid hormone is what mainly affects your basal metabolic rate (BMR) and how much heat your body produces at complete rest, keeping it under control is needed for thermoregulation.

The hypothalamus-pituitary-thyroid axis controls the level of thyroid hormone in your body. It follows a classic negative feedback loop control pattern. The hypothalamus sends out Thyroid Releasing Hormone (TRH), which attaches to specific receptors in the pituitary. In response, the pituitary sends out Thyroid Stimulating Hormone (TSH), which attaches to specific receptors in the thyroid gland. In response, the thyroid gland sends out thyroid hormone. (See Figure 9.1 for more details.) Both the hypothalamus and the pituitary can detect thyroid hormone levels in your blood. If it's too low, they release more TRH and TSH, respectively, and if it's too high, they release less of these hormones. They use setpoints in these decisions, but no one knows how they determine what your blood level of thyroid hormone should be.

Sometimes things can go wrong with thyroid function and the level of thyroid hormone in the blood can drift too high or too low. When it gets too high, this is called hyperthyroidism. When it goes too low, it's called hypothyroidism.

People with hypothyroidism have a decreased basal metabolic rate, which means slower metabolism at rest and less heat generated. They tend to feel cold and experience weight gain, fatigue, muscle weakness, dry skin, hair loss, constipation, and a very slow heart rate that can sometimes limit activity.

People with hyperthyroidism have a higher metabolism at rest and generate more heat. They tend to feel warm and experience weight loss, fatigue, muscle weakness, excessive sweating, nervousness, tremors, diarrhea, and a faster heart rate that can sometimes lead to palpitations and life-threatening rhythm problems.

Consider what Julia experienced before going to the beach volleyball tournament. She had a hand tremor, weight loss, anxiety, and excessive sweating. This cluster of symptoms is consistent with hyperthyroidism. That would make her body warmer than usual at complete rest. Then place her in a hot, humid environment and demand intense activity from her, and you see the danger.

High-Tech Thermostat

SOMEHOW YOUR hypothalamus knows what your body's core temperature should be and acts as the body's thermostat to keep your core temperature near its target range of 97° to 99°F. It does this by combining subconscious adjustments with your conscious sense of being too hot or too cold, which spurs the deliberate actions you take to get cooler or warmer.

To help the hypothalamus keep track of your body's temperature, your body is equipped with thermoreceptors that come in two different flavors. Peripheral thermoreceptors are located in your skin. They detect either hot or cold, and warn your body when it's being exposed to extremes in temperature that may result in tissue damage. Temperatures too high can cause a thermal burn while temperatures too low can cause frostbite. The peripheral thermoreceptors also inform the hypothalamus of the temperature on the surface of your body so it can anticipate temperature changes.

Central thermoreceptors are in your chest, abdomen, and hypothalamus. They detect your body's core temperature—that is, the temperature of most of your cells. This information is also sent to the thermal control center in your hypothalamus. Based on this central and peripheral thermal information, the hypothalamus sends signals to tell the body to adjust its autonomous heat dissipation systems to meet the current need as best it can. But this may not be enough, so when needed, signals are also sent to the conscious mind that intentional action must be taken.

When the hypothalamus warns you your core is too warm, you can stop your present activity to reduce the amount of heat your body is producing. You can remove warm clothing to lose more heat to the environment. You can move out of the sun into the shade. You can turn on a fan. You can drink a big glass of cold water and pour another all over your body to help it quickly lose more heat.

When the hypothalamus warns you your core is too cold, you can increase your level of activity. You can rub your hands together. You can stamp your feet. You can move around more. You can put on heavier clothing. You can stand near a warm fireplace. Or you can book a trip to Hawaii.

Once again, we find a crucial control system in the body that takes a lot of parts, with all of them doing the right things with the right signaling, the right control logic, and the right effectors.

Your Amazing Skin

Your skin is your largest organ and, as the outer layer of your body, it of course has the greatest contact with your surroundings. It's made up of different cell types that work together to protect your body from things like friction, chemicals, and microbes.

Your skin also helps your body regulate its core temperature by varying how much heat it loses to your surroundings. For this it needs some unique properties, and for these it has specialized blood vessels and millions of sweat glands.

Being so close to your body's surface, the warm blood circulating in your skin tends to lose heat. More blood flow to your skin leads to more heat loss, and less blood flow leads to less heat loss. So, when your core temperature rises above normal, your body can lose more heat by increasing blood flow to the skin. When your core temperature drops below normal, it can reduce heat loss by decreasing blood flow to the skin.

This runs counter to the norm. For most of your organs, blood flow is mainly tied to its metabolic needs, which indicate how hard it's working at any given time. Serving those metabolic needs is the primary task of the cardiovascular system, and as we've seen, it's masterfully designed to do this effectively and efficiently.

But your skin works differently. The amount of blood flowing in your skin usually exceeds its metabolic needs. The skin incorporates special blood vessels found nowhere else in the body, which connect the arterial and venous systems directly, bypassing the narrow and constricted capillaries that service the skin's metabolism. When the body needs to lose heat more quickly than usual, it opens these connections to allow rapid blood flow through the skin by shunting blood directly from the arteries to the veins. These special blood vessels are particularly prevalent in your hands, feet, ears, nose, and lips.

The hypothalamus controls the blood flow to the skin through the sympathetic nervous system. For this process it uses a neurohormone called norepinephrine, which makes the heart speed up, as we learned in Chapter 5.

Norepinephrine attaches to specific receptors on the muscles surrounding the arterioles in the skin tissue and tells them to contract. When it detects that your core temperature is above normal, your hypothalamus tells the sympathetic nervous system to send out less norepinephrine. This relaxes the muscles around the arterioles in your skin, resulting in more blood flow. (When you see a person out in hot weather looking flushed, this is likely the reason.) It also causes your body to lose more heat. Conversely, when your core temperature drops below normal, your hypothalamus tells the same nerve cells to send out more norepinephrine. This contracts the muscles around the arterioles in your skin, lessening blood flow. (When you see a person out in the cold looking unusually pale, this may be the reason.) It also causes your body to lose less heat.

The body also employs a second nerve-controlled mechanism when it needs to rapidly shed heat, one quite familiar to most of us. Your skin has millions of sweat glands that release water onto its surface. Once on your skin, the water from your sweat glands quickly absorbs heat from your body, which causes it to evaporate more quickly. As it turns into vapor, it cools the skin via evaporative cooling. To control perspiration, the hypothalamus still uses the sympathetic nervous system, but instead of norepinephrine it sends out acetylcholine. (See Chapter 5.) Acetylcholine attaches to specific receptors on the sweat glands to control their output. When the hypothalamus detects a rise in core temperature, it tells the sympathetic nervous system to send out more acetylcholine. This generates more perspiration and greater heat loss. When the core temperature drops, the hypothalamus tells it to send out less acetylcholine, for less perspiration and lower heat loss.

Julia Recovers

IN OUR scenario of the beach volleyball player passing out in the Florida heat, she was hyperthyroid for several weeks before traveling to the tournament. Even at rest, her metabolism was on overdrive, generating a lot more heat than usual. Her body's ability to regulate its core temperature was compromised by her hyperthyroid condition. The heat and high humidity at the volleyball tournament also limited how much heat her body could shed through sweating and the accompanying process of evaporative cooling.

During the match her body screamed at her to rest and get out of the heat, but she ignored this. As her level of exertion ramped up in the heat and humidity, her body's thermoregulatory systems just couldn't compensate, her core temperature rose to dangerous levels, and she fainted. The fainting is itself one of the body's ingenious mechanisms to avoid overheating. But Julia has another strike against her. On the day of the tournament, she woke feeling a bit under the weather. She had contracted a viral illness that gave her a fever. This along with the other factors combined into a perfect storm. When her temperature hit 105° F, she didn't merely faint. She went into seizures and a coma, in what is called a thyroid storm.

In ICU, she is given rapid intravenous fluid hydration, packed in ice, and given medications to stop her seizures, lower her heart rate, and block the effects of thyroid hormone. She soon comes out of her coma and opens her eyes. Her body's natural healing and recovery systems are again humming, and a few days later she has fully recovered.

Modern medicine is a wonder, but don't miss what else is illustrated here. Take away even just one of these many strikes against Julia and she would not have ended up in the hospital. The body's thermoregulatory system is that resilient.

Insights

To SURVIVE, humans need (and have) the ability to stay active in surroundings that are very hot or very cold, and to properly manage core body temperature while doing so. This means that our bodies must be able to regulate the rate of heat loss quickly and effectively in widely varying environmental conditions, and under varying levels of activity. The mechanisms that allow for this are extraordinary, not just in their ability to solve these difficult problems in a timely fashion, but also in the sheer ingenuity of their design.

With your new understanding of how your body manages your core temperature, maybe you've come up with some questions that beg for answers. How could all this have come about? Which of the classes of causal forces would be capable of making such a system? If this system of systems came about gradually over millions of years among our distant ancestors, which parts of the system of systems came first, and how did they contribute anything to the ancestral creature without most or all of the other parts already being in place? What subsequent parts fell into place when and, specifically, how?

This book, keep in mind, isn't arguing that our bodies are free of vulnerabilities and degradation. Of course they aren't. If such were the case, we would be immortal and one of us (Howard) would be out of a job. But freedom from degradation is not the standard for engineering excellence. Rather, these pages are highlighting the plain reality that the human body is an engineering wonder, and in no small part because of its many masterfully navigated engineering trade-offs, which afford it a remarkable resilience across a long span of life, a life that includes a rich variety of activities, the ability to thrive in a wide range of diverse environments, and the capacity to reproduce itself.

And the most arresting thing of all: the many coherent interdependent systems that make up the human body—and now we add to the list the body's thermoregulatory system—all need each other for the human body to survive and thrive. This, again, poses an enormous causal challenge for evolutionary scenarios that forgo foresight and intention.

PART THREE: LIVING BEYOND HOMEOSTASIS

HOMEOSTASIS IS FUNDAMENTAL TO LIFE, BUT IT'S ONLY A FOUNDA- tion. To do most of what we do, and especially what we like to do, much more is required. Homeostasis is mostly involuntary and unconscious. Homeostasis is necessary but not sufficient for our existence. To survive and thrive, you must also be able to take action, consciously and voluntarily.

To take effective action when opportunities or threats arise, your body needs to know what's going on, both inside and outside your skin. For this it uses specialized nerve cells, each equipped to detect something specific like light, sound waves, or chemicals that you can smell or taste. You also have cells that can detect pressure, stretch, vibration, heat, and cold. And you detect tissue damage (pain) from trauma, inflammation, and noxious organic molecules (like lactic acid).

When a sensory nerve cell detects its specific "something," it sends a signal through the peripheral nerves to the central nervous system (the spinal cord and brain) for analysis, making you aware of the sensation.

To live beyond homeostasis, your body also needs a skeletal structure specially tuned for purposeful movement. The skeletal muscles usually come in pairs—one muscle to flex a joint, and its complement to extend it. To prevent a tug-of-war, nervous controls ensure that when one muscle contracts, its counterpart relaxes.

Together, these systems enable you to monitor and engage your environment. They allow you to be conscious and to see, hear, feel, smell, taste, think, communicate, move around, stay balanced, and handle things—to act in the world.

10. Seeing Is Believing

How came the bodies of animals to be contrived with so much art, and for what ends were their several parts? Was the eye contrived without skill in opticks?

—Isaac Newton[1]

Anthony is a heavy equipment operator, married and with children in high school. One day he notices that sometimes when he shifts lanes in traffic, a car seems to appear out of nowhere. Another day at work, while running a frontend loader, he has a near miss when he doesn't see a foreman walking nearby. The near miss shakes up both him and the foreman, and he's ordered to get himself checked over right away.

After a full assessment, his eye doctor tells him that, while his near and far vision are perfect, he has deficiencies in the peripheral vision of both eyes. Anthony can see things in front of him clearly. It's the things coming at him from the side that give him trouble.

The doctor tells him his condition could be serious, and possibly permanent, and it isn't correctable with glasses. Anthony faces the possibility that he will never again be able to work as a heavy equipment operator, or even drive. His wife drives him home. Along the way he wonders aloud why they can't fix his problem. "If we can put a man on the moon," he says, "they should be able to fix me!"

What Anthony doesn't realize is that the human vision system is far more complex than any that human engineers can produce.

Seeing Is Hard to Do

IN THE previous chapters we looked at many of the body's ingeniously sophisticated mechanisms, but vision makes most of our previous examples look like child's play. It's often said that the eye is like a camera. But this is backwards, because the vertebrate eye was around long before the first camera. Better to say that a camera is like an eye—albeit an eye in a much simpler form.

It turns out that sight is yet another hard problem. Light needs to come into the body, be converted into signals, and then be sent to the brain to be processed. And that's putting it simplistically. Vision requires many millions of light sensors sending data in real time to the brain, which requires massively parallel processing to convert the signals into a view of the surrounding world. All this must happen in real time, with no perceptible delay between something happening and the experience of seeing it happen. A lot of stuff will need to be "just right." And we can expect that it will, once again, involve a series of cascading problems that must all be solved at the same time for the vision system to work.

With a little engineering thought, we can predict much of what will be needed to detect and use a natural phenomenon like light:

- Sensory transducers to convert light into information that can be interpreted.
- A large array of individual sensors, precisely arranged.
- Signaling of sufficient quality and quantity (bandwidth) to send information from the sensor array to the brain.
- Substantial processing power to convert the raw signals into a consistent, whole, and timely image.
- A structure able to hold all the parts together in a precise configuration while enabling them to move or rotate as needed for their functions.
- A finely tuned optical system that can quickly adjust to different situations to provide a sharp image in a wide variety of light intensities and across a variety of frequencies.

Human Eye Structure

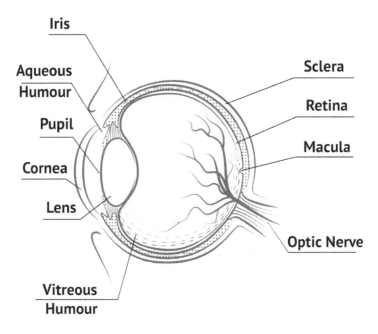

Figure 10.1. A cutaway view showing the main parts of the eye.

The most critical requirement for vision is some kind of sensor. Just as a camera's sensor (or its film) converts light into information, the eye's sensors need to convert individual photons of light into electrical signals. Figuring out how to accomplish this is a challenge demanding enough to get an engineer's juices flowing.

The retina is where this problem is solved. (See Figure 10.1.) A thin layer of tissue along the back of the retina contains two specialized types of photoreceptor cells called rods and cones because they resemble these shapes.

Each of your eyes has about 120 million rod cells in its retina, mostly scattered throughout the outer edges. Rod cells make a light-sensitive molecule called rhodopsin, which reacts to any wavelength in the visible spectrum. Because they're not picky about specific wavelengths, these molecules mainly detect luminosity rather than color. In effect, they see in black and white. Because they're mostly located off the central axis of vision, at the periphery, they provide peripheral vision.

For central vision, each of your eyes has about six million cone cells, concentrated in the macula, at the center of the eye, with the highest concentration in the center of the macula, at the fovea. Each cone makes one of three light-sensitive molecules, together called photopsins, which react to specific wavelengths of visible light—either red, green, or blue.

> The highest concentration of color-sensitive cones is right in the middle of the eye's optical axis—the macula and, in particular, the fovea. Here's where the most and best information is needed.
>
> As a result of this concentration, the sharpest acuity with the best color fidelity is available exactly along the central axis of vision—right where your eye is aimed. (Rod cells are better suited for peripheral vision and are found in abundance where they can assist in this, around the edges. More on this later.) Since each cone reacts to just a single color, full color vision requires roughly even distribution of the different color-detecting cone cells within the central area of the retina.
>
> This is a stunningly imaginative and efficient approach to capturing light waves and converting them into information that the brain can process and use.

How do these photoreceptors work? It takes some special machinery to convert photons of light (traveling at the speed of light) into something the body can make sense of.

When a photon collides with a photosensitive rhodopsin molecule (in a rod cell), the energy changes the molecule's shape, which triggers the photoreceptor to alter its signal to a nearby interconnecting nerve cell. These auxiliary nerve cells (mostly bipolar and ganglion cells) collect the visual sensory information from the nearby photoreceptor cells,

STRUCTURE OF THE RETINA

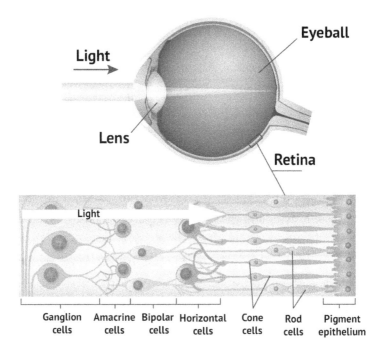

Figure 10.2. The upper image shows the location of the retina in the human eye. The lower image provides details of the retina's structure.

preprocess it, and ultimately send the results along the optic nerve to the brain. The photopsin molecules in cone cells work in a similar way.

What follows is a summary of the biomolecular process at play.[2] When a photon of light enters a rod cell, the smaller 11-*cis*-retinal molecule attached to the larger rhodopsin protein changes shape to become 11-*trans*-retinal, and this in turn causes rhodopsin to change its shape as well. This starts a cascade of several chemical reactions involving several different molecules that ultimately results in the reduction of an important signaling molecule in the cell called cGMP. The sudden drop in cGMP causes the rod cell to no longer send out its neurotransmitter (glutamate), which normally inhibits the nearby bipolar cell. With the inhibitor removed, the bipolar cell sends an electrical signal to the ganglion cell, which then sends a signal along the optic nerve to the brain. The entire process occurs in a few pico-seconds—"about the time it takes light to travel the breadth of a single human hair."[3] (A pico-second is one trillionth of a second.) Speed is essential if we are to experience vision as instantaneous. And it's crucial that we do. In most situations, it wouldn't do much good if you didn't see what was happening until some while after it occurred.

This is a lot of action, all of which needs to be just right or vision will not happen.

Curious readers might be wondering where all these precision parts come from and how they come together: what raw materials are required, how much information in the DNA is required, and how is the whole assembled and activated, but only in the exact cells where it's needed for vision? Good questions, all. But here notice that this is yet another example of the push-pull principle. We just saw that we need one irreducibly complex chemical cascade to turn a photon into a neural signal. But once a given photosensitive molecule has changed its shape in response to an incoming photon, that molecule can't react to another photon until it has been reset to its original shape. It's like a spring-loaded animal trap that needs to be reset before it can spring again.

It turns out that a completely separate irreducibly complex cascade is needed to turn the photosensitive molecule back into its original shape. Resetting the shape of the retinal (and subsequently the rhodopsin) is not simple. It's another example of a thorny problem created by an ingenious solution, with the new problem itself requiring another ingenious solution. In this case, three distinct tailor-made enzymes, working in perfect sequence, are required to convert a photosensitive molecule (rhodopsin) from its spent shape back to its ready shape. And this doesn't happen in the photoreceptor cells. It happens in a special tissue called the retinal pigment epithelium (RPE), which sits right behind the photoreceptor cell.

In yet another stage in this cascade of problems to solve, the photosensitive molecules in the rods and cones are built on vitamin A. So, if your body couldn't get vitamin A, you wouldn't have rhodopsin or the photopsins, your rod and cone cells would be useless, and you'd be blind. We won't unpack the many things required to harvest, transport, and process the vitamin A. Suffice to say, it takes several steps to absorb vitamin A in the intestine, multiple kinds of transport proteins as it moves through the body, and still other protein types, including various enzymes, to use it to build one of the photosensitive molecules needed for vision. So, yet another complete subsystem of mechanisms and controls is needed to make this happen.

Fuel for the Fire

As it turns out, the process of seeing light uses a lot of energy. In fact, the cells in the retina have the highest metabolic rate in the human body. This means they need a steady and generous supply of O_2 and other nutrients (including vitamin A), and they need to get rid of plenty of CO_2 and other waste products. For this, they need a lot of blood circulating nearby.

To support the energy-hungry retina, the eye has an especially dense network of capillaries in a special layer of tissue called the choroid, just behind the retinal pigment epithelium in the retina. These capillaries deliver just the right mixture of nutrients and remove enough waste products to support the energy needs of vision—full-time, all day long.

Poor Design?

Despite the coherent design and workings of the eye's many well-coordinated subsystems, in recent years the eye has become a folk-legend for neo-Darwinian storytellers, who have declared it to be an example of the "poor design" that results from eons of purposeless accidents driven by natural selection. Their claim goes something like this: *The photoreceptor cells in the eye point away from the front of the eye, where the light comes from. This is obviously backwards. Further, the auxiliary nerve cells that preprocess*

the visual signals are situated between the front of the eye and the photorecep-
tor cells, which surely must cause visual attenuation and distortion. This is
bad design, best explained not by reference to some all-wise designer but as
the outcome of the aimless creative process of evolution by random mutation
and natural selection.

Stories of this kind can't withstand much scrutiny, especially scrutiny from people who understand the practical necessities of real systems.
Due to the energy-hungry metabolism required for human vision and
the need to constantly reset all the photosensitive molecules, the rod and
cone cells must be very close to the retinal pigment epithelium, which
performs both these tasks. Readers who are interested in further pursuing this argument will find helpful a discussion from biologist Jonathan
Wells.[4]

We will further explore this class of argument—the poor-design argument for evolution—in Chapter 23.

The Optics of It

As ANYONE who's ever had to wear glasses or contact lenses knows all
too well, there's more to vision than merely processing light at the back
of your eyes. If it's going to be of much use, the light must get there in the
first place and be properly focused. And this leads us to the next set of
problems the body must solve: the problems of classical optics.

The cornea is a convex (curved outward) transparent connective
tissue made from a special type of collagen. It protects the front of the
eye while allowing light to enter. Since light rays coming into the eye
are either practically parallel (if the viewed object is more than about
twenty feet away) or diverging (if the viewed object is closer than twenty
feet), they must be bent (refracted) so they all come to a focal point on
the retina, preferably at the fovea, which has the highest density of cone
cells. The curvature of the cornea provides 60–70 percent of the refractive power needed to achieve focus.

Blood cells are opaque, so if the cornea had blood vessels it wouldn't
be transparent. This presents a problem for the cells in the cornea, which

still need a way to get O_2, water, and nutrients. So instead the cornea is "fed" from two sources: the tears that wash across the front of it by the eyelids when they blink, and the clear fluid (aqueous humor) in the chamber that sits between the cornea and the lens.

The lens, also transparent, is an elastic biconvex (doubly outward curved) structure consisting of connective tissue containing collagen. Like the cornea, it lacks blood vessels and gets O_2, water, and nutrients from the transparent aqueous humor.

Indeed, all the tissues and fluids between the front exterior of the eye and the retina must be transparent and colorless. Vision would be impossible otherwise. Consider how difficult that is to achieve. The eye contains the only tissue in the body that is truly transparent and colorless, and it's located exactly where it's essential for function, and nowhere else.

Once again, the right materials for the right uses, in the right places.

The lens is suspended in place by a ring of ligaments attached to a ring of ciliary muscle. When the muscle contracts, the lens bulges to enable closer focus. When the ciliary muscle relaxes, it flattens the lens for more distant vision. This action dynamically fine tunes the focus in an automatic control process called the accommodation reflex. Depending on how far away the object of interest is, the lens provides 30–40 percent of the refractive power needed to achieve focus.

> The eye's cornea and lens work exactly like a two-element lens on a modern camera, though their optical formula is simpler because the eye's sensor is curved while most photographic cameras have a flat sensor, which is optically harder to focus on. But the way the eye lens achieves variable fine-tuned focus is unlike any modern-day camera. It's better, so much so that mimicking the eye's lens would be a huge breakthrough in human-designed optics.

There's one more optical problem our eyes need to solve, and solve really well—modulating how much light enters the eye. When it's dark, it's hard to see. And when there's too much light, it's harder still. Happily, our vision system is up to the challenge.

The choroid layer of tissue behind the retina curves around the eye to the front, and at the front (and perfectly aligned with the optical axis of the eye), the choroid has an opening, called the pupil, which is surrounded by the colored iris (which is not transparent and blocks light). The iris is operated by two different muscles.

These muscles are controlled by the pupillary light reflex, which automatically controls the amount of light entering the eye. Enter a dark room and the dilating muscle of the iris enlarges the pupil to let in more light. Shine a bright light into the eye and the contracting muscle of the iris tightens to shrink the pupil. You can see this reflex in action if you look in the mirror and open and close your eyes or shine a light in them.

> The pupillary reflex is yet another example of an autonomous control system essential for good vision. It provides a critical function to the eye and a protective reflex that prevents damage.
>
> The muscles in the iris that allow for this provide for us another example of the push-pull principle. These features of the eye are so ingenious that they have been copied (albeit crudely) in cameras.
>
> Human inventors are often inspired to borrow clever engineering solutions from the biological world. This is known as biomimetics. Other examples of inventors getting ideas from nature include airplanes, hook-and-loop fasteners, suction cups, sonar, the light bulb, and tape. And of course, many of the mechanisms in the field of robotics.

When the light gets painfully bright, another reflex automatically closes the eyelids as a further layer of protection of the sensitive retinal tissues. And if it's really bright out but you still need to see, you reflexively squint, using your eyelids to further reduce the amount of light that enters your eyes.

Finally, when it's dark, as at dusk, your cones are too light-hungry to function well. But this is where the rods come into their own. Rods, recall, can't detect color like cones can, but rods gain something in the trade-off. They are much more sensitive to light than the cones are, making them ideal for vision in poor light. (Rods also are better at detecting motion.)

The Supporting Cast

Just as the lens and image sensor of a camera need the other parts of the camera, your eye needs a host of other systems and structures to work properly.

Five bones, each tailored to its role, make up the orbital cavity in the skull. These protect about two-thirds of the eyeball and provide the base for the origin tendons[5] of the six muscles that cause the eye to rotate in its socket. The eyelids and eyelashes protect the eye from dust, dirt, bacteria, and other foreign objects. A film of tears, consisting of oil, water, and mucus, is produced by the oil glands of the eyelids, the lacrimal gland, and the conjunctiva that overlies the sclera, the white outer protective coating of the eyeball. The tear film lubricates the eye, protects it from infection and injury, nourishes the surrounding tissue, and preserves a smooth surface to aid in optical focusing.

The vitreous is a thick, transparent, and gelatinous substance that forms and shapes the eyeball. It can be compressed and return to its natural position, allowing the eyeball to withstand most common physical stresses without serious injury.

The corneal reflex (blinking) is a protective reflex brought on by something touching the cornea. The menacing reflex, something coming at you quickly, and the optical reflex, sudden exposure to bright light, cause the blink reflex as well. The latter two depend on visual sensory information sent to the brainstem.

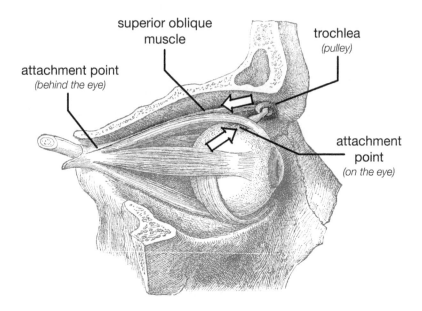

Figure 10.3. The trochlea in the right eye, viewed from the side. The ar-rows indicate the direction of the pulling force when the superior oblique muscle contracts to rotate the eye. The trochlea acts like a pulley to re-direct the force.

The trochlea is a good example of a thorny assembly problem and its solution. (See Figure 10.3.) The eye is fixed in a bony socket, with six muscles attached. Each muscle rotates the eye in a different direction. But there's a problem. Due to the shape of the skull and the position-ing of the eyes, there's no suitable attachment point for one of the six muscles. So the eye employs a clever pulley system to redirect the energy of one of the muscles. "Trochlea" is Latin for "pulley," and as you can see in the illustration, this is exactly how it works.

Assembling this structure involves something like "threading the needle." How is a structure like this made during fetal development? How are the assembly instructions encoded?

One of the keys to vision is the ability to track a moving subject. And once again, it takes some interesting mechanisms to make this work.

The vestibular-ocular (doll's eyes) reflex is a functional reflex that helps stabilize the retinal image. When you're in motion, unless you focus your view on something specific, your surroundings move across your visual field at the same speed as you do. Without the ability to control your eye movements when your head moves, what you look at would be blurry. Look into a mirror and focus on your eyes as you rotate your head from side to side and up and down. Notice how your eyes automatically move in the opposite direction of your head so you can keep your subject in focus and in the center of your visual field.

> Like every other part in your body, the eyes can't just be floating around. It also wouldn't do for them to roll out of your head and fall to the floor whenever you turned your head quickly. They need to be anchored, and they need to be held in the right configuration, with specialized structures surrounding them and protecting them, while at the same time being directly exposed to the light outside the body. As if this weren't challenge enough, the eyes also must be allowed to rotate up and down and side to side.
>
> For human eyes, this involves five specially shaped bones forming a ball-and-socket structure, with six muscles for each eye, with their tendons attached at just the right points to the bones, with eyebrows, eyelids, eyelashes, various tear and oil glands, pressurized internal gel, and various nervous reflexes (which in turn require signaling back and forth with the brainstem).
>
> Each of these parts must be correctly specialized, organized, and assembled. This is coherence of the highest order.

The brain combines sensory information from the eyes with angular information about head motion from the semicircular canals in the ears to reflexively move the eyes to maintain a stable retinal image. This means we can visually track objects no matter how fast or in what direction they (or we) move.

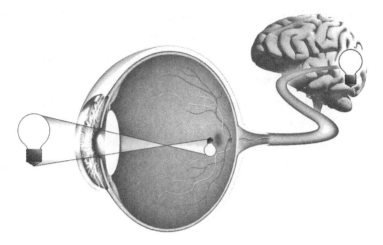

Figure 10.4. The optical inversion of the image at the retina.

Even with all the other visual mechanisms discussed above—the sensors, biochemistry, optics, and so on—we'd be functionally blind without this intriguing ability to focus on a subject and track it as we (and/or it) move.

Optical Pathways

ALL THE above are necessary if we're to see the world around us. But we still haven't explored how the visual information from all those rods and cones gets to the brain, or how the brain turns those signals into a unified and complete visual image.

About 20 percent of optic nerve impulses veer off early to provide sensory data to the brainstem, which controls the various reflexes discussed above. Because these go to the brainstem, we can diagnose brainstem function using the reflexes in the eyes. If the brainstem is working right, touching the cornea with a wisp of tissue should make both eyes blink. Shining a light into either eye should make both pupils contract. And twisting the head from side to side should make the eyes move in the opposite direction the head is moving.

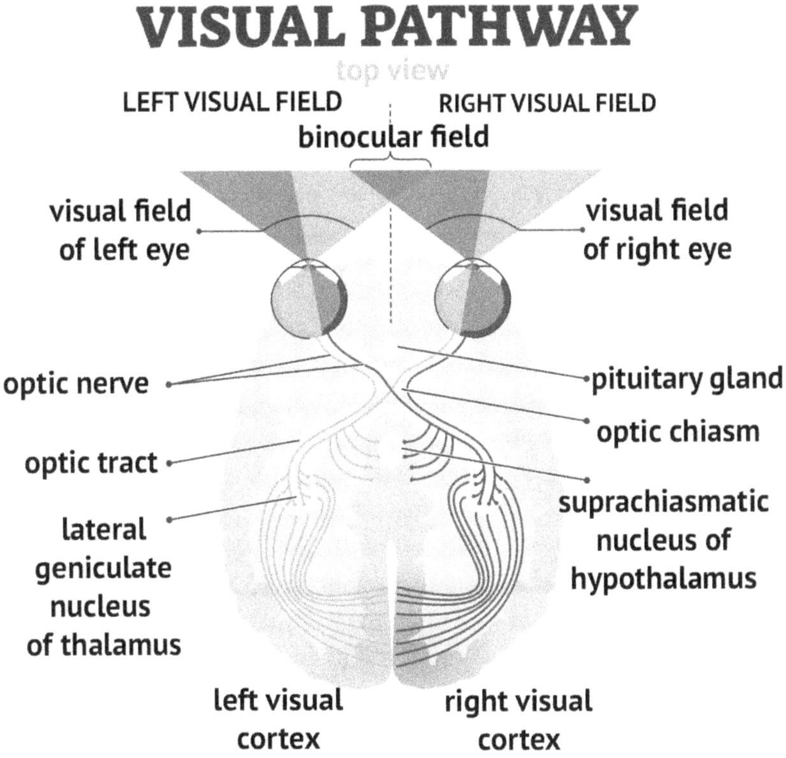

VISUAL PATHWAY
top view

LEFT VISUAL FIELD   RIGHT VISUAL FIELD

binocular field

visual field
of left eye

visual field
of right eye

optic nerve

pituitary gland

optic chiasm

optic tract

lateral
geniculate
nucleus
of thalamus

suprachiasmatic
nucleus of
hypothalamus

left visual
cortex

right visual
cortex

Figure 10.5. The pathway for visual information from the retina to the visual cortex.

What about the other 80 percent of the signals from the optic nerves? These go to the visual cortex, but they don't take the path you might expect.

Just as a camera lens forms an inverted image on the sensor, so too does the retina. (See Figure 10.4.) What you see in the upper part of your field of view is sensed in the lower part of your retina, and what you see to your left will be sensed in the right side of your retina. This means that the image is physically backwards and upside-down on the retina. This is just simple optics, but the brain's vision-processing system needs to properly decipher these signals so you sense the world as right-side-up and skillfully navigate through it.

There's another complicating factor. Your vision is split vertically in each eye, and each half of the visual signal—the inside (nasal) and the outside (temporal)[6]—takes a different path to the visual cortex.

Life on our planet depends on the electromagnetic energy that radiates from the sun. The sun throws off an enormous range of energies, from very long radio waves (with wavelengths in the millions of meters and frequencies from ten to a few hundred waves per second) to high-energy gamma rays (with wavelengths around 10^{-15} centimeters and frequencies around 10^{25} waves per second). Between these extremes are AM and FM radio waves, microwaves, infrared rays, the visible light spectrum, ultraviolet (UV) rays, and X-rays.

Visible light makes up an infinitesimally narrow band in the middle of the electromagnetic spectrum—a fraction almost unimaginably small. Michael Denton compares it to "a few playing cards in a stack stretching beyond the galaxy of Andromeda,"[7] and he calls it the "Goldilocks" portion. This visible light (along with a small portion of the near-infrared and the near-ultraviolet) is indeed special—the only slice of the entire spectrum that supports photochemistry, the process of stimulating molecules for chemical reactions. This includes all forms of photoreception and photosynthesis.

At frequencies lower than this band, photons lack the energy to drive chemical reactions. At higher frequencies the photons are so energetic they destroy the delicate molecules necessary for life, which is why living organisms cannot survive much radiation at the higher frequencies. Fortunately, the sun emits most of its light in the life-friendly region. Plus, the Earth's atmosphere lets the visible band through, while blocking almost all the damaging higher frequencies.

Imagine a vertical line going through the middle of the retina. All the photoreceptors to the right in both eyes—the inside (nasal) half from the left eye and the outside (temporal) half from the right eye—send their messages to the right side of the brain. (See Figure 10.5.) Similarly, the photoreceptors to the left in both eyes—the outside (temporal) half from the left eye and the inside (nasal) half from the right eye—send their messages to the left side of the brain. But because the image on the retina is inverted, the right visual cortex processes everything in the left visual field of each eye and the left visual cortex processes everything in the right visual field of each eye. The information pathways cross over and go their separate ways at a point called the optic chiasm.[8]

There's one more complication. Each eye sees from a slightly different perspective, a property that makes it more challenging to assemble a complete visual image. But the complication is worth it, and not just because having two eyes provides redundancy (lose one eye and you can still see). Having two eyes also allows you to sense distances—depth perception. That each eye sees an object from a slightly different angle enables the brain to calculate the resulting differences and accurately determine how far away various objects are. From this, your brain builds a real-time, 3D model of the world around you, which comes in handy for spearing a fish moving through a stream, hitting a moving target with an arrow, or catching a fly ball in center field.

Putting It All Together

Now IT's time for the brain to do its job. It must take this conglomeration of photon-generated nerve impulses—turned around, upside down, split-up, overlapping, with a blend of color and black-and-white info, and with two holes in it (from the blind spots in each eye, where the optic nerve exits the retina)—and turn it into the unified whole we experience as vision. And it must do this so fast that we can't detect a lag between the experience in the world and our vision of it.

Though we can describe many parts of the overall vision process, no one really understands exactly how it works. How, exactly, does our mind make sense of the jumble of data it receives from the many millions of photoreceptors from two eyes? It seems that the more we learn, the more profound the mysteries we discover.

Since each rod or cone in the eye produces its own signal, it acts a bit like a single pixel in a digital camera sensor. It's imperative that the signaling and interpretation system(s) keep track of (know?) where each signal is coming from and how that pixel relates to the others around it. It just wouldn't do if the pixels arrived in random order and could not be reassembled in the right order. How does the brain know where each signal is coming from? How does it assemble all these signals across different pathways into a coherent visual whole? The task is so outlandishly complicated that scientists have yet to unravel how your body manages it.

What's Wrong with Anthony's Vision?

THE ABOVE survey of human vision is, keep in mind, a massively simplified overview of a far more complicated system of systems. But with this basic understanding of visual signaling pathways, and one or two additional details, we have enough to get a handle on what is messing up the peripheral vision of Anthony the heavy equipment operator.

An untrained person might guess that Anthony has a defect in his cornea or lens, an aberration along the sides that obstructs peripheral vision. But, no, everything in his eyes looks normal. The problem lies elsewhere, and the eye doctor quickly arrives at a provisional (and classic) diagnosis: given the different pathways the visual signals travel, the most likely location of Anthony's problem is where the signals for the outer (temporal) field of vision for both eyes run together but where the signals for the inner (nasal) field of vision (for both eyes) may not be affected. This only happens in one place in the body—the optic chiasm, where the two information pathways from your two eyes cross before going their separate ways.

The eye doctor soon pinpoints Anthony's precise condition: bilateral loss of peripheral vision likely due to a pituitary tumor. That's because the pituitary gland sits just below the optic chiasm. A tumor there can press on the nearby nerves, rendering them non-functional. (Nerves don't work well under physical pressure, like when you hit your funny bone.)

Anthony's eye doctor orders a brain MRI, which verifies his suspicion. A neurosurgeon removes a large benign (non-cancerous) pituitary tumor. Eventually Anthony's peripheral vision returns to normal, and he is able to go back to work.

The story of Anthony illustrates just how critical the signaling pathways in the body are. Even if all the other components of vision are present and working properly, a limit on the signals from the eyes to the brain can significantly diminish eyesight. It's another case of the interwoven dependencies among the body's systems. Dependencies like this are common to highly complex human-engineered systems, suggesting that they are unavoidable for systems this sophisticated. This brings us back to one of this book's central questions for evolutionary theory: Could an organ system of such sophistication, necessarily involving so many layers of dependencies, have evolved in a series of incremental and functional steps? If so, how?

Darwin was himself concerned about whether the eye could ever be explained adequately by the mechanisms of his theory. He was right to be concerned.[9]

A Chemically Fine-Tuned Biomechanical Electro-Optical Signal-Processing Vision-Interpretation System

THAT VISION is possible at all is startling. Vision requires more solutions to more difficult problems than perhaps any other system in the body. It combines perfectly tuned biochemistry with solutions to complicated engineering problems involving general physics, optics, and electrical engineering, all at a level of nanotechnical sophistication that makes even the best human engineers drool. Our vision requires perfectly tuned physical structures with orchestrated motion, transparent tissues and fluids (in all the right places and in none of the wrong ones), unique supply chain solutions, constant delivery of energy to energy-hungry cells, layers of complex control systems, high information signaling systems, and information processing and image assembly on a scale we've barely begun to understand. And all this happens with no perceptible delay and no conscious effort, so you can focus on what you're seeing rather than how you're seeing.

Vison is both a wonder and an enigma.

11. Hearing Is Believing

The design of the human ear is one of nature's engineering
marvels…. It is not only a perfect design but also a low-cost
design…. In terms of performance, the human ear design is very
impressive and serves as an inspiration for designing products in
industrial environments.

—Sundar, Chowdhury, and Kamarthi[1]

Ludwig von Beethoven is one of the top composers of all
time; his music has only grown in popularity since his death in 1827.
His exceptional musical talent was evident at an early age, but he started
going deaf in his mid-twenties. His hearing continued to deteriorate
until, by the time he composed his Ninth Symphony and its celebrated
final movement, "Ode to Joy," he was all but completely deaf.[2]

While nobody is certain what caused his deafness, some have noted
that his symptoms suggest a common inherited condition—one that
modern medicine can effectively treat.

But to understand what may have caused his deafness, we first need
to understand how our hearing works.

What Is Sound?

We hear sounds. A simple enough statement, but what is sound? Sound
occurs when pressure oscillations (waves) move through air. More specifically, sound is due to air molecules alternating between being packed
together in areas of high concentration (compressions) and spread apart
in areas of low concentration (rarefactions). Think of an accordion or a
slinky.

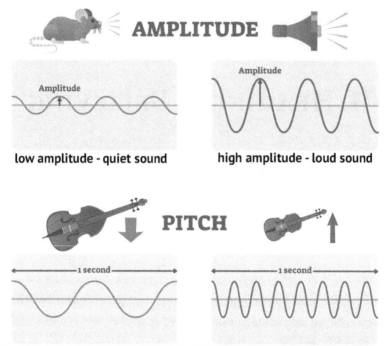

Figure 11.1. Amplitude and pitch in sound waves.

These compressions and rarefactions form longitudinal pressure waves of sound that travel through Earth's atmosphere at about 340 meters/sec (760 mph). Light travels at 300,000 kilometers/sec, meaning it is almost a million times faster than sound. This is why we see the light from a distant lightning strike well before we hear the corresponding thunder.

Sound waves vary in amplitude and frequency, as illustrated in Figure 11.1. Amplitude is perceived as the volume of the sound. Higher amplitudes sound louder and lower amplitudes sound quieter. Amplitude is measured in decibels (dB), named after Alexander Graham Bell, the inventor of the telephone.

The decibel system compares sound intensity to the lowest level at which the human ear can detect sound. Thus, zero decibels (0 dB) is the minimum threshold for human hearing. Conversational speech is normally around 50 dB. A jet engine can be as loud as 150 dB. In between are rustling leaves (20 dB), a garbage disposal (80 dB) and a chain saw (120 dB).

The decibel system is logarithmic, so the scale represents changes in the order of magnitude. A difference of ten decibels equals ten times the loudness, so normal speech at 50 dB is 10^5 (one hundred thousand) times louder than the threshold of hearing; and a jet engine, at 150 dB, is 10^{10} (ten billion) times louder than conversational speech.

Frequency is the number of cycles per second. One cycle per second is one Hertz (Hz), named for Heinrich Rudolf Hertz, a German physicist instrumental in developing the radio and radar. Higher frequencies have shorter wavelengths (more wave cycles per second) and are higher in pitch. Lower frequencies have longer wavelengths and are lower in pitch.

Hearing—A Symphony of Parts

To HEAR, the body must collect acoustic signals from the environment (pressure waves in the air), channel them to the right locations, convert them into nerve impulses, send them to the brain, and correctly interpret them into experiences like speech and music. And, just as with vision, if any one of those parts works incorrectly, or even just a bit less efficiently, hearing is either severely degraded or impossible.

The human ear can detect sound when the eardrum is displaced by as little as one-tenth the diameter of a single hydrogen atom. Yet it can also hear and correctly interpret sounds with acoustic pressure levels approaching the loudest sounds produced in nature (~1 kilopascal (kPa)).

And you can do more than register sounds of varying pitch and volume. From an early age you could tell from the sound of your mom's voice just how much trouble you were in, and which direction she was calling from (so you knew which way to run). These and other features of human hearing require—and by now this should come as no surprise to readers—not just one or two clever engineering solutions, but a suite of ingenious solutions upon ingenious solutions.

ANATOMY OF THE EAR

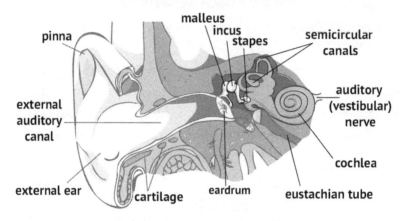

Figure 11.2. The parts of the ear.

Figure 11.2 illustrates the main parts of the body's auditory system. Its many parts work together to gather sound waves from the environment and transmit them accurately and efficiently to the cochlea, where a subsystem called the organ of Corti converts them into nerve impulses and sends them to the brain.

The ear is divided into three regions: the outer (external) ear, the middle ear, and the inner (internal) ear. We'll walk through these parts in order—that is, following a sound wave as it moves from outside the body to the inside where it's converted into information and eventually into an experience.

The Outer Ear

THE OUTER ear is made up of the pinna (ear flap), the ear canal, and the tympanic membrane (eardrum).

The pinna acts like a satellite dish, collecting sound waves and funneling them down the ear canal. But it does more than just collect. The pinna's ridges and folds reflect and absorb certain frequency components of incoming sound waves. Since the pinna is not circularly symmetric, sounds coming from different directions have slightly different acoustic characteristics. This means certain frequencies in a sound will be slightly softer or louder depending on the direction they enter the ear. This allows you to tell the direction a sound comes from. This is why we instinctively look up when we hear a sound coming from above us.

To further help with this, we have two ears for stereo sound. We can detect differences as small as ten microseconds in the time of arrival of the same sound in each ear. We can also detect subtle differences in loudness between our two ears. Coupled with the fine-grained sound-shaping done by the outer ear, this allows us to tell the direction of a noise and hear in three dimensions. That is, our minds can generate a three-dimensional understanding of what's going on around us based solely on sounds.

Close your eyes and listen carefully to the sounds you hear. Where are they, both in direction (left or right, front to back, up or down) and distance away from you? If you have good ears and are used to exercising this skill, your hearing should prove informative on this score.

The ear canal is a hollow tube about two centimeters long. It forms an acoustic channel between the pinna and the eardrum. The ear canal may not seem interesting at first glance, but its length plays a crucial role in hearing.

Much like a pipe in a pipe organ, the outer ear consists of a rigid tube open at one end and sealed at the other. Incoming waves bounce off the closed end and create standing waves in the tube (ear canal). This amplifies sounds at or near the tube's resonant frequencies (constructive interference) and dampens sounds at other frequencies (destructive interference). This increases sensitivity to particular frequencies while diminishing the amplitude of others. Basically, it's a passive amplifier!

For the human ear, this amplification is strongest at around 3,000 Hz. While this is higher than the central frequencies of human speech, it's exactly the range where the percussive elements of the consonants in human speech are most prominent, and the consonants are essential for distinguishing the nuances of human speech.

The net effect is that the outer ear preprocesses incoming sound waves to maximize sensitivity to the natural frequencies of human speech. That is, our ears are fine tuned to hear best at the same frequencies we naturally speak.

The human ear can hear sounds from 20 Hz to around 20,000 Hz. Normal human speech ranges from 80 to 2,500 Hz. The lowest note on a tuba is 16 Hz, middle C on a piano is 262 Hz, and the highest note on a flute is 2,093 Hz.

The eardrum (tympanum) is a small membrane, about one centimeter in diameter, at the inner end of the ear canal. It's a durable piece of skin tightly stretched across an opening in the bony skull. The eardrum vibrates at the same frequency as an incoming sound wave, enabling it to accurately and efficiently transmit sounds from outside the body to the inside. All the while, it maintains a barrier that seals the delicate inner workings of the ear from foreign matter and bacteria.

> The eardrum is perfectly engineered to perform two distinct and opposing tasks. First, it must provide a barrier to prevent harmful contaminants from reaching the inner ear. For this it must be durable and fairly rugged. Second, it must be thin and lightweight to transmit sounds from outside the ear to inside the ear, with acoustic accuracy and without appreciable degradation or damping of the sound's energy.

The Middle Ear

THE MIDDLE ear is an enclosed air-filled chamber, beginning at the inner surface of the eardrum and ending at the cochlea.

The middle ear contains the ossicles, the three smallest bones in the body. These are the malleus (hammer), incus (anvil), and stapes (stirrup). They were given these familiar names because they resemble those objects in shape. Together, they transmit the vibrations of the eardrum into the inner ear.

THE MIDDLE EAR

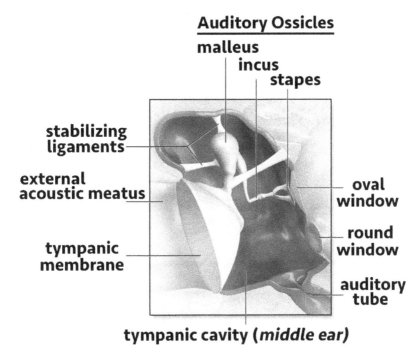

Figure 11.3. The parts of the middle ear. The oval and round windows are parts of the cochlea.

To do this, the malleus is attached to the eardrum and the incus, the incus is attached to the malleus and the stapes, and the stapes is attached to the incus and the oval window of the cochlea, as shown in Figure 11.3.

Sound waves make the eardrum vibrate, which vibrates the malleus, which vibrates the incus, which vibrates the stapes, which vibrates the oval window of the cochlea. But the key to hearing is how these bones are precisely shaped and interconnected to modify incoming vibrations. We'll look at this below.

Interestingly, these bones are fully formed at birth and do not grow as the entire body around them grows from infancy to adulthood. These are the only bones in the body with this property.

How does the body grow all its other bones while keeping just these specific ones from growing? What mechanisms and control systems are needed? So far, neither medical science nor biology has answers, but engineers know that such things don't happen by accident, so there seem to be many interesting discoveries yet to be made.

As you'd expect by now, there are some less-than-obvious problems with hearing that the body needs to solve.

First, just like all the body's cells, the cells in the tissue surrounding the middle ear need oxygen for respiration. Since the middle ear is filled with air, these cells have direct access to a ready supply. But they will gradually absorb all the available air, causing a vacuum effect, which would reduce eardrum movement and impair hearing.

Without a way to replenish its air supply, the ear would quickly lose hearing acuity. To solve this problem, it uses a small tube, called the eustachian (auditory) tube, that connects the middle ear to the back of the throat. When you swallow or yawn, this tube opens, allowing fresh air to enter the middle ear. This equalizes the middle ear's air pressure with the pressure outside the body. This tube can get clogged, as during a head cold, preventing the middle ear from equalizing pressure, which, as we all know, degrades hearing and causes earaches.

> Sound is composed of pressure waves. For the ear to be able to accurately register these pressure waves, the air pressures on either side of the eardrum must be equal. When the air pressure between the middle ear and the surrounding environment is different, your hearing must fight against this difference. This affects both the amplitude (loudness) and the tonality (pitch) of incoming sounds.

As a second and more formidable problem, sounds entering the body come through the air, but the cochlea is filled with fluid. The cochlea's fluid, as we'll see, serves a vital purpose, but it presents a thorny acoustic problem for accurate hearing. Because air is much less dense than liquid, and far more compressible, without some skillful engineering most of the energy of the sound wave would simply be reflected back into the ear canal. A rough analogy would be throwing a rubber ball at the sidewalk. Most of the ball's energy is reflected in the ball's bounce back to the thrower. Very little is transmitted to the sidewalk.

For proper hearing, then, the body needs to amplify the signal between the eardrum and the cochlea. The best way to do this is with a lever system. Since the malleus is attached to the eardrum and the stapes to the cochlea, this leaves the middle bone, the incus, to serve as a lever. But not just any lever will do. Only a very specific configuration of that lever will properly translate the pressure waves in the air into corresponding pressure waves in the fluid.

The middle ear must provide a mechanical advantage to accurately bridge the different densities of air and fluid, and do so with minimal loss of either loudness or tonality. Mechanical engineers call this *impedance transformation*, a tricky problem to overcome in even a simple system.

The ear's solution involves the precise shapes and configurations of all three bones of the middle ear. The malleus has a larger surface area than the stapes. Also, the two arms of the incus's lever have different lengths. Each provides mechanical advantage. Pressure waves hitting the large area of the eardrum are concentrated into the smaller area of the stapes so that the force of the vibrating stapes is nearly fifteen times greater than that of the eardrum. This makes it possible to hear even the faintest sounds.

These bones can only do their job effectively when surrounded by air. If they were immersed in fluid, the viscosity of the fluid would degrade their mechanical properties. This drives the need for an air supply to the middle ear.

The three bones of the middle ear, and the ways they're held in place by various tendons, act as a four-bar mechanism. The specific configuration in the ear is called a double-crank rocker. Engineers use four-bar mechanisms to fine tune mechanical relationships in systems where exacting precision and sophistication are needed, as they most certainly are in the middle ear. To achieve the necessary mechanical advantage, the

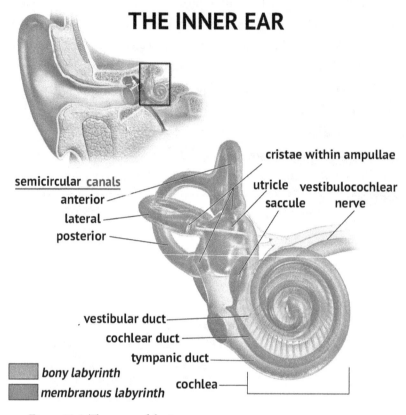

THE INNER EAR

cristae within ampullae

semicircular canals
anterior
lateral
posterior

utricle vestibulocochlear
saccule nerve

vestibular duct
cochlear duct
tympanic duct

bony labyrinth
membranous labyrinth

cochlea

Figure 11.4. The parts of the inner ear.

shapes of the parts and the positions of the several hinge points must be precisely tuned, with little room for error.

So, hearing hinges on the precise configuration of these three tiny bones. Chapter 3 discussed how the very specific shapes of various bones are essential to their purposes. Nowhere do we see this more clearly than in the bones of the middle ear.

The Inner Ear

THE INNER ear is the most complicated part of the auditory system. It's so complicated that its exact workings are not yet fully understood. It consists of the bony labyrinth, a hollow cavity with a system of passages that includes the cochlea and the vestibular system. The cochlea is a heli-

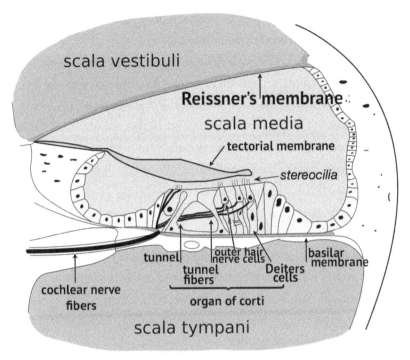

Figure 11.5. The three fluid-filled chambers of the cochlea.

cally shaped bony structure, something like a snail shell but with three parallel, fluid-filled chambers which spiral together for about two-and-a-half turns. The vestibular apparatus consists of the three semicircular canals, the utricle, and the saccule.

If the cochlea were uncoiled, it would be 3 to 3.5 centimeters in length. The three chambers that run its length are shown in cross-section in Figure 11.5, above. The upper and lower chambers are filled with a fluid called perilymph, chemically similar to the other extracellular fluids in the body, with high concentration of sodium ions (Na^+) and low concentration of potassium ions (K^+). In contrast, the middle chamber (the scala media), contains endolymph, a unique extracellular fluid with high K^+ and relatively low Na^+ concentrations, much like the fluids inside the cells. This is the only place in the body we're aware of where a fluid with this kind of chemical balance exists outside of individual cells. Though its purpose is not understood, it appears that this specific chemical composition is essential to hearing.

Sound waves enter the cochlea's first channel, called the scala vestibuli. The stapes acts like a piston to transmit sound waves to the fluid in this channel through the membrane of the oval window. This sets up pressure waves in the fluid that correspond to the pressure waves that were in the air outside the ear. The pressure waves travel through this channel from its base to the far end, called the apex.

At the apex, the scala vestibuli connects through a small gap (the helicotrema) in the bony cochlear partition, into the third channel, called the scala tympani. Here, the pressure waves return toward the base of the cochlea. At the base end of this channel is a highly flexible membrane called the round window, which bulges in and out as the pressure waves move in the fluid. This allows pressure waves to be absorbed at the end of the channel, preventing pressure waves from bouncing back and creating standing waves inside the cochlea.

Unlike air, the fluids in the inner ear are not readily compressed. So without the cochlea's pressure relief system, the ear would have little freedom of movement, and hearing would be severely degraded.

> Why is the cochlea of the inner ear coiled? Perhaps to better fit with the surrounding structures of the head. The human head crams a large array of systems into a remarkably compact space. The cochlea's coils may be the most compact design possible for a structure of this kind and complexity. In total, the human head presents a marvelous solution to a difficult packaging problem.

The middle channel is where things get really interesting. This is called the scala media, since it sits in the middle between the other two channels. A partition called the basilar membrane separates the middle channel from the third channel, the scala tympani. (See Figure 11.5.) As pressure waves pass through the third channel, they cause the basilar membrane to bounce up and down, like a toy boat floating in a bathtub.

The basilar membrane is specially shaped to differentiate frequencies in sound. It tapers in width over its length, from its narrowest point at the oval window (about 0.04 mm) to its widest point (around 0.5 mm) near the apex at the helicotrema. This allows different wavelengths of sound (frequencies) to be maximized at different distances from the oval window.

The end closest to the base is tuned to higher frequencies, while the end closest to the apex is tuned for lower frequencies. In effect, the basilar membrane acts as an acoustic filter to separate the frequencies in sounds and direct them to different hair cells along the length of the cochlea.

The organ of Corti is attached to the basilar membrane. It has about 20,000 specialized "hair cells" which have thin bundles of fibers, called stereocilia, protruding from their top. A small bony "roof" called the tectorial membrane overhangs this area, such that when the basilar membrane moves up and down, the stereocilia are pushed back and forth at an angle against the tectorial membrane.

The hair cells differ in length by minuscule amounts and have different levels of resiliency to the fluid in the middle chamber. This means each hair cell is specially tuned to a particular frequency of vibration. When a sound wave's frequency matches the natural frequency of the hair cell, that cell resonates with greater amplitude and induces the cell to release an electrical impulse into the auditory nerve, which sends it to the brain.

So, the acoustic properties of the basilar membrane, combined with the fine tuning of the hair cells, produce our amazing ability to make fine distinctions in frequencies.

Battery-Powered Hearing

Hearing requires electrical signals to be generated in the inner ear and sent to the brain, and for this the ear uses a remarkable mechanism that differs from anything else in the body.

Within the inner ear, the hair cells in the organ of Corti pump positive ions like sodium (Na^+) out of the cell, leaving a net negative internal charge of about −40 millivolts relative to the normal extracellular potential of the body. This is their resting potential.

The stereocilia of the hair cells protrude into the middle channel, which contains endolymph. Because endolymph is rich in potassium ions (K^+), it has a positive charge at around +80 millivolts. It's believed that this positive charge is generated by specialized cells that line the walls of the scala media. (Note that it takes yet another system to maintain the special charge needed in this fluid.)

Engineers have a special term for this kind of arrangement: it's called a battery, which in this case has its negative terminal inside the hair cell and its positive terminal outside, on the upper surface of the cell. When the stereocilia bend, the cell opens small ion channels, which allow K^+ ions to flow into the hair cells from the endolymph to equalize the electrical potential, in a process known as depolarization.

> The inner ear's hair cells open potassium ion (K^+) channels, allowing K^+ ions to flood into the cell to depolarize it. This is both unique and a bit surprising, as every other nerve and muscle cell in the body (as far as is currently known) uses sodium (Na^+) ion channels for depolarization. While the exact purpose of this is not yet known, we suspect that this unique property will one day be shown to be essential to hearing.
>
> Still, the fact that depolarization here uses the exact opposite approach as used in all other cells in the body makes the prospect of an unintentional evolutionary origin all the less likely.

When the hair cell becomes depolarized, the voltage rise in the cell opens specialized calcium (Ca^{2+}) channels, so calcium enters the cell, causing the hair cell to release a neurotransmitter.

Auditory nerve cells surround the bottom and sides of the hair cells. As it detects the hair cell's neurotransmitters, the nerve cell "fires," opening its own ion channels at the synapse, which raises the voltage in the nerve fiber. A domino effect ensues, which causes a wave of depolarization to propagate along the nerve, all the way to the brain.

Protecting the Ears

EARS ARE sensitive things, so they're vulnerable to a range of threats. Fortunately, the ear possesses several defenses.

Perhaps the humblest of these defenses is ear wax, produced in the ear canal of the outer ear. Ear wax provides lubrication to keep the skin healthy while protecting the eardrum from dust, dirt, and invading microbes and insects.

But by far the greatest threat to hearing is damage to the tissues of the most sensitive parts of the inner ear. Remember, your tissues have physical limitations. Just as you can injure your elbow by hyper-extending it, extremely loud sounds, such as a nearby explosion, can injure your eardrum, ossicles, and microscopic components of the cochlea by causing sudden and excessive movement.

Curiously, two skeletal muscles are located in the middle ear: the tensor tympani, attached to the malleus where it meets the eardrum, and the stapedius, attached to the stapes where it meets the oval window of the cochlea. (See Figure 11.3, above.) When the ear detects an extreme movement in the eardrum, a protective reflex instantly contracts these muscles, stiffening the sound transmission mechanisms of the ear, mechanically damping the transmission of sound through the middle ear to the inner ear. This protects the inner ear's most sensitive parts by reducing their relative movement.

Even though the physical reduction in amplitude is real, your brain seems to still perceive this as a noticeably louder sound. Surely this involves additional feedback systems that we don't yet understand.

Making Sense of Sounds

AUDITORY NERVE cells react to signals from the hair cells in the inner ear and transmit them to the brain. There doesn't appear to be any difference based on frequency in the signals that different auditory nerves send to the brain, so as best we can tell the frequencies in sound are encoded on the basis of what nerve cells are involved. This is known as *place coding*.

Differences in amplitude are encoded in the rate the nerves fire. When the sound at a particular frequency is louder, the hair cells at that frequency fire more quickly, which in turn causes the associated nerves to fire more frequently. This is known as *rate coding*.

Between these two signaling mechanisms, both frequency and amplitude information are sent to the brain.

If place coding is how different frequencies are sent to the brain, distinguishing various frequencies must occur in the brain. How does the brain's hearing center know which nerve signals to associate with which frequencies? How does the hearing center know to interpret more frequent signals as louder volume? How are these connections assembled during fetal development? Where is this encoded in the DNA? (Or is it encoded somewhere else?)

While the body's solution to the challenge of getting sound-based signals to the brain is a good one, it does pose a problem. Around 20,000 hair cells from each ear can each send a signal to the brain at any given time. Each of these represents a different frequency, and the variations in firing rate represent different degrees of loudness. Given all this, the brain's auditory center has a lot of work to do in order to convert all this raw information into meaningful sounds. How your brain performs this feat is not yet fully understood. The bottom line is that assembling individual nerve impulses into coherent sounds is an enormously difficult problem.

Because the hair cells nearest the base of the cochlea respond to higher frequencies and the nerves closest to the apex respond to lower frequencies, the nerves mirror this arrangement, terminating in roughly linear order from front to back along the primary auditory cortex (the brain's hearing center). At least logically, this arrangement should make it a little easier for the brain to understand differences in frequencies.

The Experience of Hearing

FINALLY, THE mind needs to actually hear. To this end, it not only assembles all the individual nerve impulses into a real-time auditory whole, but it also uses the fine nuances in the quality and direction of sounds to assemble a three-dimensional understanding of what's happening around the body. When coupled with visual signals, we're able to know the space around us with remarkable accuracy.

Further, our minds track and appreciate relationships in sounds over time. We know without looking whether a car is moving toward us or away from us. We understand spoken words and sentences by comparing many different frequencies and amplitudes over time. And we appreciate chord structures and transitions in music.

The rich bundle of capacities that is human hearing enables us to experience many nuances in volume, tonality, harmonics, timbre, cadence, direction, distance, movement, and more. Hearing gives us a richness of information about our world, and a richer way to experience the world around us. It's an amazing gift that enriches our lives.

Contemplating the gift of hearing should spur us to experience wonder and gratitude, but also the curiosity to ask questions such as, Why do we perceive auditory information differently than visual information? Both are received as electrical signals by the brain, but they are translated into very different experiences. How do we know to do this? How do we do this?

Takeaways

THE NEEDS of hearing are simple to state, but incredibly difficult to achieve:

1. Capture acoustic pressure waves in the surrounding environment.

2. Amplify the most important range of the sounds, where importance is defined by the needs of the person, not the needs of the ear itself.

3. Convert the mechanical energy of those waves into electrical impulses.

4. Transmit those impulses to the brain without loss of information.

5. Generate a three-dimensional auditory "image" of your surroundings.

6. Animate this "image" to understand—and in many cases, enjoy—how the sounds are changing over time.

How many possible ways could hearing go wrong? Surely in many thousands of ways. In almost all cases, a failure or error would severely degrade or eliminate the experience of hearing.

As with all the systems in the body, each part of the hearing system of systems must be in the proper position. The middle ear, for example, must mechanically transform waves in the air into waves in a fluid, and this is only managed when each bone has the correct shape, fits with its neighboring bones, and is held in exactly the right places and with the right pivot points. Only with extreme fine tuning can mechanisms of this kind work properly.

Each part of the ear must be tuned for a specific purpose: the eardrum and oval window must have the right surface tension, the fluid in the middle channel must have the right electrical properties, and so on.

The ear needs resilience mechanisms to protect against damage when sounds are too loud, else hearing would quickly degrade and you would lose both the information and the rich human experience hearing provides.

The shapes of the ear's many parts must have just the right acoustic properties. This includes the shape of the pinna, the diameter and length of the ear canal, the holes in the bones of the skull, the curling bony structure of the cochlea, the taper in the basal membrane, and many others.

Hearing requires specialized cells, and some of these cells, like the hair cells in the inner ear, must be precisely tuned to specific audio frequencies. Signaling between the ear and the brain must carry all the necessary information, and in a way that enables the brain to make proper sense of the sounds. And as with vision, the entire system must operate so quickly you cannot perceive any time lag between the arrival of a sound and the brain's processing of it.

Hearing is an easy-to-understand example of how having the individual functions of the system is not enough. They must be strung together correctly in a continuous process from start to finish.

Human hearing requires solutions to many difficult engineering problems, and solves them in a strikingly elegant and efficient way, yielding acoustically accurate sounds, with an emphasis on the frequency range most central to human existence and human relationships.

In short, our hearing system is an extremely clever (and near-optimal) set of solutions to a tough set of engineering problems.

Touch, Taste, Smell

WE WON'T take the space to do a similarly deep dive into our other human senses, but let's touch on them briefly before moving on to other extraordinary systems in the human body.

Our sense of touch allows us to sense our environment by physically contacting objects in it. We can sense vibrations and stresses while doing heavy labor, yet we can also sense minute offsets less than the thickness of a sheet of paper, which helps us align parts while doing fine craftsmanship. We can feel hot and cold. We can feel wet and dry. We feel the differences between oily and watery substances. We feel differences in smoothness. We feel pain when the hammer misses the nail and hits our thumb.

Our sense of taste allows us to sense our food in our mouths, enabling us to detect its quality and condition before we consume it. And, of course, enabling us to *enjoy* eating.

Our sense of smell allows us to sense and differentiate airborne molecules. This augments taste, enabling us to better enjoy different flavors and foods. But it also gives us important environmental cues. We can smell smoke before we see it, handy for avoiding a wildfire. We can smell when food has gone bad even before tasting it.

We can also sense a variety of conditions inside our body. We sense when we have a fever. We sense when a bone is broken. We know when we need a drink of water, and we know when we've inhaled water. We know when we need to rest.

The problems that must be solved for these senses to work must be similar, at least in some ways, to those for vision and hearing.

- The body must detect and convert a signal from the environment (or an internal system) into electrical impulses. For taste and smell, this involves specialized cells with external receptors to detect hundreds or even thousands of different chemicals.

- These specialized cells, when stimulated by a chemical, must generate a matching signal and send it to the brain. So, the sensor cells must connect to the nervous system.

- The brain must interpret these signals correctly. How does the brain know the cell has detected salt in the food, and how is that signal differentiated from the signal for sugar?

- The brain must combine signals from many receptors at the same time and correlate them. How does it detect the difference between a lemon and a lime?

- The brain must interpret the millions of signals across all the senses, and the mind merge them into a unified experience.

When all of these are in place, for all our senses, we are able to maintain our internal systems and experience the richness of the world around us.

Back to Beethoven

GIVEN THE complexity of the ear and the interplay of so many different parts essential to hearing, there are obviously many ways hearing can fail. A failure in any part can cause deafness: damage to the eardrums, a buildup of pressure or fluid in the middle ear, auditory nerve damage, or a stroke affecting the hearing region of your brain.

So, what caused Beethoven's hearing loss? Many medical practitioners believe it was caused by otosclerosis. This is an inherited condition that usually starts to affect hearing in young adulthood (as with Beethoven). It's often associated with ringing in the ears and intermittent dizziness (as with Beethoven). And it usually progresses slowly over many years, eventually leading to near or total deafness (again, as with Beethoven).

The middle and inner ear are housed in and protected by a rigid section of the temporal bone called the otic capsule. In otosclerosis this bone grows abnormally, thickening and scarring. Eventually this impacts the nearby tissues of the middle and inner ear. It can damage the oval window of the cochlea, but more often affects the ossicles, particularly the stapes.

The stapes must vibrate freely to conduct sound waves, so when it becomes hardened and fixed by otosclerosis it loses its ability to conduct sound, resulting in deafness. In our day, surgically removing the stapes and replacing it with a prosthetic one can solve this problem.

More recently, another possible cause has been suggested for Beethoven's deafness, in conjunction with his many other ailments. Paget's disease is a chronic disorder in which certain bones become enlarged and deformed. This is a painful condition usually affecting the spine, pelvis, and femur (thigh bone), but it can also affect the skull, leading to headaches and hearing loss.

Beethoven suffered greatly during the final years of his life. Besides ringing in his ears, dizziness, and deafness, he also suffered from headaches, bone and abdominal pain, and various other abdominal complaints. It's said he asked his family to have an autopsy done so the world would know what had caused him to suffer.

The autopsy revealed that Beethoven's skull was twice the normal thickness; his auditory nerves were atrophied; he had multiple kidney stones and abscesses (which indicate high levels of calcium in his blood);

and he suffered from gout. These symptoms are consistent with Paget's disease.

To relieve himself of his chronic pains, Beethoven tended to drink a lot of cheap wine, which in those days was illegally fortified with lead sugar. All this eventually led to his death from alcohol-induced hepatic cirrhosis and chronic pancreatitis, possibly aggravated by lead poisoning. Beethoven's deafness and premature death are, of course, tragic. We can only wonder what richness of music we'd be blessed with today if he had lived longer than fifty-six years. What if his Tenth Symphony had been even better than his Ninth?

At the same time, Beethoven's story underscores a couple of key points. As with all the medical cases we discuss, his hearing loss illustrates how many things must be just right for a coherent body system to function, and how little it often takes for that system to fail. And, once again, the key question in all this is not why the body's systems sometimes fail, but rather why they ever work, given all the things that have to be just right for them to work at all.

Finally, it's extraordinary that Beethoven was able to compose and conduct the masterpiece that is his Ninth Symphony while he was almost completely deaf. This testifies to the powerful and mysterious capabilities of the human mind.

Insights

LET'S BRIEFLY review our quick dive into hearing and the other complex biological systems considered in previous chapters:

- Coherence of the parts is always required for the function of the whole. To change one part invariably requires changes to other parts, often many other parts. Coherent processes, like hearing, require that the parts be fine tuned to enable the whole.

- Systems and subsystems are almost never understood in isolation. Interdependencies are common and usually critical to outcomes.

- The various systems and subsystems in the body exhibit recurring design patterns, even when they're solving completely different problems. This becomes clear when we compare, for example, vision and hearing.

And an overarching takeaway: It's probably rash to draw firm conclusions about the origins of a biological system before understanding how it actually works. Only then does one have enough data to make a proper assessment of competing causal theories.

12. Balance and Movement

You move because you are built for movement, because your
heartbeat and respiration are involuntary. Though you feel the
part of you that is always dying, the rest moves forward, squeezed
between destiny and choice.

—Cai Emmons[1]

I (Howard) have seen almost the whole range of neurological disorders in my over forty years of medical practice. Diagnosing the precise cause isn't always easy. Imagine a patient enters the office—let's call her Emily—and tells you that recently she's been having problems with her balance and coordination. When walking down a hallway, sometimes she suddenly lurches from one wall to the other. If she closes her eyes while taking a shower she may fall into the wall. In her jewelry business she's having more trouble handling small items, writing in her ledger, and sometimes even speaking clearly.

What could be causing Emily's problems? To understand, you'll need to know what it takes for the human body to stay balanced and coordinated—two things essential to purposeful movement.

Falling for Gravity

The mass of our bodies is drawn inexorably to the larger mass of the Earth. We depend on this fact for nearly all human activities. An object's center of gravity is the point around which its weight is evenly distributed. Place a wooden block on a table and slowly push it off the edge. It will fall when its center of gravity is no longer over the table. Your center of gravity while standing or lying down with your arms at your sides is in the midline, near your belly button.

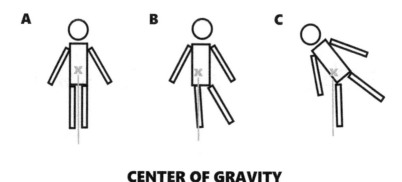

CENTER OF GRAVITY

Figure 12.1. The body's center of gravity moves as the body flexes.

When you're standing, your center of gravity must stay between your two feet; otherwise, you'll fall to the ground. Moving your arms or legs away from your body or bending your spine in any direction changes your body's center of gravity. When you carry an object, your center of gravity is averaged with the object's center of gravity, based on its weight and how far it is from your body. In effect, this moves your center of gravity toward the carried object and makes it harder to keep your balance.

Walking or running means staying balanced while in motion, which makes the balance problem harder to solve—hence toddlers' need for lots of practice to master walking.

In short, your body's ability to move and change its center of gravity makes it an inherently unstable object. The body needs to take control to stay balanced. Your neuromuscular system solves this problem using reflexes that help maintain posture, and active controls across hundreds of muscle groups to maintain balance. But this wouldn't work without a lot of sensory information related to balance, and without ways to process the information quickly and effectively.

Balance Information

THE SENSORY information your body uses to stay balanced comes from four main sources: visual cues from your eyes, the organs of balance in the inner ear, pressure sensing in your feet, and proprioceptors that sense the positions of your many moveable parts. Most of this occurs subconsciously.

Vision

Your eyes provide visual cues about your body's position relative to the horizontal. To test this, and assuming you don't have brittle bones or other risk factors, find a flat, safe area, and get someone to stay close to you in case you start to fall or veer into something. Now close your eyes and walk, gradually increasing your speed. You'll find that without the use of your eyes, it's much harder to stay balanced, even on a flat surface.

Inner Ears

Your inner ears have a special mechanism for balance known as the vestibular apparatus. This mechanism uses five fluid-filled chambers: the utricle, the saccule, and three semicircular canals. (See Figure 11.4.) Each of these has hair cells, and when they bend, they generate nerve impulses that are sent to the brain.

The hair cells in the utricle and saccule detect small changes in the pull of gravity as your head nods up and down. At the same time, the three semicircular canals sense movement, and because they are arranged at right angles to each other, they can detect head movement in three dimensions. As the head moves, the fluid in one or more of the canals moves, causing that canal's hair cells to bend, acting as accelerometers and generating nerve impulses. Together, the five chambers (in each of your ears) tell your brain how fast and in what direction the head is moving.

To test how this works, move your neck quickly in all directions. As you do, the semicircular canals on each side of your head send strong alternating signals to your brain, and this makes you feel dizzy and off balance. Now, move your body quickly back and forth, side to side, and jump up and down. These movements activate the utricle and saccule but don't make you so dizzy. Signals from the vestibular apparatus also help stabilize your eye's retinal image, in a process called the vestibular-ocular (doll's eyes) reflex, discussed in Chapter 10.

Though they reside in the inner ear, the fluid, nerve cells, and hair cells of the semicircular canals serve no role in hearing. Instead, they act as accelerometers, enabling the body to detect both gravitational fields and movement in time. This solution to the balance problem involves fluid dynamics, mechanical engineering, complex molecular interactions, and electromagnetic impulses. These combine to generate yet another true engineering masterpiece.

Skin

Your skin incorporates many types of sensors—for touch, pain, vibration, hot, cold, and pressure. Pressure sensors, like the Merkel's discs in your feet, tell your brain about your body's weight distribution relative to its center of gravity. Notice this by standing, planting your feet firmly on the ground, and concentrating on the pressure you feel on the bottom of your feet as you lean from side to side and back and forth. Pay attention to the difference in the pressure sensation you feel in each foot with these movements and how it affects your feeling of balance.

The feet play another role in balance, one less often noted. Each foot has three main points of contact with the ground, offering a stabilizing platform just like a tripod. Others in the simian family, like chimpanzees and gorillas, lack this feature, and instead have feet more suited to climbing and walking on all fours than for upright posture and walking.[2]

Proprioceptors

Your body can't control its actions if it doesn't know what its muscles and joints are doing. Proprioceptors are stretch receptors situated within your muscles, tendons, and joints. They detect changes in length and the rate of change, using mechanically gated ion channels, and send this information to your brain. Some of these proprioceptors are responsible for initiating the automatic stretch reflexes that allow you to maintain your position and balance. (See Figure 12.4, below.)

The brain monitors the position and movement of your muscles and joints to gain a continuous picture of how the body is configured at any given time. To experience this, bend at your neck and at your waist in any direction. Note how this affects your feeling of imbalance as your center of gravity shifts in one direction or the other. Your core, ankles, and feet compensate to keep you from falling over.

> To maintain fine control over balance while moving, your body must employ its many individual sensors to continually feed real-time positional information to the brain, and the brain must assemble these (also in real time) into a holistic view of the body's position as it moves, adjusting future movements accordingly.
>
> Here we see one of engineering's most useful tools: feedback loops. To control balance, the system's controller needs to monitor the effects of its commands and adjust them as needed. For example, when you reach to pick up an object, your mind estimates the force needed and sends appropriate commands to the muscles in your hands, arms, and core to maintain your balance. If the object is much lighter or heavier than expected, your brain detects this via feedback from those muscles and joints, and quickly adjusts the signals it sends to the muscles.
>
> Virtually all control systems in your body (actually, nearly all control systems everywhere) use one or more feedback mechanisms. Without them, your body would quickly spin out of control.

Coordination and Control

MAINTAINING YOUR balance is a demanding engineering challenge, to be sure; but it's just table stakes in the world of movement. Another collection of hard problems must be solved to coordinate all the muscles and muscle groups needed to perform useful tasks.

Your musculoskeletal system consists of more than two hundred bones and over six hundred muscles. The muscles reach across dozens of joints. Skeletal muscles work by contraction and are controlled by motor nerves.

Since muscles work by contraction, a given muscle can move the eyeball or the bones of a joint in only one direction. To move them back requires another, complementary muscle. And, to avoid a "tug of war" when one muscle contracts, its opposite must relax.

> We see the push-pull principle in the mechanics of movement. It takes one muscle to pull your arm outward and another to pull it inward. There's also built-in choreography, as the nerve impulses must be coordinated to contract the "push" muscle while relaxing the "pull" muscle, and vice versa.

Skeletal muscles attach to two different bones across a joint, so the length of the muscle at any given moment, as detected by the proprioceptors in that muscle, corresponds to the angle of the joint. When you flex your fingers to form a fist, each finger and knuckle joint goes through about 90 degrees of motion. The muscle spindles in your flexors decrease to a minimum while those in your extensors increase to a maximum. The muscle spindles in your finger flexors and extensors inform your brain where, within the 90 degrees of possible motion, your finger and knuckle joints are.

Of course, skeletal muscles wouldn't be much good if they didn't span a joint between different bones. Fortunately, they are in the right locations and attached in just the right places to enable the right range of motion.

For complex bodily movements to work effectively, one other thing is needed: all the right signals must get to all the right muscles at exactly the right times. Consider how your muscles work. Your eyes and eyelids, mouth and jaw move very quickly. Your fingers move much faster than your toes, and with more precision and control. The same goes for your wrists compared to your ankles; your elbows compared to your knees; your shoulders compared to your hips; and your neck compared to your upper and lower back. So to coordinate whole-body movement, the brain needs to send signals with precise timing adjusted for each muscle group.

Each skeletal muscle consists of numerous muscle fibers. When stimulated by a motor neuron, the muscle fibers contract, and the angles between the bones that the muscle is attached to will be changed. The group of muscle fibers controlled by a given motor neuron is called a *motor unit*.

> The body needs different levels of fine motor control for different muscle groups in different parts of the body. It achieves this using two separate mechanisms. First, the number of positional sensors (muscle spindles) are apportioned as needed, with the highest concentrations in exactly those muscles that need the most precise control. Second, the nerve-to-muscle granularity is engineered with just the right number of control signals (motor neurons) for the needed level of control.
>
> By combining these two mechanisms in different ways, the body achieves appropriate levels of coordination and movement for the thousands of physical tasks it needs to do. The body cleverly places these mechanistic resources exactly (and only) where they're needed for differing levels of dexterity and strength.

Different muscles have different numbers of muscle fibers in each of their motor units, according to their purpose. For the coarse strong movements of the back, legs, and arms, a single motor unit will have from hundreds to several thousand muscle fibers. For the fine and precise movements of the eyes and fingers, a given motor unit might have as few as five to ten muscle fibers.

More refined muscle control takes more refined feedback, so more muscle spindles are embedded in those muscles that need finer and more precise action, while fewer are present in muscles that need only coarser and less precise action.

There's more still to motor control. The movements of the body need the simultaneous coordination and control of multiple muscle groups—a sort of choreography of movement.

Touch your nose with your left index finger. What's the actual complexity of this "simple" action? How many body parts move, which muscles do what kinds of activities, and what is the timing and relative strength required from each muscle involved? Despite its complexity, your mind coordinates the many needed signals without specific conscious controls.

For this to work, the brain must precisely coordinate different signals to many different muscles at the same time. The body would be immobilized if this kind of coordination were missing and the many muscles involved were not given coordinated signals regarding contracting and relaxing. And of course, the body would be significantly hobbled if any of the components of these movement systems were missing. Imagine being able to extend your arm but not bring it back in.

A Moving Experience

ALL THE above is necessary for movement, but not sufficient. Purposeful movement takes many more functions, all working together. There are five main parts of the body's motor control system: the spinal cord, the brainstem, the cerebrum, the basal ganglia, and the cerebellum.

Spinal Cord

The spinal cord and the millions of peripheral nerve bundles that branch out from it to the rest of the body make up the body's main wiring system.

Your spinal cord has nerves responsible for travel in two directions, inbound and outbound. Each peripheral nerve is the beginning of an in-

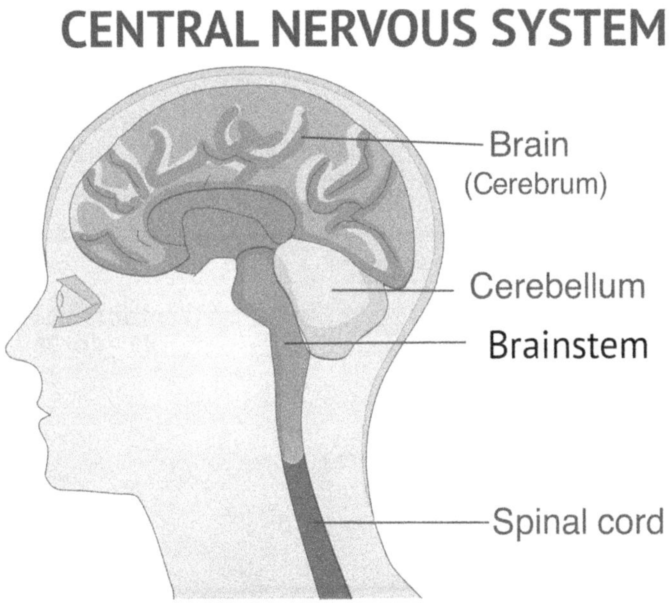

CENTRAL NERVOUS SYSTEM

Brain
(Cerebrum)

Cerebellum
Brainstem

Spinal cord

Figure 12.2. The nervous system contains five main parts. Four are noted here. The fifth, the basal ganglia, reside deep within the brain.

bound pathway for each specific sensor or motor spindle, a pathway going all the way to the brain. There is also a dedicated outbound pathway for each muscle motor unit.

Your brain, spinal cord, and nerves are what is known in network systems as a spoke-and-hub network, or star topology. Each part is connected directly to the central processor (the brain). A star topology provides a simple way to understand where each signal comes from and therefore what it means—a property essential to properly interpreting signals from the body.

The spinal cord also houses most of the body's reflexes. A reflex is an involuntary, pre-programmed automatic motor response to a stimulus. Reflexes occur without direct action from the brain, via special interconnecting neural pathways called interneurons, which redirect certain signals from the body's sensors to an appropriate motor nerve. Bypassing

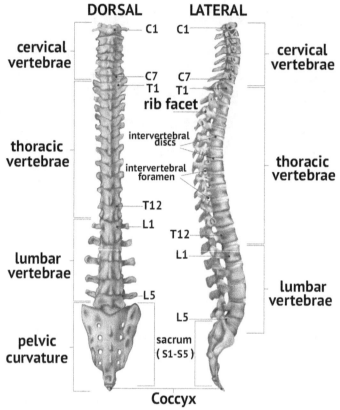

Figure 12.3. The bones of the spinal cord. Each segment serves a specific region of the body.

a complete neural circuit to the brain and back provides a much shorter pathway for the stimulus, affording a much quicker response. Most of the body's reflexes work this way.

A well-known example is the patellar stretch reflex, also known as the knee-jerk reflex. With the knee bent, your lower leg reflexively shoots out when the patellar tendon is tapped with sufficient force. Tapping your patellar tendon stretches the proprioceptors in the muscles (quadriceps) that extend your knee. The ensuing signals are sent to the spinal cord, shunted through an interneuron to a motor nerve, and then returned to a motor nerve that tells the quadriceps to contract. That's why your leg immediately straightens out.

The Stretch Reflex

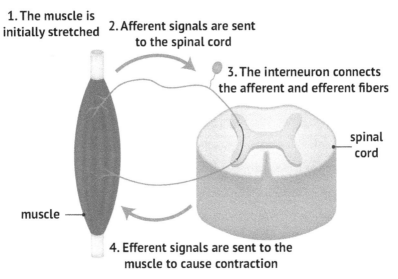

1. The muscle is initially stretched

2. Afferent signals are sent to the spinal cord

3. The interneuron connects the afferent and efferent fibers

spinal cord

muscle

4. Efferent signals are sent to the muscle to cause contraction

Figure 12.4. The stages of the stretch reflex mechanism.

This response is essential for upright posture. When you stand, your quadriceps maximally contract, causing your legs to straighten. After a while, the quadriceps can tire and flex a bit, which stretches their proprioceptors. The patellar reflex quickly sends motor signals to the quadriceps to contract more, automatically correcting your posture, which allows you to concentrate on something other than staying in the upright position.

Most of the time this works well. But nerves malfunction under physical pressure, slowing the speed of the signals passing through them. Some people, especially as they age, experience damaged or compressed disks between the vertebrae in the third lumbar region (L3), which is where the nerves to the quadriceps exit the spinal column.

Like all natural forces, gravity is not particularly forgiving—it simply doesn't care if you're vertical or horizontal. If reflexive signals to the quadriceps are slowed down by compression of the nerves, knee exten-

sion may not happen fast enough, and an unexpected fall can easily occur.

From a standing position, it takes about a half second to hit the
ground in a fall. That's not much time for your neuromuscular system to react. Your body needs to react almost instantaneously.

Different types of nerves have different signaling speeds. The
speed of a nerve is faster if it's larger in diameter and coated with
a fatty substance called myelin. It's slower when it's smaller in
diameter or lacks a myelin sheath.

The nerves servicing the knee-jerk reflex, which comes to the
rescue when we stumble, are large and myelinated, with a conduction velocity of about 100 meters per second (200 mph).
The distance from your knee to your spine is about half a me-
ter, so the conduction time is around 0.005 seconds. Thus, it
takes 0.01 seconds for nerve impulses to travel to the spinal cord
and back (0.005 + 0.005). Since it takes 0.5 seconds to hit the
ground, your body typically has plenty of time to react before
falling down.

In contrast, the conduction velocity of the small unmyelinated
nerves that inform your body about deep pain is only about 1
m/sec, a hundred times slower. If the conduction time for the
knee-jerk reflex were this slow, it would take about one second
for the signals to travel to and from your spinal cord (0.5 +
0.5). This means that the sensory signals from your quadriceps
would have only just arrived at your spinal cord by the time you
hit the ground. This would render any activity requiring upright
posture untenably dangerous.

The thousands of functions of a coherent, working body require a
wide range of signaling solutions. Fast conduction speeds are essential
for reflexes, but also for many other functions like handling objects and

doing intricate work. Slower speeds work better for other functions, like the signals for pain. Different needs demand different solutions, but different solutions are expensive. Because the speed of a given nerve is defined by two variables in the way it's constructed (the diameter of the nerve and the presence and quality of a myelin sheath), the body is able to have signaling speeds fine tuned to the specific needs of different body systems. And this is exactly what we see. Each part of the body has the nerve conduction speeds needed for its given work.

Once again, the body has an elegant solution—using the same basic mechanism (nerves) but tuned to meet different needs. And once again, the body seems to be optimized—the right responses for the right conditions in the right places and in the right timeframes—maximizing both precision and efficiency.

The Brainstem

The brainstem sits between the spinal cord and the rest of the brain. It works a bit like a distribution panel or switchboard, transmitting sensory information from your eyes, ears, and body through its peripheral nerves to the other regions of your brain, and relaying motor instructions from the brain's various centers back through to the body's many centers of action.

While this is essential to control balance, coordination, and movement, the brainstem performs many other vital functions:

- It controls your consciousness, arousal, alertness, sleep cycle, breathing, heart rate, blood pressure, swallowing, digestion, and many other life-essential jobs.
- It provides some of the protective reflexes, like the blink, corneal, and pupillary light reflexes, coughing, sneezing, and vomiting.
- It also receives sensory information from your face and controls many facial expressions and eye movements, including the vestibular-ocular (doll's-eyes) reflex.

The Cerebrum

Your cerebrum's motor cortex initiates purposeful movements. It does this by evaluating the current position of the body based on feedback information coming from the cerebellum, the basal ganglia (more on the basal ganglia below), and other regions of the brain, then determining which signals to send to what muscle groups.

There are five general keys to any action, and these all apply to purposeful movement. These are five things the motor cortex must account for:

- *Intention:* A desired outcome or future state. The intention can be conscious or subconscious.
- *Information:* The current state of the body's positioning, usually as it exists relative to the external world. For manipulating objects with the hands, for example, this would include information about the current state of the object(s) in question. Enormous amounts of raw sensor feeds must be understood in terms of the whole.
- *Control logic:* Decision logic that will turn the intent into a plan—a sequence of purposeful actions that moves the body from its current state to the desired future state, in the desired timeframe. The control logic needed to solve purposeful movement problems is far beyond an on/off switch or a simple if/then conditional.
- *Signals:* Indicators to initiate the actions according to the plan—specific signals sent to control specific muscles in specific ways.
- *Feedback loops:* In real-world scenarios, the plan is rarely perfect, the muscles don't respond exactly as expected, or conditions change as the plan unfolds, so continual adjustments are needed to reach the goal. Thus, the brain needs to monitor the situation and continually re-run its control logic to adjust the plan as it unfolds.

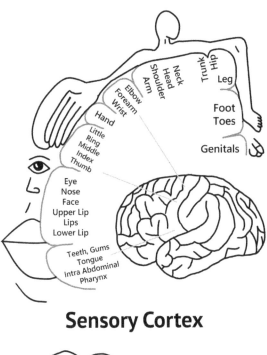

Sensory Cortex

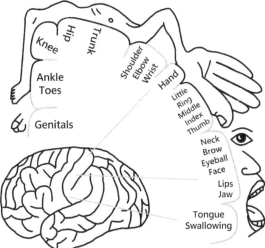

Motor Cortex

Figure 12.5. The cortical homunculus, a representative map of brain function conveying the amount of cortex devoted to various parts of the body.

For example, when a baseball outfielder realizes a fly ball is heading his way, he quickly estimates where he'll need to be to catch the ball, his mind forms a plan for how and when to get there, and his motor cortices (left and right) execute that plan by sending the requisite signals to all the needed muscle groups. Along the way, of course, he'll continue to watch the ball and adjust the plan in real time. All changes to the plans are executed by his motor cortices.

If his plan was reasonably well calculated and he made appropriate adjustments along the way (based on sensory feedback), he should arrive in the right place at the right time to catch the ball. All the while, he needs to stay balanced and upright, as it just wouldn't do to fall over while fielding a baseball. And of course, all this planning and executing happens almost instantaneously and without much conscious effort.

Both the sensory (input) and motor (output) strips of your cerebrum are arranged somatotopically, meaning they're arranged relative to the body parts they serve. Some regions need greater coordination, and these receive more sensory information and deliver more motor instructions. This has been mapped in what's called the homunculus (little human body), shown in Figure 12.5. Note the outsized importance of hand, eye, lips, and facial sensory input and motor output.

The brain processes signals on the side opposite their origin: the right side of the brain controls the left side of your body, and the left brain controls the right side. Motor signals travel from the motor cortex through the brainstem and spinal cord to the motor nerves. Eventually, they cross over to the other side and are then bundled together within the peripheral nerves that travel out from the spinal cord to your muscles. The motor cortex also sends messages to the basal ganglia and cerebellum to tell them what's happening.

The motor cortex processes signals from the entire sensory system, including vision, skin sensors, joint and tendon receptors, and the muscle spindles, in addition to the basal ganglia and the cerebellum. This continual feedback enables the motor cortex to make ongoing adjustments to the force needed for a given voluntary action.

The Basal Ganglia

The basal ganglia are a group of nerve-connecting centers deep within the brain, just below the cerebral hemispheres. They're connected to both the sensory and motor neural circuits and are believed to help process and integrate sensory data from many different sources, information which is then used to regulate motor activity. Little of what they do is well understood. Most of what we know about how they work comes from seeing what happens when they don't work—namely, what are known as "movement disorders" like Parkinson's disease, a degenerative condition that usually starts with a resting tremor, muscle stiffness, and slow movements, leading to poor control of posture and balance and loss of coordination and facial expression.

Cerebellum

Your cerebellum (little brain) receives sensory information from the proprioceptors in your muscles and tendons, and the receptors in your skin, joints, and ligaments. These tell the cerebellum the position of your limbs and what's going on in your muscles and joints. Your cerebellum also receives sensory data from the vestibular region in your brainstem, helping to maintain your body's posture and balance.

Your motor cortex informs the cerebellum of what actions it's planning, giving the cerebellum moment-to-moment knowledge of all the muscle activity in your body. It integrates this information and sends signals to make constant adjustments, allowing you to stay coordinated and balanced.

Wiring the Body

AT THE heart of balance, coordination, and movement is a complex network of nerves. And just as we saw with the pathways taken by the optic nerves, the wiring plan is extraordinary. Sensory nerves are segregated into sensory nerve bundles, as are the motor nerves. The sensory and motor nerve bundles stay separated in the brain, through the spinal cord, and as they exit the spinal column. Each nerve exits the spinal column at a specific place to service a specific location in the body.

As they exit the spinal column, sensory nerves (inbound from the body's sensors to the brain) and motor nerves (outbound from the brain to the muscles) are routed to their respective endpoints, either in a specific sensor or a specific muscle unit.

The wiring framework, which consists mainly of the bones and soft tissues of the spinal column, needs a precise set of shapes to support and protect the delicate nerves within (see Chapter 3), yet with all the right holes, both centrally to the vertebrae and for nerve egress, to enable proper function without adding pressure to the sensitive nerves (and thereby slowing or stopping nerve impulses).

When engineers design wiring systems, they often must make what is referred to in the business as a "horrible great hole" through a structure. This is exactly what we see at the base of the skull where the spinal cord exits the cranial cavity—a big hole, though one that is exactly the right size and shape to accommodate the spinal cord.[3] Each vertebra, with its own unique shape, must have a similarly perfect hole. And all the holes must be properly aligned, or the spinal cord won't survive much movement.

> The specifications and assembly instructions for the wiring of the body must be specified somewhere and encoded somehow. This specification must be read and applied during fetal development in order to build a working nervous system and to keep it working as the body grows into adulthood. And it must be interwoven with the development of the surrounding structures and connected both in the brain and with all the appropriate sensors and muscles in all the right places throughout the body.

From an engineer's point of view, all this is extraordinary. Designing a wiring harness for complex systems with similar capabilities involves many constraints that often conflict:

- The range of travel required as the machine (or body) moves and changes its shape in three dimensions.
- The required flexibility and extension for each part of the wiring. Loops are common, to avoid stretching due to movement, assembly, thermal loads, or maintenance.
- Redundant routing and multiple pathways.
- Routing to avoid other bodily systems and subsystems.
- Minimal bulk and weight.

In systems like this, with conflicting needs and goals, engineers apply fine judgment (usually acquired through long experience) to work out the best solution.

A Diagnosis for Emily

LET'S RETURN to our story of Emily, a composite character, and review some of the problems she has been progressively experiencing. And note that the descriptions below borrow the wording from actual patients with similar problems.

- "Experiencing tingling off and on in my hands and feet."
- "Having problems with my balance."
- "Lack coordination in the hands."
- "After sitting awhile, difficult to get into walking mode."
- "Writing is illegible."
- "Voice is hoarse and sometimes non-existent."
- "Sometimes have problems swallowing."
- "Feel dizzy when I stand up or turn my head."

These issues with balance and coordination suggest a problem in the nervous system. In such cases, doctors review symptoms and then seek out the source of the problem—the where.

Emily undergoes an MRI (magnetic resonance imaging) study, which verifies that she has a chronic autoimmune inflammatory condition called multiple sclerosis (MS). In MS the immune system attacks the myelin sheath that covers the nerves. This slows down the impulse conduction, making it harder for the nerves to work properly and interact with each other. These inflammatory plaques can occur anywhere in the central nervous system, and in Emily's case she has them mostly in her cerebellum but also in her basal ganglia, brainstem, both motor cortices, and spinal cord. Despite being put on aggressive treatment, within a few months she has gone from being a vibrant and active businesswoman to a debilitated and dependent invalid.

A Few Thoughts

EMILY'S STORY reminds us just how vulnerable our bodies are. While they have amazing resilience and strength, the fact remains that we are never much more than one or two new problems away from debility or death. Should our bodies lose control of any of hundreds of factors, our archenemy, *equilibrium with the environment*, is ready to take over. Our bodies are continuously working, breathing, maintaining, and enabling the human experience, but the environment never rests in its quest for total equilibrium.

Our lives depend on our balance and coordination, and these require many essential systems, subsystems, and parts to function. Further, almost every human activity requires purposeful movement, so all the systems and subsystems required for purposeful movement must be present and working properly if we are to survive for any length of time, barring heroic medical interventions.

The motor control system acts as a master controller for the body's movements, initiating and managing both conscious and unconscious activities. The signaling pathways are exacting. The coordination of signals and the timing of those signals must be spot-on. Together, the body's cognitive systems, and the number and precision of their interconnections, are humbling to human engineers.

Here is yet another example of how only a fully coherent, interdependent, finely tuned system of systems can deliver the crucial bodily capabilities that meet its needs. We don't usually think about these things because they happen subconsciously, but when something goes wrong, it affects almost everything we experience.

Once again, this overview has only scratched the surface of the true complexity involved. But even our quick flyover urges several questions. How does the body know how to build the specific nerves needed in each part of the body? How does it know where to route these? Where does it store the information that determines the right conduction speeds for the right nerves (i.e., the information determining the diameter of the nerve and the presence or absence of a myelin sheath)? How is that specification communicated to each of the millions of individual cells involved in building the thing? No one knows. It's possible the answers will be among the last and most profound discoveries in medicine and biology.

Part Four: Surviving the Jungle

The body is an amazing system of systems. But the world is fraught with danger. Injuries happen. The skin may get punctured, torn, or burned. Bruises are common. Bones can break. So the body must be able to repair itself, else its lifespan will be short.

The body is also an amazing banquet—unpleasant to think about, but true. It's constantly bombarded by microorganisms like bacteria, viruses, and fungi that would like nothing more than to set up residence inside the body's moist buffet of nutrients and build large, healthy families. So the body must actively defend itself against these freeloaders or else, again, its lifespan will be short.

The body also needs subsystems that prevent failure. Engineers understand this because this is how they must design their systems. And invariably, the subsystems designed to prevent failure are separate and distinct from those that enable function.

In short, the body must be resilient to withstand the challenges it faces over a long lifecycle, and this requires several sophisticated systems and subsystems.

13. Clotting

A chain is no stronger than its weakest link, and life is after all a
chain.

—William James[1]

Picture a pair of fraternal twins, George and Geoffrey.
Their family has a history of bleeding disorders going back several
generations. Many of their male ancestors suffered from the "royal disease," so called because Queen Victoria had been a carrier and passed it
to many of the ruling families of Europe. The most famous royal sufferer
was Prince Alexei, heir apparent to the throne of the Russian Empire,
who was executed in the Communist Revolution.

When George and Geoffrey are born, their parents are on the look-
out for any telltale signs of bleeding, given their family history. And sure
enough, as George begins to be more active, he's found to bruise easily
and have recurrent nosebleeds, and his knees swell from internal bleeding. He and his brother love to roughhouse, but George's bleeding problem makes this dangerous.

Geoffrey never has this problem, but one day he complains of pain
and swelling in his leg, and of chest pain when he breathes. His parents
figure he is trying to get more attention since George is usually the one
sick and getting everyone's sympathy. But Geoffrey becomes short of
breath and looks a bit blue. They call 911 and he's rushed to the hospital.

That's when they learn he has a clotting disorder (which, if it was in
their family history, they knew nothing about it). The main vein in his
right leg has formed a clot, which broke off into little pieces and traveled
to his heart and then to his lungs. The doctors remedy this problem only

in the nick of time. Tests show that Geoffrey's problem is genetic, just as his brother's is. The two both have blood disorders, but diametrically opposite ones. George bleeds too easily. Geoffrey clots too easily.

The brothers are fictional, but their disorders are very real.

Hemostasis

YOUR BODY uses pressure to circulate blood. When a blood vessel is damaged, that pressure pushes blood through the opening, much like what happens when a water pipe bursts. To minimize blood loss, which could lead to death, your body needs a way to quickly mend any holes with patches strong enough to hold against the blood pressure.

This process is called hemostasis and involves three coordinated actions—vasoconstriction, platelet aggregation, and fibrin clot formation. Together these form a patch to stop the bleeding and allow healing to begin at the site of injury. But clots in the wrong places and at the wrong times can be deadly, causing heart attacks and strokes.

To function properly your body needs to be able to control hemostasis so that it turns on only when needed and turns off and stays off when it's not. A fine balance between the forces that promote clotting and those that prevent clotting is essential. Without this balance, debility or even death awaits.

Clotting

YOUR BLOOD vessels are set up so that clotting won't happen under normal conditions, fortunate since under normal circumstances, you need your blood flowing, not clotting. But when an injury occurs that causes blood to leak out, the cells at the site release chemicals that trigger the muscles surrounding the blood vessel to go into a spasm that shrinks the opening in the blood vessel, thus slowing blood loss. This process is called vasoconstriction.

That's the first line of defense. The next involves platelets, cell-like structures made in the bone marrow. They float freely in your blood and don't normally interact with each other, but when a blood vessel is

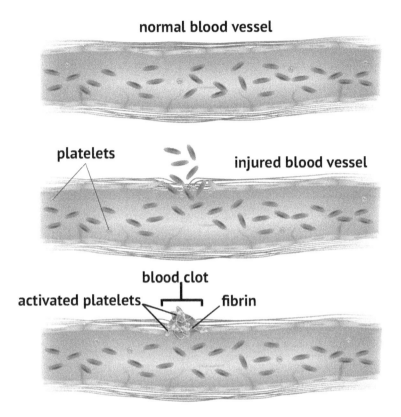

Figure 13.1. Clotting.

injured, the injured tissue releases chemicals that trigger the platelets to stick to each other. As they zero in on the injury site, they clump together to form a soft plug. Together with vasoconstriction, platelet aggregation further slows the bleeding.

But vasoconstriction and platelet aggregation aren't usually enough to stop the bleeding, so your body needs its third line of defense—specialized proteins in your blood called clotting factors. Just like platelets, which don't interact with each other apart from a blood vessel injury, the clotting factors in your blood are normally inactive. Most are made in the liver and are released into your blood, where they circulate until needed.

Clotting Factor I is a protein called fibrinogen that circulates in the blood. When it passes by the site of a blood vessel injury, it attaches, hand-in-glove, to specific receptors on the activated platelets. As the platelets pile on to each other to form a soft plug, thousands of fibrinogen molecules stick to them. Once they have attached to the binding sites on the platelets, they still need to be chemically converted (activated) to fibrin to make a solid clot strong enough to stop the bleeding.

A specific enzyme, called thrombin, chemically snips off a piece of the dissolved fibrinogen molecule, which activates it and makes it a solid fibrin molecule. But thrombin is only made when clotting Factor II is activated. Factor II is a normally inactive protein called prothrombin, which is also dissolved in the blood. To chemically snip off a piece of prothrombin and convert it to thrombin so it can activate fibrinogen to bring about a firm fibrin clot requires another enzyme called prothrombinase. And prothrombinase is a protein molecule made up of activated Factors V and X. (See Figure 13.2.)

So, like a chain reaction, the prothrombinase, made of activated clotting Factors V and X, converts prothrombin into thrombin, which then converts fibrinogen into fibrin, which forms the clot that stops the bleeding. The key to starting the clotting process is prothrombinase. But where does this enzyme come from? There are two known pathways in your body.

The quicker pathway is called the *extrinsic*, or Tissue Factor pathway, because with external injury it requires a molecule called Tissue Factor (clotting Factor III), a protein on the surface of the tissue that supports the blood vessel, so is extrinsic to (not carried in) the blood. When an injury occurs, inactive clotting Factor VII in the blood activates when it touches Tissue Factor. Once activated, Factor VII snips off a piece of Factor X, activating it. Activated Factor X then joins activated Factor V to form prothrombinase.

The slower pathway is called the *intrinsic*, or contact activation pathway, because it involves the clotting factors in the blood. Blood vessel

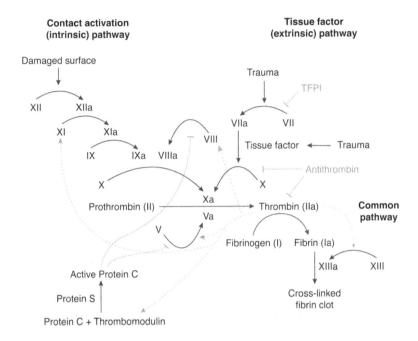

Figure 13.2. The blood clotting cascade and some of the anti-clotting factors. Each "a" indicates an active form of the enzyme.

injuries cause blood to come in contact with various cells, proteins, and other chemicals. This activates clotting Factor XII, which then snips off a piece of, and activates, clotting Factor XI, which then snips off a piece of, and activates, clotting Factor IX. Activated Factor IX, with the help of activated Factor VIII, then snips off a piece of, and activates, clotting Factor X. Activated Factor X then joins with activated Factor V to form prothrombinase. Thrombin also activates clotting Factor XIII, which allows the thousands of fibrin strands surrounding the soft platelet plug to link up across each other to greatly strengthen the fibrin clot.

This process is known as the coagulation cascade. But a cascade evokes water falling, a relatively simple process. This is more like an assembly line, where a specialized task is performed at each step to achieve a larger and more challenging goal. An external or internal injury to a blood vessel launches the assembly line process, which creates a fibrin clot at the injury site, stopping the bleeding and allowing healing to begin.

The first twin brother in the scenario above, George, suffers from a deficiency of clotting Factor IX. This deficiency is also known as Christmas disease. Russian Prince Alexei Romanov suffered from Christmas disease, which might well have killed him if a Bolshevik bullet hadn't found him first. Nowadays this genetic disorder is called hemophilia B, in contrast to hemophilia A, which involves a deficiency of clotting Factor VIII.

You can see in Figure 13.2 that both these clotting factors are specific and critical to fibrin clot formation. A defect in, or a deficient supply of, either clotting factor would result in a potentially deadly bleeding disorder due to recurrent or severe blood loss. And it's not just those two. If any one of the clotting factors from Figure 13.2 were missing, in short supply, or improperly formed, your body would have a bleeding disorder. And without clotting, the body is in constant danger of bleeding out from even a minor injury.

Blood clotting is another great example of the many protein and enzyme cascades that operate much of the body's most critical systems. The intricate, interconnected chemistry of these cascades boggles the mind. That the entire blood clotting cascade happens so quickly and efficiently, and only when and where it's needed, is engineering genius.

But this is only half the equation. Hemostasis involves a delicate balance between the forces that promote clotting and those that prevent it. And, as you'd expect by now, every delicate balance requires precise controls. The push-pull principle predicts that the process of preventing clots is likely very different from the process that forms them.

Anti-Clotting

THIS BRINGS us back to the second brother in our scenario, Geoffrey. Rather than bleeding too easily, his blood tends to clot in his veins even absent an injury. Clots in the large veins of the leg can break into little pieces, called emboli, which then move with the flow of blood to the right side of the heart. From there they can travel through the pulmonary arteries to the lungs, where they can lodge in the downstream blood vessels, blocking blood flow and preventing adequate gas exchange. Depending on the number and size of the emboli, this can quickly lead to severe debility and even death.

Far from passive actors, the blood vessels are set up to actively prevent clotting until an injury occurs. Under normal conditions, the tissue lining the inside of the blood vessel (endothelium) releases localized anti-clotting factors. These help deactivate and neutralize some of the clotting factors in the blood nearby.

When the endothelium is disrupted by injury, these localized anti-clotting factors are no longer produced, which helps to launch the coagulation cascade (along with the extrinsic or intrinsic pathway) so that clots form. Since the vessel walls on either side of the injury are still intact, they continue to inhibit activation of the clotting factors in either direction from the injury site. This restricts the fibrin clot formation to the site of the injury.

Besides making most of the clotting factors, the liver also produces a protein called antithrombin, your body's main inhibitor of thrombin. (Thrombin, keep in mind, is key to activating fibrinogen to form a fibrin clot.) Antithrombin works by entrapping thrombin like a fly in a spider web, rendering thrombin unavailable to do its job. But in its initial form, antithrombin doesn't bind well to thrombin. To help it, normal endothelium produces a chemical called heparan sulfate, which attaches to antithrombin to change its shape, increasing its ability to bind to thrombin by more than a thousand-fold.

Antithrombin also blocks activated Factor X and, to a lesser degree, activated Factors IX and VII. These clotting factors are needed in the cascade that produces thrombin. Antithrombin (made in the liver) and heparan sulfate (made in the endothelium) work together to prevent clot formation.

Normal endothelium also produces another anti-clotting factor called Tissue Factor Pathway Inhibitor (TFPI). It grabs and deactivates activated clotting Factor X. On top of that, the resulting complex molecule can attach to and prevent Tissue Factor from activating clotting Factor VII in the extrinsic pathway. Both actions help prevent clotting.

The endothelium also produces thrombomodulin, which attaches to thrombin. When combined, they activate protein C, produced in the liver. Activated protein C is an enzyme that neutralizes activated clotting Factors V and VIII. Both factors are essential to the coagulation cascade. So, the combination of protein C (made in the liver) and thrombomodulin (made in the endothelium) also work together to prevent clotting.

> The many components required for clotting circulate freely throughout the body, always at the ready, but in their inactive state. When the right trigger occurs (caused by an injury), a chain reaction begins, consuming the raw materials, each in order, to produce the desired outcome—in this case, a timely and effective repair to a leak in a pressure vessel.
>
> Further, this effect is localized to just the injured area. This is critical to sustaining life to adulthood. The alternative, where clotting occurs in the wrong places or at the wrong times, is generally deadly.
>
> These separate systems are perfectly orchestrated to achieve this delicate balance of clotting and anti-clotting. Once again, we have different parts made in different places, in just the right quantities. The result can be deployed almost instantly in the exact places where needed, and only when needed. The systems are ingenious, perfectly orchestrated, and amazingly efficient.
>
> Here we see another common design pattern in the body: global capabilities, ready for action, yet with localized triggers and application.

The chemistry in all this may seem complicated (mainly because it is), but the basics are quite simple. Proper clotting results from a delicate balance of opposing forces, those that promote and those that inhibit clotting. Normally, anti-clotting factors are in control, but when a blood vessel is injured, anti-clotting factors are no longer produced and the coagulation cascade produces a clot, local to the exact site of a blood vessel injury.

To Clot, or Not to Clot?

GEOFFREY'S AND George's genetic disorders mean they each have trouble keeping their coagulation cascades within the narrow Goldilocks zone that's necessary for life. Geoffrey illustrates the commonest clotting problem, Factor V Leiden. This condition produces an abnormal Factor V that, when activated, resists being broken down by activated protein C. This results in blood with high levels of activated clotting Factor V, at high risk for clotting. His brother is at the opposite extreme. George's blood doesn't clot when it needs to. Geoffrey has to be on blood thinners all his life, and George has to have infusions of clotting Factor IX all his life. Without modern medical interventions, people with these disorders would be unlikely to survive into adulthood.

The delicate balance between clotting and not clotting is another example of the Goldilocks Principle. The forces of chemistry and physics are very picky about what works and what doesn't, and they're not very forgiving when something goes wrong.

So we're faced with the same question. Rather than asking why these systems sometimes go wrong, we need to ask how it is that they ever go right.

14. Immunity

God heals, and the doctor takes the fee.
—Benjamin Franklin[1]

Our bodies are expert at harvesting the building blocks of life from the world around us, breaking them down into the right bite-sized parts, then circulating them throughout the body for our roughly 30 trillion cells to enjoy.

But the world is a dangerous place. Many other organisms would love to join in the feast. While many of these organisms return the favor by providing resources or functions that help the body, like the many types of bacteria that live in your gut to help break down the foods you've ingested, others are less friendly and don't mind if they kill your cells as they feast.

In fact, your body is constantly exposed to unfriendlies—mainly bacteria, viruses, and fungi, but also protozoa and worms. If they infect your body and become widespread, they can cause no end of problems and possibly kill you. And any of your body's systems can be affected. Pneumonia is a lung infection that makes breathing difficult and can lead to respiratory failure and death. Gastroenteritis is a gastrointestinal infection that causes vomiting and diarrhea, and can lead to dehydration and death. Meningitis is a brain infection that causes headache and confusion, and can lead to coma and death.

These and many others can end badly, so the body needs ways to fight back. But invasive microorganisms are too small to be seen with the naked eye. They can't be detected with the senses or easily avoided through deliberate actions. To counter such attacks, your body uses a

Lymphatic Circulation

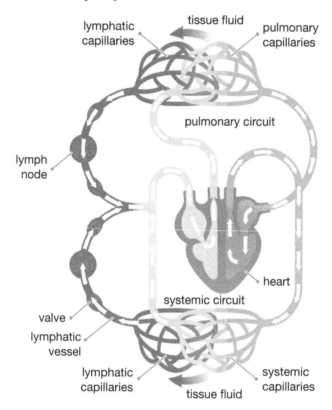

Figure 14.1. The lymphatic circulatory system.

three-pronged defensive strategy. The first is a passive barrier of epithelial tissue, which forms the surface of your skin and lines your respiratory, gastrointestinal, and genitourinary tracts. As we saw previously, these cells perform many critical functions. Not least is preventing toxins from reaching the interior of the body. They also keep out most microorganisms.

Microbes that find their way past the epithelial tissues have a direct path into the lymphatic system, a network of lymph nodes and vessels that parallels the arteries and veins of the cardiovascular system (see Figure 14.1). It's composed of tiny, thin-walled channels that collect excess fluids (lymph) from the tissues and return them to the blood.

A thorough discussion of the lymphatic system is beyond the scope of this book, but it, too, involves many substantive examples of exquisite engineering. For our purposes here, we note that while this system is essential for balancing the body's fluid levels, it's also a vulnerability because it provides a way for microorganisms to enter your bloodstream and, in this way, commandeer your body's transport system to gain access to most everything in your body.

So, when microbes breach the body's first line of defense and enter the tissues below, your body is in mortal danger. Time to call in your second and third lines of defense—the innate and adaptive immune systems. Together they form a precisely orchestrated system of many different types of cells and proteins, each tailored for specialized roles in the body's defense.

The world contains many millions of different bacteria, viruses, and fungi. The disease-causing ones that breach your first line of defense are called pathogens. In your body's life-or-death battles with attacking pathogens, time is of the essence. Though a pathogenic infection usually involves only a small invading force, that force can grow rapidly. With food and water generously supplied by your body, pathogens can multiply exponentially if your body can't quickly get them under control.

Like seatbelts in your car, the innate immune system comes standard on the human body. It engages invading microorganisms right away. But many pathogens remain invisible or resistant to the innate immune system's efforts, which allows them to proliferate. Your body also needs more specialized forces, ones that can learn about a new invader, adapt to its idiosyncrasies, and build precision weapons to target it with high specificity. That's your adaptive (acquired) immune system. Rather than being fully functional at birth, it continues to develop as your body is exposed to different microbes. It usually takes your adaptive immune system a few days to figure out a new invader, but when it's ready to swing into action, it partners with the innate immune system to beat back the attack. And as a bonus, your acquired immune system is now stronger for its efforts.

If any of the three parts of the immune system (passive barriers, innate immune system, adaptive immune system) is on the fritz, your body is in big trouble. Short of high-tech medical interventions, no one can survive long without a fully functional immune system.

Built-In Immunity

YOUR INNATE immune system, which does not need to be educated like the adaptive immune system, detects the presence of microbes and determines whether they should be destroyed (pathogens). The first thing the system must determine is whether the microbes are host cells (parts of your body) or foreign cells. If your innate immune system gets this decision wrong, it could attack your own cells. So, just as in hemostasis, it's important that your immune system turn on only when and where it's needed and stay off when it's not.

> Pathogens are either foreign cells or viruses. But your body consists of trillions of different cells and contains trillions of other friendly cells that are not pathogens. So the immune system must differentiate the body's own cells (and its friendly visitor cells) from invading cells that will cause harm.
>
> Further, your immune system needs to identify exactly which of those millions of different possible pathogens are attacking.
>
> This poses an extraordinary set of problems, yet somehow your immune system normally knows the difference and doesn't defend against your own cells or these helper bacteria. How your immune system distinguishes the good from the bad, and works with the good, is not well understood. (But we should be thankful that the body is smart enough to figure it out, even if the scientific community hasn't yet.)

Further complicating matters, the body carries roughly as many bacteria on your skin and in your nose, mouth, and gastrointestinal tract as it does of its own cells—an estimated 30+ trillion bacterial cells for an average human body. For the most part, these bacteria play important roles for the body, working with your immune system to keep you alive. So your immune system needs to be able to further distinguish the good microbes from the bad.

As near as we can tell, cells have just one way to know what's going on around them: they interact through sensors sticking out from their cell membranes. An innate immune cell has receptors (sensors) on its membrane that can attach to specific chemicals or proteins on the surface of another cell. These work mainly by shape and by chemical and electrical attraction and repulsion, akin to a complicated key in an equally complicated lock.

The innate immune system consists mainly of mast cells, macrophages, and dendritic cells, together with white blood cells (called neutrophils) and a protein complex known as complement, which circulates in the blood. Mast cells, macrophages, and dendritic cells are dispersed throughout your body's tissues. These are the first responders to microbial invasion. Each has about a thousand different kinds of receptors on its surface. And each can detect (attach to) specific foreign proteins on the surface of a microbe. When a receptor identifies an invader, it activates the cell, triggering its built-in defense mechanisms. The "target pattern" that an immune cell uses to identify an invader usually consists of the specific arrangement of just a few amino acids on a very large protein molecule. These target patterns are called antigens, since they trigger *anti*body *gen*eration.

When a receptor on the surface of a macrophage or dendritic cell attaches to an antigen, that cell becomes activated and will engulf, kill, and digest the microbe. In a fascinating process called phagocytosis, the immune cell extends its membrane to surround and absorb the pathogen. But pathogens are dangerous (by definition), so the pathogen is enclosed in a special vesicle called a phagosome, which isolates the pathogen so it can't damage the immune cell. Next, the cell injects a special packet of digestive enzymes, called a lysosome, into the phagosome, which kills the invading bacterial cell and breaks it into harmless pieces, which are then expelled from the cell. Both macrophages and dendritic cells also process some of the pieces from the killed microbe to present critical information about the pathogen to the adaptive immune system.

> A macrophage is an extraordinary nanobot—a specialized and brutally thorough assassin and factory all rolled into one. It migrates, detects, captures, kills, and dismantles harmful cells, then sends the remains out to be recycled. It also places bits of proteins from the killed microbe onto its own surface, thereby exposing (presenting) it to the adaptive immune system for training purposes. With these protein fragments on its surface, it's called an antigen-presenting cell (APC).

When activated, all three types of innate immune cells release cytokines, which are chemical messengers like hormones. Mast cells also release histamine. Cytokines and histamine signal to surrounding cells that a battle has begun. These chemicals increase local blood flow and cause nearby capillaries to become leaky, dumping fluid into the nearby tissues. Together these cause the familiar signs of inflammation—swelling and redness at the site of infection.

The next defender in the innate immune system's arsenal is a white blood cell called a neutrophil (granulocyte, see below). Like other blood cells, neutrophils are made in the bone marrow. After being outfitted for battle they move into the blood, where they hunt for microbial invaders. Using cytokine receptors on their cell surface, neutrophils detect and then rush toward higher concentrations of cytokines and nearby microbes, a bit like how sharks move toward their victim by following an increasing concentration of blood in the water.[2]

Because the capillaries near infected tissue have leaky walls, neutrophils passing by will detect that this is the place and leak out of the blood and into the tissues. The battle is joined. More neutrophils arrive and enter the fray. This continues as long as the infection remains.

Just like macrophages and dendritic cells, neutrophils become activated once their receptors lock on to the foreign proteins on the surface of an invading microorganism. Once activated, a neutrophil kills the pathogenic microbe by phagocytosis and then the neutrophil also dies. Dead neutrophils make up most of the pus that's commonly associated with infection.

Neutrophils need the bloodstream in order to move freely around the body but then must have a way to exit the blood and enter the body's inner tissues exactly where and when needed. Once again, we see amazing orchestration. The capillaries in the neighborhood start leaking in just the right places, allowing the neutrophils to exit and move into the infected area. Neutrophils sense where they need to go, hurry there, and give their lives to kill the pathogen.

Neutrophils and other types of white blood cells circulate throughout the body as a general resource. When an infection is detected, they swarm to the specific locations where they're needed to join the battle, and they will continue to do so as long as necessary.

This is a remarkable engineering achievement. You would not be reading this right now if this system didn't work. And it's another example of a design pattern that also cropped up in the chapter on blood clotting—global resources brought to bear quickly at precise locations.

The body's survival capacity depends on the number of neutrophils in the bloodstream, how fast they can be deployed from the blood into the tissues, and their firepower once deployed. Blood needs at least 1.5 billion neutrophils per liter to defend the body from serious infection. Since neutrophils can't multiply like microbes can, and generally only live in the blood and tissues for a few hours, your bone marrow must

produce about 100 billion every day—about one million new neutrophils per second.

This must continue even when you're not actively fighting an infection. To maintain this level of production, support cells in the bone marrow release a special cytokine called G-CSF (Granulocyte (neutrophil)
Colony-Stimulation Factor), which tells immature stem cells in the bone
marrow to develop into neutrophils. In response to infection, some activated immune cells also release G-CSF, which increases production to
double or triple the number of neutrophils in the blood. So, although
neutrophils can't multiply on their own, certain immune cells can stimu-
late the bone marrow to increase neutrophil production as needed so you
can live to fight another day.

How do activated immune cells signal the bone marrow's cell factory
to increase production of immune cells? The process takes many parts,
all of which must be precisely tuned to achieve the exact capacity the
body requires to stay alive. When a person has a defect that compromises this subsystem, we see just how important it is. So, for instance, when
someone has cancer that requires chemotherapy, the chemotherapy has
the unfortunate side effect of suppressing bone marrow. This often leads
to very low neutrophil levels in his blood, which in turn limits how well
the innate immune system works. Consequently, the patient often has to
go to the hospital to be treated for life-threatening infections.

Several specialized proteins are needed to round out the innate
immune system. These proteins, which also leak into the tissues when
inflammation takes place, are collectively known as the complement system, because they complement the function of the innate immune system's cellular components.

The complement system consists of around thirty proteins. Like the
clotting factors, these proteins are mainly produced in the liver and enter
the blood in an inactive form. And as with clotting, a complex, multi-
step chemical pathway is involved in activating these proteins.

Once activated, complement is particularly deadly. The four steps in this process are as follows. (1) Surface proteins on the foreign microbe (or an antibody that has attached to its surface) activate the complement proteins, which then move toward the microbe. (2) The complement proteins link together into what is known as a *membrane attack complex*, which drills a hole in the microbe's cell membrane. Typically, a pathogen will have several holes punched into it around its perimeter. (3) Extracellular fluids rush into the microbe through the holes. (4) Entering fluids swell and rupture the microbe, killing it.

Not surprisingly, anywhere there is such an effective cell killer, there's the potential for "friendly fire" incidents, where this kind of killing power is inappropriately turned toward the body's own cells. When this happens, it's just as awful as it sounds, and can quickly lead to debility or death.

It's essential, then, to apply the same kind of strict controls to the complement system that we saw with clotting. The complement system must have accurate targeting to ensure that when it's activated it doesn't turn its destructive powers on cells that the body needs. Complement must be activated only when and where it's needed. The body uses yet another set of finely tuned control systems for this purpose, including special proteins to inhibit complement activation when it's not needed.

Adaptive Immunity, with Memory

ALAS, MANY microbes have ways of thwarting the innate immune system. Defeating these invaders falls to your body's third line of defense, the adaptive immune system. While the innate immune system reacts quickly, the adaptive immune system offers a slower but more tailored response to invasion. Since it needs to adapt to pathogens it hasn't seen before, it usually takes a few days to ramp up.

Each cell in the innate immune system has the same thousand or so different receptors, allowing each cell to react to around a thousand or more different pathogens. In contrast, each of the cells in the adaptive immune system has around 100,000 identical receptors, with each cell responding to only one specific chemical pattern and therefore only one (or just a few similar) pathogens. But the adaptive immune system has a clever trick up its sleeve. It's constantly generating vast numbers of cells, each with a different receptor. And because each cell has 100,000 copies of that receptor on its surface, it will be much more difficult for a corresponding pathogen to escape detection.

Though all the details of the process aren't yet known, these receptors are composed through a complex combination of different genetic *exons*, or gene segments. Due to the nature of combinatorics, this produces a massive number of possibilities from a much smaller number of variables. Estimates of the number of possible receptor patterns in the adaptive immune system range from around a trillion to as high as 10^{30} (a billion billion trillion). In other words, no one knows exactly, but it's a lot. Taken as a whole, the system can detect and target a trillion or more different antigens to kill their host pathogens.

> The adaptive immune system can detect an enormous variety of pathogens using relatively few resources, quickly producing large quantities of immune cells with just the receptors needed to thwart a specific attacker. In the software industry this property is known as elasticity, which describes systems that can quickly ramp their resources up or down based on rapidly changing needs.
>
> The adaptive immune system also remembers the specific attacker so it can respond even more quickly if and when it sees the same attacker in the future. A handy ability since, if a particular pathogen has been detected once, there's a higher probability it will appear later.
>
> Here we have a just-in-time army—quick and made to order, exactly when needed.

But there's a problem. Your body just isn't big enough to hold millions of copies of each of these trillion-plus cell/receptor combinations.

(Remember, there's only an estimated thirty trillion cells in an average adult body.) And when a particular cell with its particular receptor is needed, millions of copies (or more) will be required to get the job done. The solution? The acquired immune system adapts its resources dynamically as it faces new threats. It starts with a limited number of cells with each specific receptor, but when one is effective against a pathogen, the system quickly ramps up production of just those immune cells with that specific receptor.

The main actors in the adaptive immune system are specialized white blood cells (lymphocytes) called T-cells and B-cells. T-cells respond mainly to infections inside the body's cells, while B-cells respond mainly to infections outside the cells, either in the body's tissue fluids or in the blood.

Like all blood cells, lymphocytes are made in the bone marrow. Some migrate to and mature in the thymus gland, between the breastbone and heart, becoming T-cells ("T" for thymus). Others mature in the bone marrow, becoming B-cells ("B" for bone marrow).

As lymphocytes mature, they gain their specificity—the specific receptors that will enable them to bind to specific antigens. Though medical science hasn't yet figured out the details, the cells appear to use programmed mechanisms to rapidly modify the gene segments that make these receptors. (The two mechanisms known to date are somatic hypermutation and V(D)J recombination, a form of somatic recombination.) The variations seem to be largely random, but they always happen in specific, non-random locations—in what are known as the *variable regions* of the immunoglobulin genes, where the specific receptors are encoded. This enables the immune system to rapidly generate vast numbers of different receptors, increasing the chances of finding one that will bind to the new threat (pathogen).

After they mature, both T-cells and B-cells circulate from the blood to the lymph system and back, patrolling for foreign antigens. (Antigens, recall, are proteins found on the surface of pathogens.) T- and B-cells tend to aggregate in the tissues of the lymphatic system, which includes the lymph nodes, spleen, tonsils, adenoids, and appendix. As pathogens float through the lymph system, they're running the gauntlet, exposed to the billions of specialized immune cells that are waiting to kill them.

T-Cells

T-CELLS MAINLY target pathogens that infect the body's cells. There are two types of T-cells: cytotoxic T-cells, also known as killer T-cells, and helper T-cells, which coordinate the immune response. These cells work together to defend the body.

T-cells can only recognize an antigen if it's "presented" to them by other immune system cells—usually dendritic cells or macrophages from the innate immune system. As noted above, these are called antigen-presenting cells (APCs). Dendritic cells and macrophages are embedded in various tissues throughout the body. During an infection, APCs add antigen fragments from the pathogen to their cell membrane and then migrate via the lymphatic vessels to the lymphoid tissues.

T-cells are waiting in the lymphoid tissues. If a killer T-cell with specific receptors for the presented antigen is in the area, it will "recognize" the antigen. If a helper T-cell with receptors for this specific antigen is also nearby, it will communicate with the killer T-cell to confirm this antigen as a foreign invader. (Helper T-cells perform the same confirmation function for B-cells.) The helper T-cells thus act as controllers for the adaptive immune response.

With both recognition and confirmation, the killer T-cell becomes activated, and this triggers a series of reactions in a swift, coordinated attack. The APC releases cytokines that tell the activated T-cell to begin rapidly dividing, multiplying into thousands of identical clones. The clones include two types of T-cells: *effector* T-cells, released into the body's lymph system to seek and destroy pathogens, and *memory* T-cells, which remain in the lymph node, ready to be activated if the same pathogen later infects the body again.

Effector T-cells exit the lymph node, into the lymph ducts, blood vessels, and intracellular fluids. When they encounter a cell with the target antigen on its surface (indicating the cell is infected), the effector T-cells release cytotoxic molecules called granzymes, which penetrate the infected cell's membrane and instruct the cell to die. This is a form of apoptosis, a critical process in the body in which a cell executes an internal program to kill itself—a sort of self-destruct mechanism.

Although apoptosis sounds ghastly, it's a remarkably useful tool in the body, and key to many of the body's core processes, including development. In this case of apoptosis, when the cell dies and its internal contents degrade, its membrane stays intact, so the infection inside remains contained and doesn't spread. This is crucial for isolating viruses, which can wreak havoc in the body if not contained. The body must either dismantle them or isolate and expunge them.

> Viruses are a sort of floating packet of instructions, either DNA or RNA. But they're not alive, because they lack processing machinery (to execute those instructions), metabolism, and other functions associated with life. They need a living host cell to provide the functions they're missing, which allows them to make copies of themselves.
>
> Viruses make the news when a harmful one triggers a pandemic. So it would be easy to assume that viruses are all bad. In fact, the vast majority of viruses are not pathogenic to humans. Instead, most are critical for developing ecosystems, maintaining bodily health, and controlling bacterial populations. As one epidemiologist puts it, "If all viruses suddenly disappeared, the world would be a wonderful place for about a day and a half, and then we'd all die.... All the essential things they do in the world far outweigh the bad things."[3]

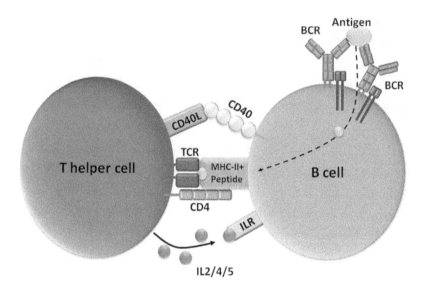

Figure 14.2. Multi-faceted signaling between a T helper cell and a B-cell. As the diagram suggests, the signaling between these cells is much more complex than we can go into in this chapter. Suffice to say that it involves multiple mechanisms and signaling proteins.

B-Cells

T-CELLS GENERALLY work well against pathogens that attack the body's cells directly. But many pathogens go after the nutrient-rich spaces between cells. These pathogens, mainly bacteria or fungi, are not trying to kill the body's cells, but are merely freeloading on the body's rich supply of nutrients.

As the lymph drains the excess fluids in the body, pathogens in the body's fluids are conveyed to a lymph node, or if they're in the blood, they eventually go to the spleen. Both locations are populated with B-cells, so either way they eventually encounter B-cells. In the following, we focus on the lymph node, though it works much the same in the spleen.

The receptors on the surface of the B-cell's membrane can recognize antigens directly on the surface of a pathogen. They don't need an APC to "present" them like the T-cells do. But activating a B-cell works in much the same way as activating a T-cell, in three steps: (1) Recognition occurs when a B-cell's specific receptors lock onto the antigen on the surface of the pathogenic microbe. (2) Verification happens when a helper T-cell (that's been activated by its specific receptors locking on to the same antigen) and the activated B-cell exchange a series of complex signals that confirm for the B-cell that this is a pathogen. (See Figure 14.2.) (3) Proliferation begins after the activated helper T-cell confirms the presence of a pathogen and releases cytokines, stimulating the activated B-cell to multiply and become thousands of identical clone cells.

Just as with the T-cells, the B-cell makes two types of clones: effector B-cells (called plasma cells), which secrete molecules called antibodies that recognize the same antigen as the one that activated the B-cell; and memory B-cells, which will rapidly respond to this same pathogen if it appears later.

Each plasma cell produces millions of identical proteins called antibodies. Each antibody has the same chemical pattern as the specific pathogen receptors on the surface of the B-cell that produced it. Thus, it matches the specificity of the parent cell and will target the same infecting pathogen.

Antibodies

SPECIALIZED PROTEINS called antibodies (also called immunoglobulins or gamma globulins) allow the adaptive immune system to collaborate with the innate immune system, in effect drawing the innate immune system into the battle.

The key to an antibody's effectiveness is its structure. The antibody molecule consists of four chains of amino acids bonded together, two identical pairs of heavy and light chains joined together in the shape of a Y. The two connected heavy chains provide the basis of the Y-shaped structure while each light chain is connected to the outside of the branching portion of the heavy chain. (See Figure 14.3.)

The tips of the Y-shaped antibody molecule consist of the amino acids from the ends of each identical light and heavy chain. Together they form the variable region, a specific chemical pattern with a three-

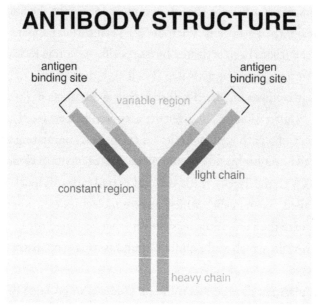

Figure 14.3. The structure of an antibody. The upper portions of the "Y" are the variable region while the bottom portions of the "Y" form the constant region.

dimensional shape identical to the antigen receptors on the B-cell that produced them—the cell that attached to and verified the antigen on the surface of the pathogen.

The variable regions of the antibody molecule act as specific antigen-binding sites and are known as the Fab portion (fragment antigen-binding). The amino acid structure that makes up the base of the Y-shaped antibody molecule remains constant—it's non-specific to any particular antigen—and is called the Fc piece (fragment crystallizable).

As effector B-cells generate new antibodies, the antibodies flow into the bloodstream and are pumped throughout the body. When the Fab portion attaches to a specific antigen, the Fc portion is activated, making the antibody ready for action. The antibodies don't kill target pathogens directly. Rather, the antibodies bind to the surface of the pathogen's membrane (via the Fab), precipitating several beneficial outcomes:

- *Targeting Sneaky Pathogens*: The cells of the innate immune system have receptors that will bind to the activated Fc portion of an antibody. With the Fab portion bound to a pathogen, the Fc portion is exposed in its activated form, giving the innate immune system a target to attack. The cells of the innate immune system recognize this and attack the cell bound by the antibody. Now pathogens that evaded and resisted the neutrophils and macrophages of the innate immune system have lost their advantage. The antibodies enable the innate immune system to see and defeat these pathogens.

- *Activating Complement*: Some complement proteins will attach to the activated Fc portion of bound antibodies, which triggers the complement process, killing the pathogen. Also, fragments of activated complement (such as C3b) attach themselves to the surface of these microbes. Neutrophils and macrophages also have receptors for C3b, enabling them to identify and attach to the pathogen and kill it.

- *Blocking Attachments*: Many bacteria and viruses have structures on their outer surfaces that allow them to grab a human cell and attack it. When antibodies attach to the antigens on these outer structures, they may prevent the bacteria or virus from attaching to a cell, thereby blocking the pathogen's ability to infect a cell.

- *Binding Toxins*: Some bacteria release toxins that attach to receptors on the body's cells and cause damage. Antibodies can bind to the specific molecular patterns on these toxins and prevent the damage.

- *Immobilizing Pathogens*: Many microbes have flagella or cilia that enable them to swim in the body's fluids and spread throughout the body. Antibodies can bind to these structures, blunting their ability to move around freely.

The Best Defense Is a Good Offense

A QUICK review will help drive home the immune system's elegant orchestration.

In the body's first-line defense, the body's epithelial tissues repel most attackers. But when that line is breached and pathogens enter, the innate and adaptive immune systems provide a powerful offense that can counter most attacks. These two systems must detect the presence of microorganisms where they may not belong, determine whether they present a threat the body's seen before, generate appropriate countermeasures, deploy those countermeasures at scale and to the right places, defeat the threat, and even recycle the leftover parts—all before the invaders can reproduce to levels that might overwhelm the immune system's resources.

Since many pathogens can reproduce in minutes or hours, there isn't much time to react. To accomplish all this, the many parts of the body's immune system act in a series of interconnected processes. Without any one of these parts, or if not properly coordinated, the whole would not work properly. And, as you've come to expect by now, failure in any of these areas would make it unlikely for any human to survive long enough to reach maturity, much less to successfully reproduce a next generation.

The cells of the innate immune system are dispersed throughout the body, ready to respond quickly to any threat. Since all are outfitted with the same receptors, they all respond to the same pathogens and can work together as a large fighting force. They're everywhere, and they're all available, all the time.

The cells of the adaptive immune system are more specialized, and while each can only respond to just a single antigen, together they're able to detect at least a trillion different antigens. Because there are relatively few cells that can respond to any particular antigen, these circulate via the blood and lymphoid tissues, which optimizes their chances of finding a pathogen early; and when a pathogen is detected, the body quickly ramps up production of the cell that found that given pathogen, so the defense can quickly scale to meet the challenge.

The body retains memory cells for the pathogens it has seen, allowing them to detect and defeat them even more quickly if those pathogens come back later.

Making all this work means signaling, handshakes, and coordination across many different types of cells and various protein machines. (A specification for this system's interactions would make an interesting research project, especially if it went into all the known details of these systems.)

And it's a good thing it does work, or none of us would be here. The human immune system is amazingly effective at deflecting and defeating infections of many different types. At the same time, it's remarkably good at not attacking good cells, both those that have your DNA and those that do not, like the essential bacteria in your gut. And we can't ignore the ingenious efficiency of this system, which expends the bulk of its resources only when and where needed. Yet it's able to mount a timely deterrent to most threats. Once again, the body does just the right things at just the right times, and rarely at the wrong places or at the wrong times.

The human immune system isn't bulletproof, of course. Some pathogens are downright insidious and can reproduce and kill more quickly than even a well-functioning immune system can overcome them. Also, some people have compromised immune systems (due to a variety of causes), which restricts their ability to fend off even minor infections. On rare occasions, the immune system even goes so haywire that it attacks the body.

But consider that without all the parts of this amazing system of systems, their many coordination strategies, and their remarkably efficient operations, it would take a plastic bubble for *anyone* to live long enough to reproduce, and the human species would soon cease to exist.

In the end, then, the body needs systems that make it work and systems that prevent it from failing. These are very different problems, and they must be solved by very different systems.

260 / Your Designed Body /

More Questions

How MANY different components are required to make the immune system work? How do the various cells and molecular components of these systems work together? How many ways are these components integrated? How many ways must they communicate with each other? What happens if there's a failure at any point in the process?

We've omitted many of the known details (and many more are not yet understood), but we have covered enough of the human immune system to feel some of the weight of the following question: How could a biological system with these kinds of indispensable interactions come to exist through any gradual evolutionary process when the larger system's function is essential to basic survival? Researchers have trouble explaining how this engineering marvel works, never mind explaining how it could have gradually emerged over many generations.

PART FIVE: BEGINNINGS AND ENDS

THE HUMAN BODY REQUIRES SOLUTIONS TO THOUSANDS OF HARD problems—solutions that must work all the time, that require coherent interdependent systems, that thread the needle and stay in the Goldilocks zone.

It's a hard problem to make a human body work. It's harder still to make a human body. Yet here we are.

It's easy to take the process for granted. Making a new human body happens all the time, after all, right under our noses—the beginnings of a new human life in the womb. But just because it's common doesn't mean it's easy. Making a new human body involves almost unfathomably daunting engineering challenges. As we explore this process, keep the following four points in mind:

- We never see life starting on its own. We only see life coming from other life.
- The human body comes with an end-to-end lifecycle process. From start to finish, the body appears to be executing a programmed plan.
- The information, instructions, programs, mechanisms, and orchestrations needed to operate a human body are of little use for assembling the body, a job which needs its own information-rich programs, mechanisms, and orchestrations.
- Life must be continuous. You don't get to stop it for a while, change the parameters, or build on an addition, then restart it. The body has to be alive throughout the process.

15. Vive la Différence

Sexual reproduction is the chef d'oeuvre, the master-piece of nature.

— Erasmus Darwin[1]

Your father is Henry VIII, the king of England. He came to the throne just a couple of decades after the War of the Roses. His wife of many years had failed to produce a male heir, which made him concerned about another civil war after his death, so he kicked his wife to the curb and married your mother. Finally, after your brother (from another mother) and your sister (from the rejected queen) both die, you ascend to the throne of England.

Your father's concerns notwithstanding, you never marry and never produce an heir to carry on the Tudor line. Later, you execute your cousin, Mary, Queen of Scots, whom you see as a rival to your throne. Ironically, since you never had a legitimate heir, her son, James I, becomes your heir and takes the throne of England after your death.

Given this unwelcome prospect, which you surely foresaw, your refusal ever to marry doesn't make much sense—unless you know you can't have children because you've never had a menstrual period.

What you probably don't know is that the same condition preventing you from having a menstrual period also renders you physically unable to have proper sexual intercourse. Although you have breasts and normal looking external genitalia, you don't have a uterus and your vagina is a short dead end to nowhere. You are what we now know to be an XY female, having the body of a female but the sex genes of a male.

Could this be why Queen Elizabeth I never married? It has been suggested, and it's not as crazy as you might think. The type of abnormal development described here is an uncommon condition, but it does occur about once in every 20,000 female births.

How could something like this happen? To answer that question it will help to first look at how these things are supposed to work.

The Birds and the Bees and the People

MOST ONE-CELLED organisms form offspring through asexual reproduction. The organism makes genetically identical copies of itself—a lonely but efficient business. In contrast, most multi-cellular organisms reproduce by sexual reproduction. Two different gametes, a sperm (male) and egg (female) join in a process called fertilization.

The nucleus in each human cell normally contains twenty-three pairs of chromosomes. Among other things, these chromosomes carry the genetic specifications to produce the protein and enzyme molecules needed for life. Twenty-two of the chromosome pairs are somatic (non-gametic) and one pair contains the sex chromosomes, XX for female and XY for male. (X and Y chromosomes are so named because their physical shape resembles either the letter "X" or the letter "Y.") At fertilization, the egg from the mother contributes twenty-two somatic chromosomes plus an X chromosome, and the sperm from the father contributes twenty-two somatic chromosomes plus either an X or a Y chromosome. If it's an X, the baby is female. If Y, the baby's male.

For humans, fertilization occurs through sexual intercourse between a man and a woman. The result of fertilization is a one-celled zygote, made by combining the separate genetic materials from the sperm and egg into a complete set of twenty-three chromosomes. The zygote is a new life genetically distinct from either parent—a new and unique human being.

Aside from its obvious role in reproduction, sexuality is how individuals become genetically distinct from one another.

In the Beginning

IT TURNS out that human embryos are programmed to become fertile females by default. To become a male, the embryo must invoke a precise sequence of specific molecules that, in effect, "switches on" maleness. If something goes awry in the process of making the embryo into a male, it will develop into either an infertile female or an infertile male, depending on where the mishap occurs.

In the first several weeks, the human embryo remains sexually undifferentiated and develops tissues with the capacity to develop into either the male or the female internal genitalia. The male tissue is called the Wolffian ducts and the female tissue, the Mullerian ducts.

At this point, the gonads have not yet declared themselves to be testes or ovaries. But they'll automatically become ovaries and start making estrogen unless a protein molecule called Testis Determining Factor (TDF) is present. TDF is, in effect, the master switch that tells the body to use the "male" development program rather than the default "female" program.

As you might expect, the genetic specification for TDF is on the Y chromosome, so only males can manufacture this special molecule. As the embryo begins making TDF, the undifferentiated gonads take the cue to become testes.

But there's much work needed to develop the male internal and external genitalia. As the testes develop, they use several additional enzymes, encoded on different somatic chromosomes, to convert cholesterol into testosterone.

The cells of the Wolffian ducts have androgen (male hormone) receptors on their surface. As the fetal testes begin to produce testosterone (one of the body's male hormones and thus an androgen), it attaches to these androgen receptors and triggers them to develop into the epididymis, vas deferens, and seminal vesicle (see Figure 15.1). The male internal genitalia store sperm and support its movement out of the body. If there's not enough testosterone, or the androgen receptors on the Wolffian

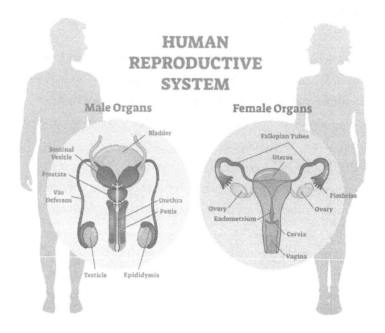

Figure 15.1. The male and female reproductive systems.

ducts don't work properly, the body will kill the Wolffian ducts in a form of apoptosis (programmed cell death). Since the female embryo's ovaries mainly produce estrogen and not testosterone, her Wolffian ducts will automatically die.

In contrast to the Wolffian ducts, nothing is needed to tell the female embryo's Mullerian ducts to automatically develop into the uterus, fallopian tubes, and upper vagina (see Figure 15.1), which are necessary for fertilization and gestation in the womb.

However, male embryos need to ensure that this female tissue doesn't form and thereby interfere with the development of their male internal genitalia. To solve this problem, the testes also produce Anti-Mullerian Hormone (AMH). The cells of the Mullerian ducts have AMH receptors, so when AMH attaches to them it triggers apoptosis of the Mullerian ducts. Apoptosis is a process by which the body kills certain unneeded cells. It serves a critical role in many areas of fetal development, including sexual differentiation.

A female embryo's ovaries do not produce AMH, so there is nothing to stop the Mullerian ducts from developing into the female internal genitalia. If a male embryo's testes don't produce enough AMH, or the AMH receptors are absent or not working on the Mullerian ducts, female internal genitalia will develop inside the male, rendering him sterile.

> How does the body know when to kill cells, and which cells to target? What signals tell these cells to self-destruct? Where do these signals originate, and how are they sent only to the proper cells? Or do the cells somehow know internally that they must die at a certain time and place?
>
> Many unsolved mysteries surround apoptosis, a process indispensable to our development, including the development of reproductive function.

In much the same way as the internal genitalia are formed, the undifferentiated tissues destined to become the external genitalia will become the female lower vagina, labia, and clitoris, unless acted upon by male hormone. But for them to become a normal male penis, prostate gland, and scrotum, they require much more stimulation of their androgen receptors than testosterone can provide. The solution: these cells in the male employ an enzyme called 5-alpha reductase to change testosterone into the more powerful dihydrotestosterone, which is able to do the job. Without 5-alpha reductase the male external genitalia become deformed, causing infertility.

So, without TDF, or the enzymes that convert cholesterol into testosterone, or the androgen receptors, or AMH, or AMH receptors, or 5-alpha reductase, the human embryo becomes either an infertile female or an infertile male. If any of these six molecules ceased to exist, human reproduction and species survival would become impossible.

As with so many of the systems we've reviewed so far, the system for developing a fertile human male is irreducible. Take any component away and the result is an individual who cannot reproduce. But put them together, in the proper ways and in the proper quantities, and you have a coherent system that can produce an outcome (a fertile human male) that none of the parts could produce by itself.

How could such a developmental system come to be, when the whole is necessary before the next generation can come to be?

The XY Female

IN THE rare case of an XY female, the TDF on her Y chromosome makes her undifferentiated gonads become testes. They produce testosterone, but the androgen receptors on the cells in her body don't work properly. This is called Complete Androgen Insensitivity Syndrome (CAIS) and because her androgen receptors can't respond to testosterone, her Wolffian ducts degenerate and die, just as they would in an XX female (whose ovaries don't produce testosterone). So, the XY female doesn't develop any male internal genitalia.

Her testes, however, also produce AMH, which attaches to the AMH receptors on the cells in her Mullerian ducts, so they also degenerate and die. As a result, she has neither male nor female internal genitalia.

Further, because her androgen receptors don't work, even in the presence of suitable levels of dihydrotestosterone, her external genitalia default to become female just like they do for the XX female. Consequently, at birth an XY female looks like a normal female. Even though the genes say the person is a male, the body that results is female. This is an XY female.

Here, the XY female problem causes one outcome to fail while preventing the other outcome from succeeding. Fortunately for the human race, our bodies usually avoid this problem and develop normally.

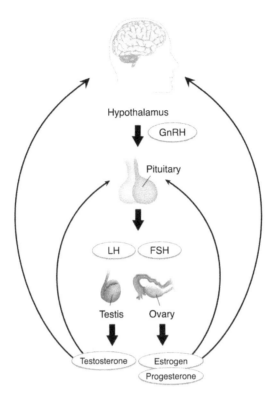

Figure 15.2. The hypothalamus-pituitary-gonadal axis.

Sexual Development

WHILE HUMANS are sexually differentiated as male or female at birth, they're obviously not yet able to reproduce. Before this can happen, the body has a lot more work to do.

Most children begin to show early signs of sexual development by the end of their first decade. In subsequent years they undergo further sexual and bodily development in a process called puberty, a constellation of changes that prepares males and females to reproduce, and to perform their natural roles in the family as fathers and mothers.

Puberty is stimulated, at the right time, as the body begins to produce more sex hormones under the direction of the hypothalamus and the pituitary gland, both of which are in the brain. The hypothalamus secretes a hormone (signaling molecule) called Gonadotropin-Releasing Hormone (GnRH). Cells in the pituitary gland have receptors for GnRH. When it's detected, the pituitary sends out the gonadotropins Luteinizing Hormone (LH) and Follicle Stimulating Hormone (FSH).

In the male, LH and FSH attach to specific receptors on certain cells in the testes, instructing them to make testosterone (male sex hormone) and, later, to turn on sperm production. In the female, they tell cells in the ovaries to make estrogen (female sex hormone) and, later, to turn on egg development.

Together, the hypothalamus and pituitary control the concentrations of the sex hormones in the blood. They continuously monitor these hormones and in response to the detected levels either increase or decrease production of their own hormones (GnRH, LH, and FSH) such that the proper sex hormone levels are maintained.

The sensitivities of the hypothalamus and pituitary change with the seasons of life. In the first decade of life, even minimal levels of testosterone and estrogen are enough to prevent the hypothalamus from releasing GnRH, and the pituitary from releasing LH and FSH. So, prior to the onset of puberty, the blood levels of testosterone in the male and estrogen in the female remain very low.

What triggers puberty is not well understood, but one effect of the trigger is to make the hypothalamus and pituitary progressively less sensitive to the levels of the sex hormones. With these changes, output of GnRH from the hypothalamus, and of LH and FSH from the pituitary, increases. By the time puberty is in full swing, the levels of both the gonadotropins and the sex hormones are up significantly.

For males, increased LH and FSH instruct the testes to produce more testosterone and sperm. These changes also progressively increase and coarsen facial, chest, axillary, abdominal, extremity, and pubic hair, along with enlargement of the vocal cords and deepening of the voice. The associated increase in the pituitary's release of Growth Hormone (GH), causes a significant linear growth spurt and development of the musculoskeletal system. Puberty also enlarges the penis, scrotum, and testes. In addition, testosterone plays a major role in the desire for sexual relations. Finally, testosterone is important in giving the male the ability to maintain an erection for adequate penetration into the vagina and ejaculation during sexual intercourse. Together, these changes convert the body of a boy into the body of a man.

For females, increased LH and FSH tell the ovaries to produce more estrogen and prepare to develop an egg. These changes also increase pubic and axillary hair and initiate breast development in preparation for future breastfeeding. As with the male, the pituitary's increased GH production causes a significant linear growth spurt and development of the musculoskeletal system, though this development in females is notably less dramatic than that of males. Puberty also enlarges the external genitalia and increases mucus production in the vagina and uterus. Finally, along with the capacity for egg development, the increase in LH, FSH, and estrogen allows for ovulation, where an egg is released and enters the fallopian tube.

In post-puberty females, ovulation occurs approximately every twenty-eight days. Just after ovulation, the ovaries switch to mainly secreting the pregnancy hormone, progesterone. The lining of the uterus detects the changes in these hormones and responds by thickening and producing more mucus, in preparation for a pregnancy.

If sexual intercourse occurs at this time, sperm from the male swim into the uterus and eventually up into the fallopian tube. As the egg travels down the fallopian tube, a sperm and egg may successfully join to make a new human—a single-celled zygote.

If pregnancy does not occur during this time, the hormone levels drop precipitously, which causes the lining of the uterus to shed. This is menstruation. A girl's first menstrual period marks the beginning of her fertility, and menstruation will usually recur monthly for the next thirty or forty years. Together, these developments convert the body of a girl into the body of a woman and prepare her for the miraculous job of producing a new human baby.

> When pregnancy occurs, the developing embryo signals the mother's body that he is present in the uterus. This prevents menstruation, which would wash the embryo out of the uterus. This is the first communication of many that must occur between the bodies of developing child and mother.

Back to the XY Female

DURING PUBERTY an XY female will develop normal breasts and look like a normally maturing woman. However, as time goes by and she fails to menstruate, the obvious questions will lead to further investigation, which will uncover the problem, until then likely unknown even to her. Since she has no female internal genitalia, there's no uterus to menstruate from. And when examined by her physician, her vagina is found to be a very short blind sac which would make sexual intercourse very difficult or impossible.

However, she'll have normal breasts because breast development depends on the ratio between estrogen and testosterone, rather than on the absolute amount of estrogen. During puberty the normal XX female produces lots of estrogen and only small amounts of testosterone, so her breast tissue develops. During puberty the normal XY male produces lots of testosterone and small amounts of estrogen, so his breast tissue does not develop. Although an XY female has testes that produce lots of testosterone, because she has no androgen receptors for it to have an effect, it's like she has none at all. This lets the small amount of estrogen she does produce dominate and cause normal breast development. Also, the testes in an XY female are internal—they don't descend and thus are externally invisible.

A Few Thoughts

THE PROCESS by which humans (and other sexual organisms) reproduce is sensitive to even minor perturbations. Even without exploring the details at the molecular level, it's clear that human reproduction is a hard problem that can only be solved with coherent parts working according to precise sequencing. Many specialized molecules are needed: TDF, enzymes to make testosterone, androgen receptors, 5-alpha reductase to produce dihydrotestosterone, AMH and AMH receptors, GnRH and its receptor, FSH and LH and each of their receptors, estrogen and its receptor, progesterone and its receptor, along with several other protein signals we've omitted for readability. What's the use of having any one of these if the whole system fails without all of them, present and regulated to the appropriate quantities? Even a fully functional male without a female, or vice versa, isn't sufficient.

So many of the body's functions only work within the context of its carefully orchestrated life processes. In this case, the processes run for decades. Yet all the functions must work correctly, and the coordination of the parts must be precise. Even relatively small errors in the workings of these systems means no next generation.

How does the body track its progress over decades? How could human reproduction come to exist when so many essential parts must all be in place and perfectly coordinated? Given that the process is so sensitive to errors, where did the fine tuning come from if reproduction fails without it?

When we witness a child being born, it's as if we are watching a miracle. Based on what it takes for that to happen, perhaps a miracle is exactly what it is.

16. FERTILITY

The world must be peopled!
—BENEDICK, WILLIAM SHAKESPEARE'S
MUCH ADO ABOUT NOTHING

AS ALL OF US WHO HAVE HAD THE BIRDS-AND-BEES TALK KNOW, human reproduction occurs when the male and female come together in sexual intercourse. This intimate physical union requires the man, during the sexual act, to ejaculate semen containing sperm near the cervical opening of his mate's uterus. Over the next several hours, aided by the cervical mucus, the sperm use their flagella to swim up through the body of the uterus toward the fallopian tubes. If one of the woman's ovaries has recently released an egg, one of the sperm may be able to penetrate the egg's outer shell to form a zygote, in a process called fertilization. Over the next several days the developing zygote migrates into the uterus and implants in the uterine lining. At this point the zygote becomes known as an embryo. The embryo develops into a fetus in a process called gestation. About nine months after fertilization, the fetus will exit the mother's body as a newborn baby.

An almost unimaginable number of things must go right to get from A to Z.

The Male's Sexual Function

FOR THE male to reproduce, his body must perform two critical tasks:

1. Produce enough healthy sperm cells (fertility).

2. Deposit the sperm cells deep inside the vagina of the female (potency).

The first task involves his fertility and is done by his testes. His pituitary makes LH and FSH, which tell his testes to make testosterone and sperm. Fertility depends on sufficient testosterone and sperm production, which can only happen when there is enough LH and FSH, the testes' specific receptors for these chemicals are working properly, and the testes can properly manufacture testosterone and sperm. It takes ten to twelve weeks for the testes to make a mature sperm cell, but roughly 100 million of them reach maturity each day, meaning there are around eight billion immature cells being nurtured in the testes at any given time.

Prior to release, the sperm is mixed with nutrient fluids from the seminal vesicles and the prostate gland to form semen. The normal volume of semen needed for adequate fertility is about two milliliters (mL). The concentration of sperm should be greater than twenty million per mL.

Also, the structure of the sperm (morphology) and their ability to move (motility) are essential. The front tip of the sperm cell is shaped a bit like a knife and coated with digestive enzymes that can break down proteins in the egg's membrane. Between this cutting shape, the dissolving enzymes, and the driving force of its tail, the sperm has the tools to bore its way into the egg.

A sperm is a specialized cell with remarkable abilities. Its task is to swim under its own power (the circulatory system can't help), carry just the right half-chromosomal payload, find a fertile egg, and cut and dissolve its way through the egg's outer membrane. Once inside the egg, it must fuse its half-chromosome payload with the egg's half-chromosome to form a new human being.

Cell shape, chemistry, motility mechanisms (motors), information payload, and many molecular signals and machines are required for the sperm cell to accomplish all these tasks.

The second critical capacity of the male is potency. This means having a firm enough erection to penetrate deep enough into the vagina and

Cross Section of a Penis

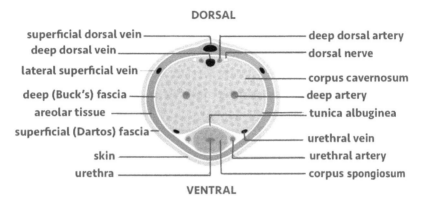

Figure 16.1. Cross-section of a human penis.

then ejaculate semen. To achieve this, the male must have a normal penis, with normal nerve and vascular function.

A penile erection is achieved by hydraulic pressure. Running the length of the penis, surrounding the urethra (the duct through which urine exits the body) are the corpus cavernosa, as shown in Figure 16.1. These tube-shaped venous chambers are surrounded by strong fibrous tissue. Sex-related thoughts and stimulation of the penis and pelvic region activate one set of nerves (parasympathetic). These nerves activate valves that increase the flow of blood from nearby arteries into the chambers and, at the same time, reduce the outflow of blood from these chambers into the veins. Together, these actions increase the blood pressure within the chambers, causing an erection.

After erection takes place, with continued stimulation another set of nerves (sympathetic) kicks in to bring on ejaculation—the release of semen, usually with a pleasurable feeling called orgasm. Soon after this happens the first set of nerves turns off and the penis becomes flaccid again.

All this requires the precise orchestration of multiple valves and signaling to change hydraulic pressure at just the right time. All the parts needed, in the right places, must work together in precise ways to achieve the required overall function. This, in turn, requires precise timing and coordination among all the parts.

Getting Jack Back in the Game

THE MALE reproductive system is an engineering marvel, but as with anything this complex, sometimes things go wrong. Consider the case of a hard-working executive—we'll call him Jack—working long hours and frequently meeting with clients over drinks. He tends to "burn the candle from both ends," so he's often too tired for sex and sometimes can't perform. Little does he know that his lifestyle and alcohol use are not only causing him to be intermittently impotent but also have diminished his fertility.

> The scrotum has muscles that contract to move the testicles closer to the body when it's cold, and that relax to move the testicles farther from the body when it gets warm. This enables the body to optimize temperatures for sperm production and storage.
>
> Yet this is another example of design ingenuity in the body that many see as bad design. Placing the testes external to the body's core, where they are more vulnerable, seems like a poor engineering choice.
>
> Without getting into the details, the optimal temperature for the body's core is different from the optimal temperature for the development and storage of sperm. These optima are determined by the basic biology and chemistry of life, rather than some arbitrary choices that could be randomly selected.
>
> Achieving optimal sperm temperature, then, is a physical problem that the body must solve to reproduce. And here, as pretty much everywhere else in the body, the solution is near-optimal.[1]

He visits a doctor, and tests reveal that he has a very low sperm count. On top of that, many of his sperm cells are deformed (morphology) and can't move well (motility). His fertility specialist realizes that besides Jack's lifestyle and alcohol use, Jack has another problem, one which can easily be remedied.

Jack spends a lot of time working with his notebook computer placed on his lap. Further, because he is under so much work-related stress, he likes to go to the local gym and relax in the sauna for long periods. Both these things increase the temperature around his testes, which can kill sperm cells. That's why, in contrast to women who have their gonads inside their body's core where it's warmer, men have theirs outside the body, in the scrotum, where it's usually about 4°C (7°F) cooler. Sperm just thrive better at this lower temperature.

The prescription for Jack? Get the laptop computer well away from his lap, shorten the sauna time, drink less alcohol, and get more rest and exercise. In most cases that would get someone like Jack back in the game.

The Female's Sexual Function

For the female to reproduce, her body must perform three critical tasks:

1. Develop and release an egg (ovum) from her ovary, in a process called ovulation.
2. Move the egg into the fallopian tube and assist the sperm in reaching it for fertilization.
3. Provide nutritional support for the embryo once it implants in the uterus.

For the first task, the woman's pituitary sends out FSH and LH, which tell her ovaries to make estrogen and start developing some immature eggs. Prior to puberty, the release of FSH and LH is normally inhibited by a rising estrogen level. Under normal conditions, the woman's body continues to use this negative feedback to control estrogen.

However, when it's time to develop eggs, a rise in the level of estrogen stimulates her pituitary to release more LH. This is called the LH surge.

FERTILIZATION

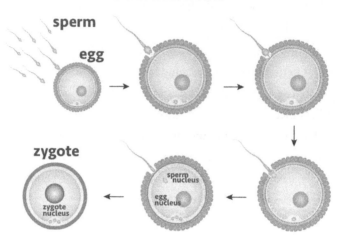

Figure 16.2. The process of fertilization.

In effect, her body switches its control from its normal negative feedback to positive feedback. How this change happens, or what drives it, is not yet well understood, but the LH surge is crucial for the release of the dominant egg.

With the release of an egg, her body must perform its second task. Located at the ends of the fallopian tubes are finger-like projections called fimbriae. The high estrogen levels that caused the release of the egg also tell the fimbriae to move in a wave-like fashion, drawing the egg into the fallopian tube. The fallopian tube sends out more mucus, and its small hair-like projections, called cilia, sweep the egg toward the body of the uterus.

The high levels of estrogen also induce the cells in the cervical opening of the uterus to secrete lots of watery mucus. This greatly assists the sperm as they swim up through the uterus to the fallopian tubes. Here, within the relatively confined space, some of the sperm may meet up with the egg, and one may break through the egg's outer membrane to enter. Once inside, it injects its nucleus and other organelles into the egg's cytoplasm, and fertilization takes place. If fertilization of the egg does not take place, it dies in about twenty-four hours.

It's essential that only one sperm be allowed to enter the egg. If more than one get in (polyspermy), the egg will not be able to divide properly into two viable cells, and the egg is programmed to fail. To prevent two sperm from getting in, the entry of one sperm cell causes the egg to deploy multiple distinct mechanisms: (1) the egg's plasma membrane depolarizes, preventing more sperm from breaking through; (2) a new layer is formed under the egg cell's membrane, which hardens it against further entry; and (3) the sperm receptors on the outer wall of the egg's membrane are destroyed so no more sperm cells will attach.

The process of fusing the sperm and egg cells (itself a tricky engineering problem) also increases the calcium in the zygote's internal fluids, which signals the cell to launch its development cycle. The developing zygote is then swept down the fallopian tube into the body of the uterus.

This leads to the third task. The increased estrogen released by the ovary prior to ovulation attaches to specific receptors in the lining of the uterus, signaling it to grow and thicken in what is called the proliferative phase.

After ovulation, the tissue that remains where the dominant egg erupted transforms into the corpus luteum (yellow body), which generates a lot of progesterone. Progesterone is known as the pregnancy hormone because it attaches to specific receptors in the lining of the uterus, telling the lining to increase its blood supply and develop more complex mucous glands (in what is called the secretory phase) so it's ready to support the embryo when it arrives.

The corpus luteum normally continues making progesterone for ten to fourteen days. If pregnancy doesn't occur, the corpus luteum, like the egg, will die. The resulting drop in estrogen and progesterone levels causes the uterine lining to degenerate and die. Menstruation is the process of this tissue being shed from the woman's body.

But if fertilization has occurred, the developing embryo makes a hormone called human Chorionic Gonadotropin (hCG), which acts like LH. This keeps the corpus luteum alive and producing progesterone (and estrogen) to support the uterine lining. About ten weeks after fertilization, the placenta will be ready to take over the job of making progesterone and estrogen.

Getting Jill Back in the Game

WE INTRODUCED the hard-working, sauna-loving executive Jack above. Let's give him a wife to illustrate the female side of the matter. Jill grew up with five older brothers and was always a competitive tomboy. In her teens, she was an athlete and played on most of her school's varsity teams. When she started having her periods, they were irregular and very light, which she counted as a blessing. This pattern continued after she married Jack.

Between Jack's focus on his career and their ongoing failure to become pregnant, she relieved her stress by spending a lot of time at the gym working out. In fact, they'd often meet up there when Jack came by for a sauna.

When the fertility specialist hears that Jill's periods are irregular and very light, he's concerned that she may not be ovulating regularly. He asks her to start measuring her basal body temperature (BBT) as soon as she wakes in the morning. After ovulation, due to the release of progesterone, a woman's BBT usually goes up 0.5-1.0°F and stays there until she has her period. The fertility specialist also asks Jill to monitor her cervical mucus. As the estrogen level rises prior to ovulation, a woman's cervical mucus becomes very watery, whereas after ovulation, due to progesterone, it thickens.

When Jill returns to the specialist a few months later, her BBT and cervical mucus charts confirm his suspicion: she isn't ovulating regularly. He also suspects the culprits. High levels of stress and extreme exercise are both known to suppress the release of GnRH from the hypothalamus. As Jill addresses these with better relaxation and less intense workouts, she begins having more regular periods.

With Jill having more regular periods and Jack's sperm count on the rise, the couple have hopes of a pregnancy just around the corner. But their problem persists. The fertility specialist runs more tests and discovers that Jill's corpus luteum isn't making enough progesterone. Even if fertilization were to occur, her uterus wasn't getting properly prepared, so a developing embryo would be unable to implant and would subsequently be ejected.

To prevent this, Jill's doctor prescribes monthly progesterone, which she's to start taking a few days after she has ovulated. And before the year is out, Jack and Jill have a baby boy.

Without advanced medical technology, such a couple could not have children, of course. Even ironing out the problems in their lifestyle habits wasn't enough. A single defect in one part of one of Jill's reproductive subsystems rendered her unable to reproduce. Again, we see from this just how much has to go right to make a new human.

Asking the Right Questions

IN THE previous chapter we focused on how, early in development, a set of generic body parts differentiate into two distinct, complementary systems, both of which are needed for making a new human person. This chapter shows how each part of these complementary systems is essential to a successful outcome.

As with most systems, we can learn a lot about how the body's systems work by observing how they fail. The reproduction process is unusually sensitive to perturbations. If even a small component goes wrong, or a small error in signaling or timing occurs, the entire process is likely to fail. Failure of the process means no new human.

Human reproduction involves having the right tissues and organs in place and working properly. The male can't contribute to reproduction unless his testes make enough healthy sperm and he can deposit them deep inside the female's vagina. And the female can't be fertile unless her ovaries produce a mature egg; the egg enters her fallopian tube; her cervical mucus helps sperm swim up to fertilize the egg; and the resulting new human can implant and develop in the lining of her uterus.

Jack's low sperm count showed the delicate balance that must be maintained in the hypothalamic-pituitary-testis axis. Additionally, all the many parts of the penis must do their jobs correctly, or potency will be reduced or lost altogether. Many diseases and defects can impair the male side of reproduction.

Similarly, Jill's inability to ovulate regularly showed the very different but equally delicate balance needed in the hypothalamic-pituitary-ovary axis. This reality is underscored by the fact that many women today struggle with infertility due to an impaired cervix or impaired fallopian tubes, caused by sexually transmitted infections.

All the same, the human reproductive system shows us an astounding property: for the human species to continue, three separate individuals (father, mother, and developing child) must coordinate their actions, each at a different point in the overall human lifecycle, or none of it works. This involves dozens of different parts, signals, controls, and programs—coordinating with each other and between organisms—to perform their different and highly specialized activities. Together they work as a coherent, multi-organism system of systems.

That it works at all is impressive. That it fails so rarely is even more impressive. This is irreducible coherence and interdependence at its most impressive—across multiple individuals. How can such things come to be?

17. Fuel for Baby

The two most important days in your life are the day you are born
and the day you find out why.

—Anonymous

THE BABY—JAMES, WE'LL CALL HIM—CRIES LUSTILY AFTER BIRTH
and looks normal and healthy. He is quickly cleaned up and put
on his mother's belly so mother and child can start bonding. But when
the pediatrician examines James, she tells his parents he has an unusual
heart murmur that will need to be watched.

No parent wants to hear these words.

Your heart normally produces two sounds when it beats: *lub* and
dub. When the ventricles contract to expel blood, the pressure in them
rises higher than the pressure in the atria, causing the mitral and tri-
cuspid valves to close quickly, causing the *lub* sound. After the blood is
pumped out, the ventricles relax, dropping the pressure in them below
the pressure in the aorta and pulmonary artery, which makes the aortic
and pulmonary valves close quickly, making the "dub" sound.

The pediatrician explains to James's parents that a heart murmur is
an unusual sound, like a swishing or whooshing or click, which occurs
between the two normal heart sounds. It can be innocent, where there's
no underlying heart defect, or it can be abnormal, possibly from a leaking or tight valve. With James she was hearing a continuous machine-
like murmur, and she thought it might have something to do with his
development in the womb.

But we're getting ahead of ourselves. Before you can understand
what is going on with James's heart, you need to know a bit more about

development in the womb—an amazing journey that takes all sorts of specialized molecules, tissues, and organs. All these are needed for a baby to be born without a life-threatening handicap.

> The heart has four chambers (two atria and two ventricles) and four valves. The valves permit flow in only one direction, and open or close automatically, based on the different pressures on either side of the valve. These pressures are generated by the muscles that surround the four chambers.
>
> In contrast to the heart valves, which are passive, the body's active valves, such as the arteriolar muscles, are opened to varying degrees by an active control system. When the opening in the arterioles is wider, they let more blood flow into the capillaries, and when it's narrower, they let less blood flow in.
>
> Both valve types are essential, and each type is deployed in exactly the right places for the body to function properly. Again, we see the human body exemplifies skilled engineering, with the right solutions in the right places.

Early Life's Essential Supply Chain

ALL CELLS need oxygen and nutrients. Early life is no exception. Fertilization results in a zygote, which multiplies through cell division to become an embryo. In the early phase, the embryo gets what is needed by diffusion from the surrounding fluid. This works when there are only a few dozen cells. But within several weeks the embryo will grow into a fetus, and in a few months into a newborn with trillions of specialized cells organized into coherent, interdependent, finely tuned organ systems.

For this to be possible, the embryo needs a better way to get oxygen and nutrients, and to get rid of carbon dioxide and waste materials. If he cannot meet this challenge, he will not survive. But he's in a special situation, dwelling inside his mother, so he'll need a solution altogether different from anything else in the body's inventory—a distinct yet temporary system that can meet this need while he's developing his permanent internal systems.

We dedicated much of Part Two, Homeostasis, to the clever solutions the body deploys to solve the problems of acquiring essential nutrients and offloading waste. As we saw there, every solution to a difficult problem presented difficult new problems that also had to be solved. The result was a cascade of problems, each of which needs a precise, finely tuned solution. The system as a whole wouldn't work if any of the problems or sub-problems were not effectively solved. And each solution relied in some way on the solutions to other parts of the overall problem. They depended on each other, creating a complex array of interdependencies. The solutions needed to be interwoven.

In the womb, the human body is faced with a still more difficult problem to solve: it must generate these systems, coherently along with their interdependencies, essentially from scratch, and remain alive at all times while doing so. How do you build a series of finely tuned, coherent, interdependent systems, each necessary for life, and stay alive the whole time? It just wouldn't do if the body needed to go dead for a while, build some stuff, then come back to life when everything was ready to go.

We shouldn't pass over this problem too quickly. This is an extraordinarily difficult challenge. No human engineer has ever designed a system capable of anything remotely like this. To say the body's solutions are brilliant is a bit of an understatement. This is genius engineering beyond anything human engineers know.

What the child in the womb needs is a complete set of temporary systems to meet the respiratory needs of his rapidly growing body, to keep it alive until its own systems are ready to take over. This means that, in parallel with the developing child, other distinct systems must be developed, put into use, and grown as the developing child's needs increase. Then at birth, when they are no longer needed, these systems must be discarded as the child transitions to long-term systems.

These systems are functionally analogous to scaffolding in a building project—a temporary structure put in place to provide support while the building's permanent structural elements are assembled. Of course, the scaffolding for life in the womb is a significantly greater engineering challenge. And by now the reader will recognize that it involves a fresh set of interwoven hard problems, which require solutions that will take yet another distinct set of mechanisms and orchestrations.

The first step in this scaffolding starts when the growing embryo contacts the lining of the uterus. The growing embryo's outer tissue (trophoblastic tissue) emits enzymes that cause cells in the lining of the uterus to die. This process is not well understood, but it appears to work in two different ways. The embryo's enzymes break down the walls of some of the cells in the uterine lining (from the outside, called *lysis*), and instruct some of the cells to self-destruct from the inside (apoptosis). Both are fascinating processes. How do the enzymes target only the cells in the uterine lining, and not the embryo's own cells? No one really knows, but it's a good thing it works.

As the lining walls break down, the embryo gains an entry point into the nutrient-rich uterine lining—a place to implant. It attaches and burrows in further. For the next few weeks the embryo gets its oxygen and nutrients from the cells lining the uterus.

> The embryo's DNA differs markedly from the mother's, and yet in the great majority of cases the mother's body recognizes that this microscopic new person is not a foreign attacker, so her body doesn't deploy its defense mechanisms to kill the baby. No one really knows how this works or what mechanisms are involved, but the mother's tolerance for her baby's body is recognized in the medical community as one of the great wonders of pregnancy.

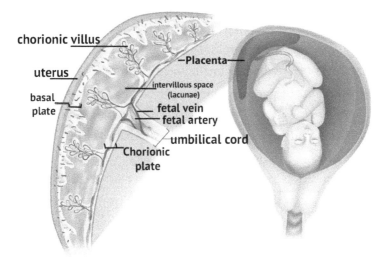

chorionic villus

uterus

basal plate

—Placenta—

intervillous space (lacunae)

fetal vein

fetal artery

umbilical cord

Chorionic plate

Figure 17.1. The microscopic view (left) of the fetal and maternal interface within the placenta. The placenta (right, above the baby) grows into an organ separate from the fetus or the mother.

Placenta to the Rescue

As THE embryo develops further, he continues making enzymes and breaking down more of the uterine lining. Eventually the outer tissue of the embryo joins with the lining of the uterus to form the placenta. The placenta, shown in Figure 17.1, is a specialized organ that brings the blood of the developing child into close proximity with the blood of the mother, permitting the chemical building blocks of life to move back and forth between the mother's and the baby's circulation while keeping their blood separate. The close-up on the left side of Figure 17.1 shows how this works. The mother's body supplies the oxygen and nutrients her child needs and gets rid of the waste products that would kill him.

This may be the most visually obvious example of the coordination required between the mother and her developing child, in which their two separate and genetically distinct bodies coordinate their activities in precise ways. In this case, tissues of the embryo combine with tissues of the mother to make the placenta—a totally separate organ that provides the scaffolding needed to keep the developing child alive. The placenta enables the mother to sustain the developing child while his internal organ systems and tissues are being fabricated, integrated, and launched. The developing child is, quite literally, on life support between the zygote phase and birth, when his body is finally ready to take over the job.

The placenta has no purpose aside from the development of the new life in the mother's womb, so it separates from the mother's uterus and is expelled from her body immediately following the baby's birth. The placenta doesn't get the credit it deserves, probably because it pales in comparison to the impressiveness (and excitement) of a newborn baby. But it invites a question: How does the placenta, a complex two-person system, come to be when that system is required for either individual to exist?

Without the placenta, it would be game over for the human race. Moreover, the placenta is just the first step in the continuous and increasing supply of essential building blocks the developing child needs. Oxygen and nutrients must be distributed to every cell in this little body, which grows by continually adding new cells over its nine-month gestation.

For this the baby needs a cardiovascular system—a heart, blood vessels, and blood—to come online soon after fertilization. And this is exactly what happens. At about three weeks, the embryo's new heart begins pumping blood through a developing circulatory system. Over the next eight months, as the embryo becomes a fetus and continues to grow and build out systems, his heart and blood vessels must grow with him to keep all the other cells alive and healthy.

A Survival Dilemma

THE DEVELOPING embryo's need for a cardiovascular system presents yet another problem that must be solved if he is to survive for more than a few weeks. The blood cycles through two loops in a sort of figure-8 pattern. The right side of the heart pumps blood through the pulmonary artery to the lungs where it picks up a new supply of oxygen. The oxygenated blood then returns through the pulmonary veins to the left side of the heart. From here the blood is pumped through the aorta and systemic arteries to deliver oxygen to the tissues throughout the body. Once the blood has given up some of its oxygen to the tissues, it cycles back through the systemic veins to the right side of the heart. This cycle repeats as long as you live. When it stops, you stop.

As with normal circulation, the fetus cycles blood from the left side of the heart through systemic arteries to the tissues. However, because a fetus's lungs don't have access to the outside air, oxygen must come from somewhere else—from the mother, via the placenta.

Blood pumped from the fetal left ventricle travels in two umbilical arteries to the placenta, where it picks up oxygen derived from the mother's lungs. The oxygenated blood then returns from the placenta to the right side of the fetal heart through its umbilical vein.

The fetus must get this oxygenated blood to the tissues. But the pathway needed after birth—through the lungs, back to the left side of the heart, and then on to the tissues (the pulmonary arterial system)—is not yet open for business. While the placenta has provided the necessary oxygen, the fetus can't send oxygenated blood through systemic arteries to the tissues they supply.

So the fetus needs a different circulatory pattern while in the womb. And with an alternative solution in place, lungs can delay developing until closer to birth. In fact, the baby's lungs won't make enough surfactant in the alveoli to allow that first breath until just before birth (see below for more on surfactant). This is why doctors have to work so hard with premature babies to establish and maintain their breathing.

A Survival Solution

THE HEART'S circulatory pathway through the lungs is essentially closed for business during fetal development, so it cannot send blood from its right side to its left side via the lungs, like it will have to do after birth. Instead, the body employs a clever solution: two shunts (openings) that divert blood from the right side of the heart so as to bypass the baby's "not-yet-ready-for-prime-time" lungs and enter the systemic arteries to supply the body's tissues with oxygen.

Heart Anatomy

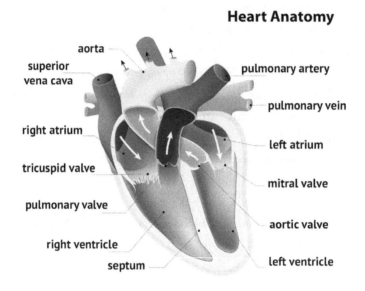

Figure 17.2. The chambers and valves of the human heart.

When a road is under construction but traffic still needs to get through, it's common to deploy an alternate but temporary route, called a detour. "Detour" comes from a French word meaning "change of direction," and that's exactly what the fetal heart does. The foramen ovale and ductus arteriosus redirect most of the blood flow to bypass the lungs while they're under construction and have no critical role.

As with road construction, the circulatory detour takes planning—the right-sized shunts in the right places, with walls able to withstand the blood pressure the heart produces. And with all temporary systems, still more planning (and work) is needed when it's time to shift the work over from the temporary systems to the permanent systems—in this case, the lungs.

The first shunt is called the foramen ovale. (See Figure 17.3.) This is a flap-like opening in the wall between the right and left atria. Since the lungs are closed and no blood is going from the pulmonary veins into

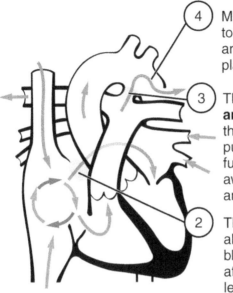

4 Mixed blood travels to the head and body, and back to the placenta via the aorta.

3 The **ductus arteriosus** connects the aorta with the pulmonary artery, further shunting blood away from the lungs and into the aorta.

2 The **foramen ovale** allows oxygenated blood in the right atrium to reach the left atrium.

1 Oxygenated blood from placenta enters right atrium via inferior vena cava.

Figure 17.3. The blood's path through the heart during fetal development.

the left atrium, the blood pressure here is lower than the right atrium. Hence, this flap acts as a passive valve, diverting blood from the right atrium to the left, from which it's pumped into the left ventricle, then through the aorta and the systemic arteries to the rest of the body.

The second shunt is called the ductus arteriosus. (See Figure 17.3.) This is a pipe-like passageway between the pulmonary artery and the aorta. Because the lungs are closed, there is high resistance to blood flow in the pulmonary artery, so its blood pressure is higher than that in the aorta. This naturally diverts blood from the pulmonary artery to the aorta and from there to the rest of the body through the systemic arteries.

Potential Respiratory Trouble in Paradise

AT SOME point this little person is going to leave the safety of his mother's womb and take on the outside world. When this happens, he will no longer be able to get everything he needs from his mother's body. Among the baby's many other birthday chores, he will need to breathe. This fact raises yet another challenge for the developing child.

The transition from inside the womb to outside is critical, as the child can only live a few minutes without oxygen. Those previously useless lungs need to come online and work, and they need to do so more or less immediately.

When you fall into an ice-cold alpine lake, your body's first instinct is to inhale deeply. That instinct may be a nuisance in an icy lake, but it came in handy in your first moments of daylight. Outside the womb feels colder than inside—generally a lot colder, especially when your body is covered with fluids from the birthing process. At the same time, the newborn's body detects a rapid rise in CO_2 levels. Together these signals cause the newborn to draw a first breath, deeply. And it's a good thing the first breath is deep. It takes considerable effort because the newborn's lungs are collapsed and filled with fluid. The fluids have high surface tension, which keeps the lungs' tiny air sacs (alveoli) closed. So the first few breaths need to overcome the natural forces of surface tension and force the alveoli to open and stay open.

At this critical transition in the newborn's life, many things can go wrong. If birth is premature (less than thirty-seven weeks of gestation), before the baby's body is fully ready, the most common complication is respiratory failure. Failure to breathe (apnea) early in life can be caused by problems with the respiratory center in the brain, weak respiratory muscles, or immature airways and alveoli.

To help get breathing started, the baby's lungs produce surfactant, a detergent-like molecule that reduces the surface tension in the lung's fluids and makes it much easier for the newborn to take that first breath. Respiratory distress syndrome (RDS) is caused when too little surfactant is present. This condition often affects premature babies born before thirty-five weeks, but occasionally also occurs with those born a few weeks later.

Here is yet another example of a seemingly modest substance playing a seemingly modest role in a much larger system—but remove this substance and the larger system threatens to break down, and at an absolutely life-critical moment.

Potential Cardiovascular Trouble in Paradise

ONCE THE newborn's lungs are working properly, he faces yet another daunting transitional challenge. He must continue to deliver all the oxygen needed for all his cells.

But before birth, the needed circulatory flow pattern shunts blood flow *away* from the lungs to the placenta, the only source of oxygen available in the womb. After birth, blood must flow *to* the lungs, as they become the only available source for oxygen. Obviously, the two circulatory shunts deployed in the womb to bypass the lungs will need to be closed. This is a major change, hitting multiple body systems at the same time. It needs to happen quickly, and permanently, else the newborn will struggle to survive.

And as any engineer will intuit, this means certain mechanisms and orchestrations must be present to do the work. Further, each of these mechanisms must be coherent—they must detect when the change needs to be made, turn on the new systems at just the right moment, and turn off the old systems, also at just the right moment.

For the foramen ovale this transition is just a matter of structure and physics. Once the lungs are open and receiving most of the blood from the pulmonary artery, they oxygenate it and send it back through the pulmonary veins to the left atrium. The rapid increase in blood flow to the left atrium raises its blood pressure, so it's higher than the right atrium, forcing the two walls of the flap-like opening between them to come together, closing it. (See Figure 17.3.) Over the next several months this tissue fuses to permanently close the foramen ovale.

However, with modern echocardiography, it's been shown that about 25 percent of the time the foramen ovale doesn't completely close, resulting in a patent foramen ovale (PFO). People with a PFO usually live normal, healthy lives. Most of them don't even know that they have a "small hole in their heart" until they undergo testing, usually for an unrelated problem.

It's possible to view this relatively high occurrence of PFO as a defect; but given its frequency and associated minimal risk, it can also be seen more as a normal variant. In contrast, while very rare, a failure to close the second shunt (the ductus arteriosus) is usually much more serious. If the ductus arteriosus fails to close at birth—a condition called patent ductus arteriosis—the result quickly becomes life threatening.

While the foramen ovale is a flap of skin that can close relatively easily, the ductus arteriosus is more akin to an open pipe, so closing it is a more complicated problem requiring a more complicated solution—an orchestrated process involving not only structure and physics, but also chemical signaling. Even though the ductus arteriosus is only for temporary use, it's nonetheless a major blood vessel with walls about as thick as the aorta and pulmonary arteries—a thickness required to support the same blood pressures. The difference is that while the aorta and pulmonary arteries never close (the result would be instant death), the ductus arteriosus must do so, and do so very soon after birth.

What kind of mechanism could solve this problem, closing just the ductus arteriosus while preventing the two associated major arteries on either side from closing? It turns out that the walls that make up the ductus arteriosus are structurally different from the walls of the aorta and pulmonary artery. Like most large arteries that handle high pressure blood flow, the walls supporting the aorta and pulmonary artery mostly consist of elastic fibers. The walls of the ductus arteriosus consist mainly of smooth muscle.

We've seen this solution before. The walls of the ductus arteriosus are structured such that it can act like an active valve, similar to the arteriolar muscles we saw in the chapter on the cardiovascular system. When the muscles of the ductus arteriosus contract enough, they can close the pipe and significantly reduce the flow. Only in this case, the valve is closed just once, in the transition after birth.

The way the process works is another remarkable story. While in the womb, the higher pressure in the pulmonary artery (because the pulmonary artery is mostly closed) causes blood flow to bypass it and go into the aorta. This pressure helps to keep the ductus arteriosus open. But two chemical factors also help to keep it open: low levels of O_2 and high levels of prostaglandins in the blood. Prostaglandins are lipid compounds which are produced in most fetal tissues and, notably, in the placenta.

Although the placenta provides O_2 to fetal blood, it's not as efficient as the lungs. Further, the blood coming from the umbilical vein to the right side of the fetal heart mixes with deoxygenated blood from the rest of the fetal body. So, O_2 levels in fetal arterial blood is only about a fourth of adult levels.

Using O_2 sensors on their surface, the smooth muscle cells in the walls of the ductus arteriosus detect low oxygen levels and respond by relaxing. They also have receptors that detect high levels of prostaglandins, causing them to relax further. So, the low O_2 and high prostaglandin levels combine to keep the ductus arteriosus open in the fetus.

With birth, the baby begins to cry, the lungs open, and blood flow increases dramatically from the pulmonary artery to the billions of capillaries that line the hundreds of millions of alveoli. As blood begins flowing to the lungs, pressure in the pulmonary artery decreases, reducing blood flow through the ductus arteriosus to the aorta.

Further, opening the lungs quickly increases the O_2 level in the newborn's blood. At the same time, the newly functioning lungs begin to break down the prostaglandins in the blood. And since the placenta isn't there to produce more of them, the prostaglandin levels quickly drop.

Together, these changes cause the smooth muscle around the ductus arteriosus to contract, in effect closing the pipe.

The most difficult stages of this exquisitely orchestrated process are now complete. With the dramatically reduced blood flow through the ductus arteriosus, the cells in its walls lose their main source of O_2, which causes these cells to die. The result is permanent closure of the ductus arteriosus, usually 24 to 72 hours after birth. The ductus arteriosus is no longer needed, so the "detour" shrivels and dies, leaving just the permanent circulatory solution in place.

> During an infant's life in the womb, the ductus arteriosis (DA) must stay open. After birth, it must close. There's little margin for error. In engineered systems, transitional stages like this are where errors are most likely to occur.
>
> The smooth muscles of the ductus arteriosus are operated by an active control system. When open (the normal state during gestation), the channel allows blood to pass through from the side with higher pressure to the side with lower pressure. Very soon after birth, this valve must close, so the smooth muscles contract to cut off the flow.
>
> Once again we find a control system well suited to the body's need, essential to the survival of the species, and needed just a single time, at just the right time.

Timing Is Everything

THIS LEADS us back to baby James.

For babies with a patent ductus arteriosus, the blood continues to flow through the ductus arteriosus after birth, causing a machine-like continuous murmur, like what was heard by James's doctor.

Premature newborns are more likely to have a patent ductus arteriosus (PDA) because their lungs haven't yet matured. Because their lungs aren't fully mature, they have trouble raising their O_2 levels and lowering their prostaglandin levels—in effect muting the signals needed to close the ductus arteriosus. So their ductus arteriosus may stay open much longer after birth.

Between 20 and 60 percent of premature babies have a PDA. But as they mature, and with medication that blocks the effects of prostaglandins, their PDA will usually close without causing much trouble.

However, a PDA in a full-term infant occurs about once in every two thousand births. This is what baby James was facing. This condition is usually due to a structural defect in the wall of the ductus arteriosus, a defect thought to be transmitted genetically. Studies show that the smooth muscle cells in the wall are to some degree replaced by collagen or elastic fibers. With less smooth muscle, the ductus arteriosus can't contract well, and so remains open while blood continues to flow through the ductus arteriosus after birth.

The main problem with a PDA, though, is not that blood continues to be sent from the pulmonary artery (the route to the lungs) to the aorta (the route to the body), preventing it from going to the lungs to pick up oxygen. Things are a bit more complicated than that.

As we saw earlier, blood encounters resistance from the blood vessels (pipes) that it flows through. A larger diameter means less resistance so more blood flow. A smaller diameter means more resistance so less blood flow. When blood comes to a fork in the road, it takes the path of least resistance. This is dictated by physics.

In the womb, the resistance to blood flowing from the pulmonary artery to the lungs (which are closed) is high, so blood is forced to travel through the ductus arteriosus shunt into the aorta where the resistance is lower. But after birth the lungs are open, so resistance in the pulmonary artery is substantially lower. So after birth a PDA allows blood to flow from the aorta directly back to the pulmonary artery.

This means that at least some of the oxygenated blood, which should be bound for the body's tissues, is instead routed back to the lungs, so less oxygen gets to the tissues. Though this abnormal situation can be tolerated for a little while, depending on the size of the PDA and the amount of left-to-right shunting of blood, it will eventually cause problems.

First, the left side of the heart must do double duty, causing strain and leading to breathing difficulty (left heart failure). Also, over time, the increased blood flow through the pulmonary arteries, due to the PDA, can cause permanent structural changes, leading to pulmonary hypertension. This causes breathing difficulty (right heart failure), and in severe cases can cause a reversal of blood flow through the PDA back to the way it was in the womb, only now without a placenta to provide the oxygen. So when the baby is outside the womb and needs a lot more oxygen, deoxygenated blood is bypassing its lungs and going straight into its systemic arteries—not a good recipe for survival. This is why failure to close the ductus arteriosus can quickly become a life-threatening problem.

For babies like James, who have an underlying structural defect, the medical solution is an operation to close the ductus arteriosus within a few weeks or months of birth.

Wonderment

Respiration is a tough problem for the body to solve at any time, but all the more so when there's no direct access to the air, as with a child in the womb. For respiration, a preborn baby must solve a cascade of hard problems, all while building out the systems he will need after birth.

As if that were not hard enough, the transition from respiration in the womb to respiration outside the womb is itself a daunting engineering challenge that requires its own set of solutions. So much needs to happen, always at the right times and never at the wrong times.

We must not gloss over the difficulty of these problems. The solutions depend on necessarily temporary systems that act as respiratory scaffolding—systems that, outside the womb, would likely cause death and therefore must be transitioned away from and discarded shortly after birth. The timing is critical. Everything must come together at just the right time, or the newborn will not survive the transition to life outside the womb.

As engineers know all too well, transitions of this kind, from one coherent solution to a different coherent solution, are fraught with the potential for errors and failures. In living systems like the human body, a transition as momentous as birth could easily lead to catastrophic failure. That such catastrophic failures occur only in a fraction of births is remarkable. Why (and how) does this ever go right, especially given that no subsequent generations are possible if this is not achieved?

18. FROM 1 CELL TO 30 TRILLION

The complexity of these, the mathematical models, and how these things are indeed done are beyond human comprehension. Even though I'm a mathematician, I look at this with a marvel of, how do these instruction sets not make these mistakes as they build what is us?

—ALEXANDER TSIARAS[1]

IN A LONG CAREER, I (STEVE) HAVE ENJOYED WORKING WITH SOME amazing people across many walks of life—from machine operators in a Mississippi sawmill to CEOs in wood-paneled offices in upscale skyscrapers. I've designed solutions to problems in healthcare, inventory, supply chain, customer provisioning, engineering, construction, payment processing, loan approvals, power distribution systems, groundwater flows, emergency management systems, sawmill automation, and many others.

I've worked as a research scientist, software developer, manager, and systems architect; in everything from research labs to telecommunications to government to manufacturing to hospital groups; with Fortune 50 companies with tens of thousands of employees and start-ups with just a couple people. I've worked on systems of systems composed of thousands of systems that were independently developed, using different technologies from different eras, systems that address different goals based on different approaches and with vastly different architectures.

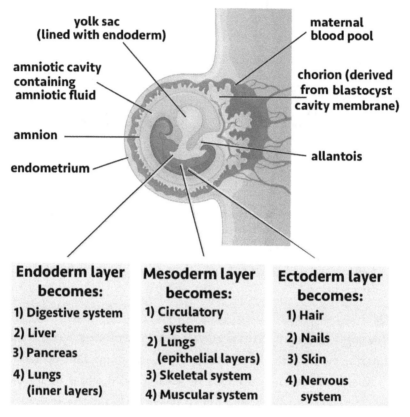

Figure 18.1. The three germinal layers of a developing embryo.

But I never once encountered a system that managed its own fabrication, assembly, and operations, from start to finish, until I turned my attention to living systems. Somehow, living systems know how to do these things.

For the human body, the process of development begins with a single fertilized cell and ends with a fully functional adult—growing from one cell to around two trillion at birth, then to around thirty trillion at maturity. But it's not the number of cells that makes this so impressive. Rather, it's the number of problems the developing body needs to solve along the way. The array of solutions required for basic respiration and nutrients, discussed in the previous chapter, is just the tip of the iceberg.

After conception the number of cells in the embryo begins to multiply and, before long, to differentiate into the hundreds of different cell types the body will need. About two weeks after conception, the embryo separates into three distinct germinal layers, shown in Figure 18.1: the endoderm (inside layer), mesoderm (middle layer), and ectoderm (outer layer). Eventually the cells in each layer differentiate into the body's many cell types, and later into the specific tissues and organs that compose the body's eleven major systems.

For this differentiation process to work, order and timing are everything. Much of what the baby will need at birth will take the full nine months of gestation to build. Some body systems can wait till near the end of the gestation process; others must arrive much sooner. Based on what we've discussed so far, which layers would you guess need to develop first if the embryo is to survive?

The cells of the endoderm will form the lungs and digestive system. But those aren't needed right away, since the mother has the duties of the lungs and digestive system covered via the placenta.

The cells of the ectoderm differentiate to form the skin and nervous system. Once outside the womb, they will allow this new human life to interact with and be protected from her surroundings. But for now, she's safe in the mother's womb, so she can do without this as well for now.

Some of the cells of the mesoderm will differentiate to form the musculoskeletal system. Once outside the womb, this system will allow this new person to move around and handle things. But for now, where does she need to go and what does she need to do? Her job is just to sit tight and let her mother provide her with what she needs to grow and develop.

Other cells of the mesoderm will differentiate to form the kidneys. Once outside the womb, they'll allow the baby to control her salt and water content. But for now, her mother, through the placenta, has that covered too.

So what's left?

We saw how the embryo quickly transitions to using the placenta for nutrition. But getting nutrients is not enough. Those nutrients must be distributed to every cell in this new little body as it grows. For this the embryo needs a cardiovascular system—a heart, blood vessels, and blood—and these also come from the mesoderm.

At about three weeks, the new heart begins pumping blood through its developing circulatory system. Over the next several weeks and months, as the embryo becomes a fetus and grows and develops, the heart provides the driving force for life.

> The cardiovascular system begins its life-critical role even as it's still developing. If it couldn't manage this extraordinary feat, the unborn baby would not survive.

Forty Weeks to a Breathing Body

THE PROCESS of building a new body from a single cell is extraordinarily complex. The timeline is short and the stakes are do-or-die. Below are some of the highlights of the process, and when they occur. In the bullet list below, T stands for the moment of conception.

1. **T:** A one-celled zygote is created—a unique, human individual with unique DNA.

2. **T + 30 hours:** The zygote divides into two identical cells.

3. **T + 3 days:** With further cell multiplication, this new life is now a sixteen-celled *morula*. The morula drifts through the fallopian tube on the way to the uterus.

4. **T + 5 days:** With further dividing, the new life is now a *blastocyst*, and enters the uterus.

5. **T + 8 days:** The blastocyst attaches to and implants into the lush endometrial lining of the uterus.

6. **T + 2 weeks:** The blastocyst is now an *embryo* with an amniotic fluid cushion, yolk sac for food, and different cell types.

7.   **T + 4 weeks:** The heart has been pumping blood through the tiny body for several days, providing nutrients to immature organs and the early skeletal system.

8.   **T + 6 weeks:** The embryo has brain waves, hands with fingers and feet with toes, and the airways are forming.

9.   **T + 8 weeks:** As the embryo enters the fetal stage, the yolk sac gives way to the placenta as the umbilical cord develops.

10. **T + 10 weeks:** The fetus begins moving her fingers and toes, the intestines are developing, and the skin is covered with fuzz.

11. **T + 12 weeks:** The kidneys are functioning, sending urine into the amniotic fluid. (The first trimester is completed at thirteen weeks.)

12. **T + 14 weeks:** A week into the second trimester, the fetus makes breathing movements and begins sucking her thumb.

13. **T + 16 weeks:** Now the fetus is growing more quickly. Bones harden, lung sacs appear, and the nerves start getting their myelin insulation.

14. **T + 18 weeks:** The brain begins developing, differentiating into distinct areas for senses like vision, hearing, smell, taste, and touch.

15. **T + 20 weeks:** The fetus has hair and fingerprints, and starts kicking as the heart and blood vessels fully develop.

16. **T + 22 weeks:** Except for the lungs, the organs have developed well enough for quasi-independent living.

17. **T + 24 weeks:** The bone marrow is making red blood cells. (Before this they were produced in the yolk sac, liver, and spleen.) The fetus is getting fatter and her intestines are moving.

18. **T + 28 weeks:** A week into the third trimester, the baby is opening and closing her eyes. She sleeps and wakes regularly.

19. **T + 32 weeks:** The baby puts on more fat and weight, her skull grows to fit her brain, and her lungs continue to develop.

20. **T + 36 weeks:** Growth continues with more fat, bone hardening, and more development of the brain and lungs.

21. **T + 40 weeks:** All the organ systems are ready, so it's time for this little one to head out, take her first breath, and meet her mother and father.

Birth and Transition

WHAT TRIGGERS labor is not fully understood. Apparently, the mother's body detects and reacts to what's happening in her womb. At the same time, the baby sends signals that tell the mother's body that she's ready to be born.

Progesterone, the pregnancy hormone, maintains the lining of the uterus for the placenta. Also, throughout the pregnancy it keeps the uterine muscle relaxed so it doesn't contract and push the baby out prematurely. The continued growth of the baby begins to stretch the uterine muscle, making it more excitable.

As the time gets close, the aging placenta struggles to keep up with the growing demands of the baby. This stresses the baby, so the placenta sends out more cortisol, a hormone critical for lung development. Cortisol also converts progesterone into estrogen, which makes the uterine muscle even more excitable.

The combined effects of maximum uterine stretching, placental fatigue, the associated rise in cortisol, and the rise in estrogen and reduction in progesterone seem to cause the uterine muscle to contract and bring on labor. As this happens, the mother's body releases other chemicals, like prostaglandins and oxytocin, which strengthen the contractions and soften the cervix for the delivery of the baby.

Once the baby is born, her body must take over all the functions she relied on her mother for, including respiration. This transition requires activating the lungs and rerouting the blood, and also many other tasks like managing water and salt concentrations, fluid balance, and tempera-ture regulation. The newborn's immune system must also be ready to go as the child enters this new (and dangerous) world.

And all this needs to happen quickly.

> Note the many ways that coordination occurs between the mother and her developing child. Their two separate bodies communicate with each other to orchestrate their activities. The programming that makes this system work in the mother was present when she herself was in the womb, when her body as an embryo was interacting with her mother's body. Several chicken-or-egg style questions come to mind.

Lessons from the Lifecycle

AFTER THE transition process, the infant continues to grow and mature, eventually reaching puberty and then adulthood, a mature human body capable of reproduction. The process of maturing is yet another crucial process to orchestrate, this time over many years. How does the body know what to do when, over a complete lifecycle that spans decades?

After the body reaches maturity, changes continue to occur. If the person doesn't meet an untimely demise, he or she goes through what in some respects appears to be a choreographed process of gradual aging and death. As we get older, our hair may turn gray (lose pigmentation) and thins. Our skin wrinkles and sags. Muscle mass diminishes. We get shorter. Bones become more brittle. The joints hurt and activities that were once easy get harder and more painful. It gets harder to concen-trate.

And then there's death. We may be able to delay it, especially with the help of a good doctor, but we cannot prevent it.

The body's final pathway to death is cardiopulmonary arrest, where breathing and the heartbeat stop at the same time. Should one of these occur first, unless there is immediate intervention, the other will quickly follow. When the heart stops, the cells in the brainstem can't get the oxygen they need. As O_2 levels drop and CO_2 builds up, these cells will die. Now there are two strikes against the body—no heart beating to circulate blood and oxygen, and no brainstem to tell the body to breathe, even if one could somehow make the heart beat. In this case it's two strikes, you're out.

Various diseases of the brain, lung, or heart can lead to cardiopulmonary arrest. So can various other chemical and physical causes. Many examples have been presented in previous chapters. We've dedicated the bulk of this book to understanding how hard your body must work to prevent that outcome prematurely, but it cannot be prevented forever.

Though we tend to take these things at face value, we can learn a lot by pondering a few odd characteristics of the human lifecycle. It has a distinct order: pre-birth, birth, infancy, early childhood, middle childhood, adolescence, adulthood, and death and dying. For those who make it to old age, these stages always come in this order. Nothing about the order is random. We commonly think of aging and dying as the result of the body's systems breaking down over time. And, of course, that's a central part of it. But aspects of the process also may be guided by some kind of internal programming. Engineers know that there are a limited number of ways to do such things, and all require some combination of timers, counters, clocks, control systems with feedback loops, and complex logic, in this case operating over decades; so as biologists research the matter, they would do well to look for such things in the human body. The jury is still out on whether and to what degree pre-programming is involved in how a person living into old age moves through the stages of life, but if we're right about the overall design of the body, the discovery of some such pre-programming would not be surprising.

One intriguing thing we do know is that the clock starts over at conception. No matter how young or old the parents are, the child always gets a fresh start. In effect, the "counter" is reset to zero. Why is this? How does it work? Would it be possible to decode this programming? It would be fun to find the answers to these questions. There's probably a

Nobel prize to be had (and lots of money) if anyone figures it out. As of now, medical science has barely a clue.

Lifecycles Macro and Micro

ANOTHER FASCINATING property of the body is that the lifecycle of the whole is independent of the lifecycles of the vast majority of its cells. Billions of your cells die every day, but the overall makeup of your body stays roughly the same, because new cells are made to replace the ones lost.

Different types of cells have quite different lifecycles:

- Sperm cells last outside the body for about five days.
- Skin cells turn over about every four to six weeks.
- Red blood cells live for around four months.
- Liver cells last about a year.
- Cells in the placenta survive for several months but die shortly after birth.
- Neutrophils (special white blood cells) only live several hours.
- Other white blood cells, like memory T and B cells, can live for years.

Interestingly, brain cells in the cerebral cortex last for the entire lifetime of the body, though they may change in important ways during that time. This suggests that brain cells have a function that cannot readily be replaced by a new cell—another mystery of the human body that would be exciting to explore.

As for all the other types of cells that die and are replaced: this is a normal and necessary part of all coherent systems, including human-engineered systems. Different parts wear out at different rates, so a maintenance regimen is developed to check the condition of the parts, determine when something needs to be replaced, and swap old for new.

Notice, too, that the human body generally manages its maintenance schedule without the benefit of outside help. For this work, the body is its own master mechanic and parts-acquisition specialist. And all this takes still more control systems—to detect how many cells there are, determine whether the numbers are appropriate, and generate new cells to replace the old. And, of course, the body needs some means to take old, worn-out parts out of service and replace them with the new ones.

These systems are essential to the resilience of the body. With them, the body is able to live much longer than any crucial parts that wear out and get replaced along the way. The body gets an independent lifecycle much greater than its weakest links—the cells that wear out the soonest.

All this is yet another kind of interdependency. The body needs separate maintenance systems to monitor and maintain its primary systems. More control systems mean more programming. This is also a large and ingenious leap in design coherence. And, without a doubt, this poses yet another series of hurdles for accidental causation.

A Plan for Unfolding the Body Plan

THE HUMAN body somehow finds a way to grow from a single-celled zygote to a thirty-trillion-celled mature adult. To accomplish a task of this magnitude requires a plan, including an order of engagement, together with many specialized systems whose jobs are to build out the body (as opposed to operating it once it's built).

The plan, together with its programming and build-specific mechanisms, must address each of the millions of problems above. Anything less would result in a body that doesn't function well or, more likely, doesn't function at all.

Given how precisely the body must do these things to sustain life, it's quite predictable, from an engineering perspective, that the process is extremely sensitive to errors. Even a small error in the development process likely will lead to a major problem in the outcome. This is generally true for systems of this kind.

The body is arranged in a hierarchy of layers—a design hierarchy. The development process must build out these layers as it goes, differentiating, assembling, and growing. Hundreds of facets of the design must be realized, from plan to body, through this process. We group these into four categories of build plans:

Differentiation

As we've seen, well over two hundred specialized cell types must be made (and possibly several hundred more that have yet to be discovered and cataloged). All contain the same DNA as the zygote (except for red blood cells, which lose their nuclei along with their DNA), but each expresses a different program and performs different functions.

This means that as the new life takes shape, some cells will divide but won't make new copies of themselves; they will make something different—a cell with a particular program selected, which will turn it into a specialized cell. This process, known as differentiation, may involve various facets of the cell, including its shape, capabilities, and role(s) in the body.

Different cell types express different genes at different times, and in different organelles within the cell, to build exactly the proteins and enzymes needed for their specific functions. Only those genes needed for their specific function are *expressed*, or turned on. This is remarkably efficient. Different cell types run different internal programs, or operating systems. They respond differently to different signals and stimuli, and they perform different tasks for the body.

But how does cell differentiation cause certain cells to run different programs? How does the body know which cells need which programs? Where do these programs come from, and where (and how) are they encoded? Remember that the body must control tens of thousands of different proteins, in hundreds of specialized cell types. How could programming of this complexity have come to be?

The body knows what machinery is needed to perform what jobs at what times in what areas of what cells. It's brilliant at producing only what it needs, and only when and where needed. The level of control required to pull this off is mind-boggling.

Further, these cells make up the various tissues and body parts, like organs and bones, and these are also highly specialized. Specialization of body parts includes shape, size, and materials. The teeth are made of very different substances than the eyes or the spleen. In fact, specialization of parts extends through the layers of the hierarchy, from the encoding of information to the body as a whole.

Organization

The specialized cells are organized according to the body's design hierarchy into tissues, organs, and body systems. The placement of various cell types in the body is precisely controlled. We've seen many examples of this, from the dispersion of light-sensitive cells in the retina, to the distribution of different types of cells in the skin, to the specific positions of the bone cells that build and maintain the precise shapes of bones.

Millions of body parts are made by these cells, together with the extracellular materials that hold them together (like the extracellular matrix, bones, and cartilage discussed in Chapter 3). Each must be precisely correct or bad things happen. Further, each part can perform its function properly only when it's in the right position with respect to other parts of the body.

Integration

The parts of the body must be integrated with precision. Each part must be held in place. Each must have the right connections and interfaces. These may be mechanical, electrical, fluid, chemical, or any combination.

Coordination

If the body is to work properly, each of its systems and parts must be properly tuned to the controls, timers, and signals it will need during its lifetime, together with the logic needed to achieve proper function.

The Parts of the Plan

EACH OF these four types of plan is quite challenging by itself. But to achieve them all is extraordinarily difficult. They must be properly "unfolded" and interwoven during development, starting from the zygote's one cell. The scope of this problem is daunting.

Clearly, all this must result from the body's higher-level development plan, so what does this plan contain? What information and programming are involved? Below we will consider what all must be there, much of which has not yet been discovered.

There are two parts to any plan of this kind: (1) the information that specifies the outcome (the *specifications*), and (2) the orchestrations and processes for building out the plan (the assembly *instructions*).

The body, recall, is made up of individual cells (along with extracellular structures). Each cell is an autonomous entity that controls its own resources, makes and consumes its own energy, and has its own goals and the programming to achieve them. At each step in the development process, these cells are doing the work. How do they know where they are? How do they know how far along in the development process they are? How do they determine what to do next?

There are two possible approaches, which we've talked about previously: *orchestration*, wherein the cells get instructions from a controller external to the cell; and *choreography*, wherein each cell determines its own course of action, based on its perception of the situation around it, combined with its internal programming.

If it's orchestration, where do the instructions come from? What systems track the development process and decide when and where to send out these instructions? If it's choreography, how do cells perceive the situation around them? What possibilities and differences can they distinguish, and how do they turn these into actions?

Most complex systems use a combination of these approaches. How the body does this is not (yet) known. But we can apply engineering knowledge to understand what must be there for the specifications and instructions to work, even if we have little idea where these things might be, or how they're encoded.

Specifications

DNA CONTAINS exact specifications for the tens of thousands of different proteins the body must produce. But what else must be specified?

Clearly, the target state also must be specified. This includes what the parts are, where they belong, and how they're interrelated. It includes all the specializations, organizations, integrations, and coordination discussed above.

But much more is required. Coordinate systems are needed to manage and inform the cells about their placement and their relative positions, such that they're able to form incredibly complex 3D shapes, like those of the vertebrae or the bones of the middle ear (ossicles), each of which must have a distinct and precise shape.

The body needs axes for lateral (left to right), longitudinal (head to toe), and depth (front to back). Placement of the parts along these axes must be precise. There is structural symmetry on the lateral axis, so there will need to be systems to maintain size and length consistency on either side. (It's helpful when both legs are the same length, and when the knee joints are in the same position along the longitudinal axis.) At the same time, many of the body's internal organs do not have lateral symmetry. The heart and the spleen are always on the left side, and the liver on the right. This also must be precisely specified.

Also included are specifications for hundreds, perhaps thousands, of control systems, through all layers of the design hierarchy. Each requires sensors, comparators, logic, and actuators. Each requires finely tuned setpoints and thresholds. Many of these must also be positioned in just the right places. How does a growing fetus know to put the special CO_2 sensors in the brainstem, and the O_2 sensors in the aortic arch?

Build Instructions

IN ADDITION to the specifications, the body needs a set of do-it-yourself instructions, an action plan for building the body. These rules tell the developing body what to do, when to do it, where to do it, and how to do it. These instructions tell the cells when to divide and differentiate.

They instruct the dispersion of different cell types in different tissues and organs. They define the routing and placement of the piece-parts, like blood vessels and nerve bundles. For this to be successful, it must minimally include all the following:

- *Fabrication instructions*, which define how to build individual parts and what materials to use.
- *Assembly instructions*, which define the precise order in which the parts and systems will be built.
- *Launch instructions*, which define the stages at which various body systems, like the heart, will start performing their function.
- A *schedule*, which understands (monitors?) the body's progress and keeps the whole works on track—in effect, keeping the project on time and within budget.

Testing and Course Corrections

SOME FORM of feedback is required during development. For human bodies to be made with so few errors, there are likely many subsystems to detect the current status (and perhaps also the trajectory) of the development process, compare it to the target plan, and make course corrections as necessary.

Much about how the body manages all of the above remains a mystery. But engineers can predict that such things must exist and will one day be discovered.

Making the Whole

EACH OF the body systems and mechanisms discussed in this book presents hard problems to that tiny zygote. If it's ever to become a mature adult, it needs to solve a lot of tough problems. There is nothing random about how these things must work if a mature human is to result.

Unfortunately, most of the specifications and instructions above are written in languages that we don't really understand and implemented in microscopic details that are hard to decipher.

These appear to be "compiled" into thousands of gene regulatory networks (GRNs) and possibly also various epigenetic systems, but at that level of detail they are extremely tough to unravel. It's a bit like trying to figure out what a computer program is doing by watching the values change in the computer CPU's registers. The observational data are at too low a level to make much sense. Sadly, we don't have access to the source code, so we're left with the long and tedious process of deciphering the signals at ground level and reverse engineering to determine the underlying logic.

So, much of how development works remains a mystery. But we're thankful that it does work, since it means we get to exist.

A Few Thoughts

MILLIONS OF new people are born every day. Because it's so common, it's tempting to conclude that it must also be easy. But nothing could be further from the truth. Life may well be, as Michael Denton has said, "the greatest discontinuity in the universe,"[2] and the making of a new human perhaps the most impressive sequence of events in the observable universe. It's the closest thing we have to a repeatable miracle.

When something goes wrong in development, we're prone to ask why, especially when it happens to the child of a friend or family member. It's a reasonable question, but we run the risk of passing over the more profound question: Why does anything in the process ever go right? After all:

- The single-celled zygote has nine months to build a complete, "standalone" human body composed of roughly two trillion cells.
- It must differentiate into hundreds of specialized cell types. Each differentiation must happen in the right place at the right time.
- Each specialized cell must be placed in just the right location to achieve its special function(s).

- Each part must be made of the right materials and have the right shape.
- Cells must be organized into tissues and organs, according to the body's design hierarchy. Different tissues have different types of cells, dispersed in specified positions. Tissues and organs must be organized into body systems. Body systems must be organized into a whole body.
- Thousands of control systems must be generated.
- Each body system must be given the right capacities, parameters, and setpoints to operate effectively.
- All the above must be done in the right times and places, such that the end result is complete and coherent.
- The process of fabricating and assembling parts must interleave systems to achieve the needed interdependencies.

And all this must be done from the inside. There is no external factory, and no external tools are involved—though, of course, the mother's body is providing raw materials and removing waste materials.

Building a self-sufficient human body from a single-celled embryo (the zygote) requires solutions to millions (billions? trillions?) of problems. The sheer complexity of this challenge, coupled with the beauty of the orchestrations involved, boggles the mind.

PART SIX: CLUES, CAUSES, AND SO WHAT?

IN THESE PAGES SO FAR, WE HAVE GONE BEYOND HOW THE HUMAN body looks, to examine how it actually works. We find coherence, interdependencies, and finely tuned dynamics everywhere we explore. These characteristics present a vast array of formidable causal hurdles, sufficient to test any theory of human origins.

As noted at the outset, there are two radically different frameworks for explaining the origin of the human form. One posits that the human body arose through purely non-intentional, material causes, a blind and gradual evolutionary process said to have overcome all the observed causal hurdles discussed in these pages. A second framework remains open to the possibility that intention was required to achieve the results we observe in the human body.

Two fundamental questions that investigators should be asking, regardless of their preferred framework, is what type or types of causes have the demonstrated ability to overcome the causal hurdles uncovered here, and how might those causes have played out in the history of life? In this final section, we will explore these questions, explore the two frameworks in greater depth, and evaluate their most profound implications.

19. Looking at the Whole

These features of biological systems, reuse of a small set of network motifs, robustness to component tolerances, and constrained optimal design, are also found in a completely different context: systems designed by human engineers. Biological systems have additional features in common with engineered systems, such as modularity and hierarchical design. These similarities hint at a deeper theory that can unify our understanding of evolved and designed systems.

—Uri Alon[1]

Years ago, I (Steve) was a principal architect at a Fortune 50 company. My responsibilities included the architecture, organization, and functional integration of a couple thousand information systems. It was a lot to juggle. I had no idea what several hundred of those systems were, who owned them, where they were, who was using them, or what their value was to the company. Such systems were built organically by people who needed a specific function and the quickest way to get it was to build it themselves, either personally or via their departmental budget. As a result, these systems often were built without architectural oversight or consideration of system-wide impacts. And, looking across the whole, they rarely produced coherent results. Asking the same question in two different systems would likely give two very different answers.

This large collection of systems had been built in different decades, for different purposes, using different technologies. Several had cost tens of millions of dollars, and a few were over a hundred million dollars. Most had internal logic and data structures that were made for the business's needs at the time they were built, with little thought for future flexibility, so they were extremely difficult to modify when the needs of the business changed.

And the needs of the business did change, often and broadly. Most of the systems' lifecycle costs were spent to integrate them with other systems, and to keep those integrations working for decades and across hundreds of system changes. That they were not designed for this made these changes difficult and expensive—a fact that management always seemed to find surprising (but not surprising to those of us who had to make the changes).

One day, the CEO announced seven sweeping strategic initiatives. All were essential to the survival of the business. All seemed simple and straightforward. All were to be implemented within six months. Two of them landed in my architectural bailiwick. With a bit of digging, we discovered that just these two initiatives would require making changes deep in the logic of about two dozen major information systems, then re-defining several dozen core business processes and retraining thousands of people.

Our early estimates pegged this at a minimum of two years with costs well above $100 million. And this was the optimistic estimate, where nothing goes wrong (and something always goes wrong). There were simply too many things that needed to be changed, all at the same time.

This story is not unusual. Even apparently simple changes can be daunting when real-world details must be considered—that is, when it has to actually work. The effort required grows exponentially with the number of systems and integrations involved, and the potential to miss something essential is high.[2]

In contrast, when evolutionary biologists hypothesize about small and apparently straightforward changes to a species during its evolution-ary history, the biologists tend to skip both the thorny engineering de-tails of what's necessary to make the system work, and the bigger picture of how any system change has to be integrated with all the other systems it interacts with. The result is that the biologists tend to massively underestimate the complexities involved.

And here's the rub: if they've massively underestimated those complexities, then they've massively underestimated the challenge for any gradual, materialistic evolutionary process to build up these systems a little bit at a time while maintaining coherence and function. Remember, at each step in this continuum of change, the pre-human body must have been alive.[3] And as we've seen, being alive is no easy task.

Hard to Build

LET'S CONSIDER some engineering principles widely established across multiple engineering disciplines and grounded in generations of engineering experience. Then we will consider how they apply to biological systems.

As all working engineers know, it's hard to build a coherent interdependent system that actually functions. Designing, building, and fine tuning such a system takes a combination of creative problem-solving and plain old hard work.

For such a system to work, many parts need to come together at the same time. These parts must be specialized, organized to fit and work together, and the whole must be operated in strictly orchestrated processes. There's a reason companies employ thousands of engineers to make complicated products like Atlas 5 rockets or iPhones. Products of this kind never just "emerge" from the properties of physics and chemistry.

> Coherence Axiom 1: The greater the number of coherent, interdependent parts (or subsystems) needed, the more work it takes to design, assemble, and fine tune them into a working system.

Given the amount of work required (decisions plus actions) to create them, coherent systems are nearly always made through relatively large, discrete jumps in functionality. This difficulty does not result from the complexity of a system. Rather, it's inherent in the design principles of coherence and interdependence. Such systems contain chicken-and-egg problems all up and down the design hierarchy, so this problem simply cannot be avoided.[4] For coherent systems, gradual increases in function are possible, but only with foresight and planning to ensure that a component is present even though it can have no function until a future revision of the design brings in another necessary part or parts to allow for the new or revised function. Including these waiting-in-the-wings parts or subsystems is sometimes useful in human-designed systems. For example, software vendors often embed modules or subroutines in their systems that have no use until future enhancements become available.

Hard to Change

ONCE A coherent interdependent system is successfully built and working, it's hard to change it into a different, coherent interdependent system. Again, this is simply an inherent property of this class of system. The more parts involved and the more ways these parts are interconnected and orchestrated to work together, the more parts, connections, and orchestrations must change at the same time to retain function through a change cycle. Further, a change in any system that another system depends on is likely to throw off any fine tuning. Goldilocks fine tuning can easily be lost, especially where multiple systems interact with each other.

> Coherence Axiom 2: The greater the number of coherent and interdependent parts (or subsystems), the more work it takes to change a working system into a different, working system.

For example, the body has separate controls for water and salt, but these chemicals interact with each other. A change in the controls for water means the body must also adapt its controls for salt; otherwise, these systems would likely oscillate, possibly uncontrollably. Failure in either of these systems, or in the interactions between them, would mean death.

Because more complex body plans have more parts, more orchestrations, and more interdependencies, they are more resistant to change, meaning changes can occur only at much higher cost and much less often than with simpler body plans. Regardless of causal force or action, we therefore expect changes in the most complex body plans to be few, infrequent, and relatively minor over time. Because of this, we're not surprised that the fossil record contains no intermediate forms between distinct animal body plans (e.g., between phyla).

A Flyover of the Human Body

THE ABOVE coherence axioms apply to the human body as well. This book has covered a lot of ground, so here we'll review the main themes, from the piece-parts to the whole, from the micro to the macro, with their integrations and coordination and orchestrations. And remember that, because they're interdependent, if pretty much any one of the smaller subsystems fails, it will take other systems with it, and this can quickly lead to equilibrium with the environment (death).

As we've seen, for life to exist, it must solve numerous thorny problems. For it to persist, it must solve still more problems. For it to reproduce, there are an especially difficult set of additional problems to solve. These problems are all interconnected, and so must be their solutions:

- The body must be fully enclosed, as must most of its organs, each of its cells, and each of the organelles in those cells. Even external materials, like foods taken into the digestive tract, cannot be allowed to float randomly in the body's internal spaces.
- The body must store, retrieve, translate, and manage information—and lots of it. Not just the specifications for tens of thousands of different enzymes and other proteins, but also for thousands of complex goal states; programs with their decision logic, instructions, and process sequencing; and operational primitives that include coordinate systems, switches, setpoints, thresholds, counters, and timers.

- The body must use thousands of different signals—chemical, electrical, or both in combination—to coordinate and control all these systems. Each signal must be triggered at the right time and place, sent over some distance, then received and interpreted at another specific location to produce a specific outcome.

- The body must transport hundreds (probably thousands) of chemicals and proteins, both within individual cells and throughout the body. Some of the required chemicals are toxic and must be carefully shielded to prevent collateral damage in transit.

- The body must disassemble the thousands of different complex molecules it takes in as food into their constituent building blocks, absorb those building blocks, then reassemble them into the thousands of specific chemicals, enzymes, and other proteins the body needs at any given time. Together, these are the catabolic and anabolic processes of metabolism. Many of these require a multi-step processing chain of highly specific enzymes and other proteins.

- The body must regulate dozens of critical parameters like fluid pressures and flows, energy production and consumption, heat management and distribution, and metabolic by-product recycling and removal.

- The body must bend and move, with parts that can perform a myriad of physical tasks, from feats of strength to ultra-fine-grained movements.

- The body must manage the exact right functional capacities, with exactly the right timing (dynamics) for all its systems, such that they can support the entire range of the body's needs. For example, the interdependent cardiovascular and respiratory systems can quickly adjust their delivery of oxygen. Thus, when you run you immediately begin to breathe faster and your heart pumps faster to meet the increased need for oxygen.

- The body must orchestrate thousands of complex processes, some nearly instantaneous (for example, in managing split-second timing between muscle groups, as in swallowing) and some over long stretches of time (for example, in managing the body's lifecycle across many decades).
- The body must defend itself from threats large and small—from predators that wish to consume it to pathogens that want to consume its resources and suck it dry.
- The body must be able to make a copy of itself (reproduction and development).

This is a lot of capabilities, and they're all necessary if the human species is to persist.

If we look across the body's design hierarchy, there is coherence at each level and interdependencies all over the place, both within each level and among the levels. All these things occur with a precision and complexity that dwarf any systems human engineers can comprehend, much less design and implement.

The Problem of Cascading Problems

SOLVING A given problem is rarely simple. It's common for a solution to one problem to present new problems that must also be solved. And each of those solutions likely presents still more problems.

Doctors constantly watch for this. A treatment regimen for a given condition often causes other issues that must also be addressed—called iatrogenic (doctor-induced) complications.

For engineers this challenge is also business-as-usual. Most problems have many possible solutions, and most solutions present new problems, which then must be solved, generating still more problems, and so on, until adequate solutions have been engineered across the whole. Only when all the solutions are brought together, and the rabbit-like proliferation of problems-from-solutions is finally corralled, does the resulting system work.

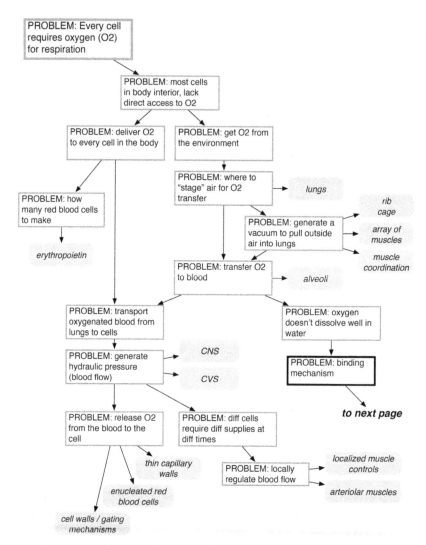

Figure 19.1a (above) and Figure 19.1b (right facing page). A problem cascade for cellular respiration in the human body. Problems are listed in boxes and solutions in ovals. Note that this illustration greatly simplifies, and therefore understates, the complexity of the problem cascade. So, for example, several of the solutions are "stubbed out" (e.g., those labeled "GIS" and "CVS") and are best viewed as placeholders for other distinct but similar problem cascades, which must also be solved in order to solve the initial problem.

from prev page

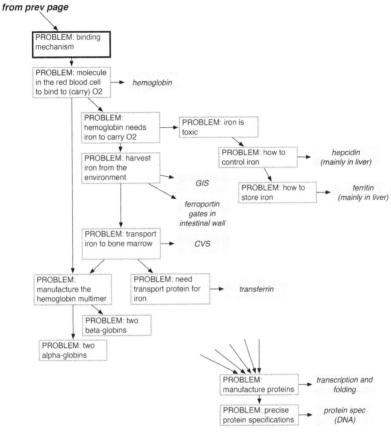

Figure 19.1b. Problem cascade for cellular respiration, continued.

We see the problem of cascading problems all over the place in the human body. The oxygen supply required for cellular respiration illustrates this well. Figure 19.1 illustrates how these problems pile up, and how each must be solved in turn to solve the initial problem of cellular respiration in the human body.

Remember, every cell must get oxygen or it cannot live. Cells that can't live don't do the body any good, and if enough cells fail, the body will also fail. It's essential to get oxygen to every one of those thirty trillion cells, but in a large body very few cells have direct access to oxygen from the atmosphere. This is a demanding problem. Even just this high-level view of the problem cascade identifies more than two dozen problems, each requiring a different complex solution composed of many specialized parts acting in a coordinated way.

Imagine you are asked to build a human body. You're given all the carbon, oxygen, water, nitrogen, metals, and other chemicals you'll need. How would you go about solving this engineering problem? If you don't solve the cellular respiration problem and all the others, you just end up with a pile of ingredients, not a living, functioning creature.

Respiration is not an isolated case. We could start with almost any problem the body must solve to be alive, and chase the cascading problems until we've touched most of the body's other systems. This tells us that the body is loaded with interdependencies. Most of the systems only work when they're in the context of the other systems they rely on. Thus, it doesn't seem possible to solve any one of the body's problems without solving pretty much all of them.

To clarify let's view this from the systems perspective. If a body must solve a couple hundred problems to be alive (the actual number is much higher), and each of the body's systems solves one or more of those problems, then it takes the whole to solve all the problems. Were any of those do-or-die problems to go unsolved, the body wouldn't survive.

This is important. When we look at the whole of the body, which of the systems, or the subsystems, or the sub-subsystems, or any of the underlying information, could be taken away before the body fails? If it can't function without hundreds and hundreds of key subsystems and parts, how could it have come to exist a little bit at a time?

In short, the body has chicken-and-egg problems top to bottom. Indeed, most of the problems the body must solve are chicken-and-egg problems. And this is not an arbitrary difficulty based on some quirky approach to engineering the human body. In every case it's a natural outcome of the laws of chemistry and physics, so the body must solve them and solve them well if it is to be alive and thrive.

The Laws of Hard Problems

THE DUAL realization that the problems are incredibly hard to solve, and the solutions must be complete (and coherent), pushes us into a corner. How can these two hurdles be overcome, and at the same time? One of us (Steve) formulated two laws of hard problems to encapsulate what will strike experienced engineers as unarguable truisms.

- Laufmann's First Law of Hard Problems: *No amount of wishful thinking will make a hard problem go away.* No amount of magical thinking can ever solve a truly hard problem. Wishing it were solved cannot make it so. Sadly, this is always true, and all the more so with the tough problems the body faces in its struggle to be alive.

- Laufmann's Second Law of Hard Problems: *Hard problems require ingenious solutions.* The mere presence of a problem does precisely nothing to make a suitable solution appear. This is because the problem itself is not a causal force. Solving problems takes a problem-solver—one with the requisite type of problem-solving skills. This is all the more so with life, where neither the problems nor the solutions are trivial.

Systems Solutions

So HOW does the body achieve its amazing array of capabilities? It takes systems to solve problems like these. A system's function is defined by its parts and the relationships between the parts.

Each part must be specialized for its particular function. Specialization can take many forms, from the more obvious—e.g., shape, size, and materials—to more subtle but equally essential ones, like the ways different types of cells respond to different types of signals—their internal programs. For example, red blood cells are programmed to eject (enucleate) their cell nucleus after they've produced enough hemoglobin, at which time the DNA in the nucleus is no longer needed. No other type of cell in the body does this. If enucleation were to fail in red blood cells, the body would not be alive since the cells would be too bulky to move through the vast majority of the capillaries. If enucleation were to occur in any other type of cells, those cells would not be able to perform their functions.

The relationships between the parts can also take many forms, from their relative positions to their integrations, to their coordination across time. Do the parts fit together? Are they properly connected? Can they be assembled? Do they work together at runtime? Can their parts be modified or replaced as needed, and if so, how difficult is it to do so?

Systems are exactly what we're looking at in the human body—a large-scale assembly of systems: a system of systems. Actually, the human body is a system of systems of systems of systems... and on down the design hierarchy.

Ingenious Problem Solving

THROUGHOUT, THIS book has stressed five main characteristics that must be all present for life. The first two are associated with dynamic capacity management (DCM), the next two with coherent interdependent systems (CIS), and the final one applies to all of the first four:

- *Controls and Capacity Management*: Hundreds of chemicals and physiological properties must be controlled within quite narrow ranges. Various body systems must have the right capacities to meet the body's changing needs at all times.
- *Dynamics*: Controls must work within critical time constraints. The time required to start and stop various systems, communications transmission speeds, capacity ramp-up and response times, and the proper "locality of effect" are all critical to life.
- *Coherence*: The body's many systems use millions of specialized parts, which must be properly fabricated, integrated, and coordinated to work together.
- *Interdependence*: The body is a closed system, exhibiting functional and process interdependencies. These may be

complex, where system A depends on system B, which depends on system C, which depends on system A.

- *Fine Tuning*: We're hard-pressed to find anything important in the human body that doesn't require fine tuning. All the systems discussed in this book do, as do all the others that we can think of.

For the human body to work, we need different types of capabilities, and each takes a very different kind of system. Each of these capabilities is implemented many times over, in various parts of the body and at different levels in the design hierarchy. Here is a partial list:

- *Enclosure*: to isolate materials and separate components.
- *Harvesting*: to get all needed materials from the environment.
- *Transport and Delivery*: to move materials from place to place.
- *Factories + Waste Recycling and Disposal*: to produce materials and recycle and dispose of waste.
- *Supply Chain Management*: to get the right materials to the right places in the right quantities at the right times.
- *Chemistry Management*: to ensure that all needed base materials and complex chemicals are present.
- *Energy Management*: to obtain the needed energy, convert it into the needed forms, and consume it.
- *Heat Management*: to ensure the body stays at the proper temperature even as the outside temperature fluctuates, and even as the body generates heat from metabolic processes.
- *Materials*: to make specialized parts out of different materials, as appropriate for their tasks.
- *Structure, Shape, and Size*: to ensure that the parts for which physical shape is essential to function are properly manufactured and assembled.

- *Motion and Strength*: to enable the needed range of motion, with strength appropriate to required tasks and fine tuned to the exact shapes and sizes of the body's structures.
- *Fluid Dynamics*: to manage fluids and pressures in various applications throughout the body.
- *Defense*: to protect the body against attackers.
- *Cleansing*: to remove unwanted chemicals and byproducts of other processes.
- *Healing and Repair*: to reconstruct damaged tissues.
- *Adaptation*: to monitor various factors in the environment or within the body, and change internal processes as needed.
- *Optimization*: to carefully monitor and control the use of potentially scarce resources.
- *Signaling and Communication*: to carry information between locations, with appropriate timing.
- *Physiological Controls*: to provide fine-grained controls over various processes.
- *Coordination Mechanisms and Programs*: to ensure that actions occur in the correct sequences.
- *Logic and Computation*: to make appropriate decisions in a timely fashion.
- *Information Processing*: to store, retrieve, and use various information resources.
- *Automation*: to control most aspects of the body's processes without conscious thought.

To make all the above processes and systems work, the body needs, among other things, a vast array of lower-level parts, or *functional elements*, that make up the body's systems. The software world knows these as *primitives*. These include:

- sensors
- machines

- timers
- counters
- switches
- logic and rules
- sequencing
- feedback and feedforward loops
- setpoints
- thresholds
- parameters
- coordinate systems
- specifications
- instructions
- plans (such as body plans)
- process definitions
- signaling
- coordination
- chemical transformations
- information

This is a lot of complicated stuff, which must be arranged in complicated ways and fine tuned to achieve complicated outcomes. Where are all these things encoded, and how and when are they decoded? It seems likely that much of this is not encoded in the DNA, but no one really knows. If it's not encoded wholly in the DNA, what possible causal forces might be able to work to change these, and how and when might they do so?

These are profound questions, with few answers so far.

The Body's Architecture

THERE IS a lacuna of great import in contemporary origins biology, one that cries out to be filled: the body is designed around specific architectural principles, ones essential to making the body work, and yet these principles are mostly absent from discussions about biological origins.

Two of these are design practices commonly used in nearly all design and engineering. Together, these work like "divide and conquer" for complex systems design. One is known as separation of concerns, wherein a large problem is solved by breaking it into separate subproblems that are easier to solve. Different concerns are solved by different subsystems. For example, among the many problems it solves, the cardiovascular system has divided the blood distribution problem into two separate subproblems: (1) generating blood pressure, and (2) channeling blood flow into progressively smaller pipes to distribute that pressure to individual cells. Human engineers apply this practice iteratively, top-down. Each subproblem is broken into still more subproblems, and so on. This is how a design hierarchy is made. This is a normal consequence of the problem of cascading problems that we discussed above.

The corresponding design practice is called the rule of composition, wherein the larger problem's solution is composed by combining the solutions to those separable subproblems. For example, the cardiovascular system only works when all its subsystems are combined. This is also done iteratively, but bottom-up, which again results in an observable hierarchy of design.

Separation of concerns and the rule of composition normally produce hierarchical architectures, with layers of design stacked on top of each other, and this is exactly what we see in the human body. (See Figure 2.1 in Chapter 2.) In many cases, the problems solved at one layer also need to be solved at another, higher layer. Cellular and whole-body respiration are a perfect example, as we saw in Chapters 1 and 4.

The body's architecture also exhibits the following three essential design principles, ones widely recognized as the best approach to managing systems complexity:

1. *Modularity*: When possible, separable solutions are implemented as modules. Modules are designed to provide a specific

set of functions using optimal means, independent of how the system as a whole or any other modules may be implemented. Generally, modules can be reused or replaced with relatively low effort. The body is composed of specialized modules all the way up and down the design hierarchy—from the amino acids, through the proteins, to the cellular subunits, the cells, the tissues, the organs, the body systems, and even up to human societies, wherein individuals specialize in certain skillsets they offer at great efficiency to a wider community.[5]

2. *Encapsulation*: The interfaces between the modules are independent of the internal design or structure of any specific module. Thus, the rest of the system (external to the module) doesn't need to know or understand how the module works, so the module and the system that encompasses the module can be designed independently. In engineering, this property makes it much easier to reuse or replace modules. For example, in a car the designer of the door doesn't need to understand the internal mechanisms of the door handle. Rather, it's only necessary to understand the interfaces the door handle presents to the door's mechanisms. Historically these have been mechanical arms and levers, but a more modern door handle might be entirely electronic, interfacing to the door through an electrical signal.

3. *Autonomy*: In many cases, modules are best when they operate autonomously, running their own internal programming and using their own internal resources. In the body, for example, each individual cell runs its own "operating system," which tells it what to do and when to do it. (A cell's operational programming is based on the type of differentiated cell it is and possibly also by the parameters by which it was initialized.)

Modularity, encapsulation, and autonomy appear to be universal principles of design. In combination, the way these architectural properties are applied will affect how easy or hard it is to make changes to a system. This, of course, depends on the specific system and the specific architecture in question. Thus, the ways a given system adheres to these principles will impact the ways it can be modified over time and the level of effort required to make those modifications, and these will impact the system's longevity.

The human body employs these exact design principles, but the ways these may have affected it over time have not received much attention, so remain relatively unexplored. Hence, there's a plethora of interesting research yet to be done. Chapter 22 explores these properties in more detail.

The Body's Recurring Design Patterns

Previous chapters explored various recurring design patterns present in the body. These are listed in summary below:

The Push-Pull Principle

In many cases, two separate subsystems are required to make the whole work—one to push and another to pull. We saw this in the muscle mechanics of the body's movements, in the ADP/ATP energy cycle, and in the chemical signals that speed up and slow down the heart rate. The principle shows up all over the place and things only work when both subsystems are precisely aligned, precisely balanced, and precisely coordinated. It would do no good if both the push and the pull were going at the same time, or exerting force in misaligned directions, or if the push overwhelmed the pull.

Global Resource Applied Locally

The body produces a resource that's available everywhere, but only deploys it where it's needed. For example, the immune system's white blood cells are freely circulating throughout the body but are only deployed in a precise location, similar to how complement proteins and clotting factors are employed.

Just-in-Time Delivery

Resources are delivered not only exactly where they're needed, but exactly when needed. We saw this in the speed of nerve impulses and the delivery of chemicals to various cells.

Dynamic Adaptation

The body adapts its systems' outputs as quickly as needed when a system demands change. We saw this in the way your lungs adjust their output when the body demands more oxygen, and in the ways the arteriolar muscles quickly adjust to meet the needs of specific muscle groups.

Functional Redundancy

The body has multiple solutions for some of its most essential functions. We saw this in the cardiovascular system's three separate subsystems that failover, each to the next, to drive the heartrate when the higher order controls fail. It's also seen in the ways the innate immune system and adaptive immune systems work together.

Specialized Materials

The body harnesses the right materials for the right jobs, often using non-organic materials to support an organic body. For example, the teeth are made of very hard enamel while the cornea is made of a transparent tissue.

Storage and Carrier Proteins

The body manufactures and applies special chemicals to mask toxic materials which are needed but that would be destructive if left to freely wander about the body. For example, ferritin and transferrin manage iron and prevent it from causing problems.

Enzyme Chains

The body converts chemicals from one form to another using an ordered series of stepwise transformations. Each step uses a different enzyme. These transformations generally work on stable chemicals, which means the transformation would happen too slowly, if at all, under natural conditions (in the absence of the enzyme). The body's thousands of metabolic processes use enzyme chains. In most cases, if any step in a chain goes wrong, the needed end result will not occur. Many human diseases are caused by failures in enzyme chains. Any single example of a successful chain is an engineering marvel; the fact that the body has thousands of these that work the great majority of the time is simply astounding.

Signals and Communications

The body coordinates activities across distances using many kinds of signals, which convey messages from the simplest, like a basic on/off switch, to semantically complex information like the visual data from the eyes. Somehow the right parts of the body seem to properly understand these signals and take appropriate actions. Signaling can be broadcast, as through the blood, or point to point, as through the nerves. This happens within cells, across cells, and across major body systems or subsystems. It occurs between the right locations and with the appropriate speed.

Coordination Strategies

HUMAN ENGINEERS use two contrasting approaches to coordinate the activities of autonomous entities. Interestingly, both are used in the body, and in ways that optimize the benefits of each:

- *Orchestration:* In this approach, decisions about what should happen, where it should happen, and when it should happen are made by a central decision-maker and communicated to the various autonomous entities that must perform those actions, as with a conductor leading an orchestra. This approach is centralized and process oriented.

- *Choreography:* In this approach, decisions about actions are made by the autonomous entities themselves, but those entities are programmed such that their respective actions coordinate with the actions of other autonomous entities. For this to work, each entity must observe the situation around it and apply internally programmed logic about what to do in the observed situation. Hence their actions are choreographed. This takes very little communication at runtime, so is advantageous in many situations. We've all seen the effects of this in the ways birds flock and schools of fish swim. This approach is decentralized and goal oriented.

Irreducibility

ANOTHER PROPERTY of complex systems is important enough to merit its own section. Across various design principles and strategies, we find an almost ubiquitous property of complex systems: irreducibility. For the system to function, the composition of solutions to the subproblems must be complete. While it may be possible for oxygen controls in the body to work with fewer oxygen sensors, it won't work at all if there are no sensors. The ability to extend your arm wouldn't be much good if you couldn't retract it again. Some minimum number of parts or controls are required for the system to work. This is *irreducibility of function*.

Each of the examples given above also involves separate processes. To extend your arm by causing certain muscles to contract is a very different problem from generating those muscles from a stem cell during development in the womb. These are not only different processes, but fundamentally different types of processes. But both are required if you're to have a working arm. This is known as *irreducibility of process*.

Different processes also require different information. The information that tells a stem cell how to make muscle tissue and attach it in a certain configuration is not the same as the information that tells a brain cell how to send a message to a specific muscle group to contract that muscle. This is known as *irreducibility of information*.

The body is loaded with interacting processes and systems. We've discussed some of the ways these systems are controlled within very narrow tolerances. But with interactions, sensitive controls can easily lead to oscillations and instabilities in the whole, which can quickly lead to death. Thus, it takes some form of super-controller to control the controls. Engineers know this is necessary, but it's not well understood in the human body. This is known as *irreducibility of control*.

The bottom line is that pretty much everything essential or meaningful in the body is *irreducibly complex*. So where did it come from, and how did it get the way it is today? Together, these ideas make a strong case that the systems that make up the human body are, as stressed early in this chapter, hard to build and hard to change.

Insights and Questions

THIS CHAPTER is mainly about considering these systems in enough detail that you can ask the right questions and realize when you're hearing inadequate answers. If someone purports to have an explanation for the origin of some complex biological system, don't be satisfied with just-so stories long on imagination and short on essential specifics. All the various classes of design problems elucidated above must be solved for a functional system to come online. Also watch for the fudge words "may have" / "might have" / "could have," especially when there's little or no supporting evidence of a capability to perform the requisite causal tasks.

When considering explanations for the origin of anything in biology, think like a good engineer playing the devil's advocate. Don't ask, What are a few things needed for the proposed system to function and flourish? Ask what *all* is needed.

These are hard problems. Beware of wishful thinking.

20. But Wait, We've Only Scratched the Surface

If most answers seem obvious in retrospect, maybe we're not spending enough time searching for the obvious.

—Frank Sonnenberg[1]

I (Steve) began my career writing software in a research lab, so the message on the guy's T-shirt immediately resonated with me. It was written like a dictionary entry:

programmer. *n. an organism that turns caffeine and pizza into software.* It only occurred to me later just how profound the message was.

Humans have an unusual but apparently innate desire to do things that only make sense if being human is more than mere survival and reproduction. Humans can (and do) turn caffeine and pizza into all sorts of amazing products. Software, yes; but also art, music, great literature (also bad literature), the designs for bridges and cell phones and spacecraft, and all the other intellectual achievements of humankind (including the invention of pizza!). Further, humans have a desire to understand the universe. They hunger for meaning and purpose, and ponder questions your dog or cat couldn't care less about: How does a physical body turn nutrition (even questionable nutrition) into intellectually creative products? Why do humans often turn to creative pursuits when they have a bit of spare time, when other creatures use their downtime to conserve energy by inactivity or sleep? And do the answers to these questions lead to other big questions, like where do we come from and why are we here?

As for the intricacies of our bodies, the chapters behind us may have felt dauntingly detailed to some readers, but we've barely scratched the surface. We've simplified and omitted thousands (probably millions) of details along the way, in many cases because they are too technical or would take much too long to explain. But many of the details that are omitted were omitted mostly because they are unknown. Science and medicine have a long way to go to fully understand how the body works.

But the body does work. And the more details and causal hurdles we discover, the more we realize how impressive the body's capabilities are, and the greater the explanatory challenges become for every theory of human origins.

What We Know

THE DESCRIPTIONS of the body in this book are accurate and uncontroversial, from both the medical and the engineering points of view. Knowledge about the body is extensive and growing rapidly. We understand, at least in broad brushstrokes, how the major body systems work. We're continually exploring new medicines and treatments that enable us to mediate the body's many behaviors, especially when things get out of whack, like when the body is fighting a disease or when a body system begins to fail.

We understand the basic workings of the cells. We've pieced together many of the organelles and structural elements essential to cellular functions, and we're exploring in ever more detail how different cells behave differently at different times.

We're also exploring the many ways our cells communicate with each other. We've begun decoding and cataloging the tens of thousands of different types of proteins in the body, the various control systems that invoke their production, and the exact locations within given cell types where that production occurs.

We have a basic understanding of how DNA encodes for the structures of proteins. We know about many of the gene regulatory networks that control these things. And we're building a basic understanding of how specific genetic "markers" affect various medical treatments, which offers the exciting potential to tailor medical treatments to specific individuals.

Through all this, we're developing a clearer view of the body as a whole. We are learning:

- How thirty trillion or more cells work together to sustain life, across hundreds of specialized cell types, forming eleven interconnected major body systems and hundreds of minor systems, producing tens of thousands of specialized proteins, each in the right places, at the right times, to perform specific tasks. And all this with near-optimal efficiency, producing them only when and where they're needed.

- How each component and system is properly fabricated, assembled, and operated.

- How these many systems interact with each other to harvest the many chemicals the body needs and transport each to the right location for processing into the form the body needs it in—while rejecting (or ejecting, sometimes forcefully) many of the harmful materials in the environment.

- How the body regulates and controls hundreds of chemicals and minerals within precise tolerances and in the right capacities and with the right dynamics—just-in-time delivery of exactly what the body needs, where it needs it.

- How the body manages tens of trillions of cells not native to the body, but which provide essential services, cells such as the many types of beneficial gut and skin bacteria, without which we'd be in trouble.

While dynamic capacity management works brilliantly at the species level, it also works well for most individuals. Each individual body—including its heart and lung capacity, water and salt controls, etc.—appears finely tuned for its individual needs, balancing inputs and outputs, controls, and capacities. Yes, the body—like all highly complex systems—is sensitive to perturbations, due to the large number of constraints on the system that are imposed by the laws of physics and chemistry. Because of this, it doesn't take much for the body to shut down—like glucose too high or too low, or calcium too high or too low. Yet, somehow, the body is amazingly resilient.

Further, the body does all these things throughout a complete life-cycle, from conception through birth, from birth through adulthood, and on through aging and programmed death.

What We Don't Know

What about all the stuff we don't yet know about the human body? As you may have noticed from the preceding chapters, many of even the most basic details of the body's workings are just not well understood. For example, where's the human "body plan"? What tells the body's cells about the specific and detailed shape of each bone, the attachment points for tendons and ligaments, and the assembly plan that "threads the needle" of the trochlea in the eye? Where's the coordinate system for left-to-right symmetry, or the plan for the head-to-toe and front-to-back layout of body parts? What tells the eyes to form in the eye sockets rather than in the spleen? Where's the plan that tells certain cells to kill themselves at specific points in the development cycle (apoptosis)?

Where's the body's operating plan? As the body takes shape in the womb, various of its systems begin their lifelong work. What tells them to start, what to do, and for how long to keep doing so? Where do these operating instructions reside? How do specific cells know what their lifecycle should be and when to die?

The list of unanswered questions is long. Most of the developmental and operational dynamics of the human body remain mysteries.

The body's information is partly in DNA, and partly in known epigenetic structures, but much of the body's information may be stored in places we don't know or understand, in forms that no one has decoded.

Some of the "missing" information may be in known locations but "compiled" into a series of regulatory signals, like gene regulatory networks (GRNs), which are difficult to decode.[2] Information encoded in such ways may take many more decades or even centuries to decipher and understand, sort of like a multi-dimensional jigsaw puzzle where each piece may have a precise fit with hundreds of other pieces.

In the early 1950s, James Watson and Francis Crick discovered the double helical structure of DNA. Since then, the biological research community has focused enormous effort (and computational power) on deciphering genetic codes. Yet even with all the progress on this front, no more than about 15 percent of the human DNA's information payload is understood, with many estimates much lower.[3] And so far, little progress has been made in deciphering the epigenetic codes. What we do know is that the combinatoric possibilities of known epigenetic information repositories is vastly larger than the storage capabilities of DNA, which is itself outlandishly large.

Given how little we understand about epigenetic information systems, it's not clear whether or to what extent any Darwinian model of change would apply. To what extent are these systems heritable? What traits can be inherited? Is much epigenetic information replicated during reproduction, and if so, how? Is it subject to random variations? If so, to what degree, and are any of these random variations ever beneficial? If we don't understand basic questions like these, how can anyone claim that a Darwinian model is demonstrably adequate to explain observed changes?

The bottom line is that, while we know a lot about the body, the amount we know is dwarfed by the amount we don't yet know. Our understanding of the body remains relatively thin. It doesn't take much digging, into any aspect of the body, to exhaust what's known and expose mysteries just under the surface.

However, engineers know quite a lot about how the kinds of functions in the body are accomplished in other domains of investigation. In the architecture of information systems, for example, we know how to build systems that do some of the things the body does. Typically, there are a handful of possible approaches, each with its own trade-offs, and the trick of good design is to make the choices that best produce the desired results across a broad range of considerations.

Based on our knowledge of how to build complex systems, we can say with high confidence that the information that makes these things happen in the human body must be extraordinarily complex. Perhaps more importantly, it must also be internally coherent, else the outcomes it produces cannot be coherent.

Further, given how much we don't know or understand, it behooves all of us, on all sides of these origins questions, to apply a heavy dose of humility as we do the hard work of science—asking good questions, humbly seeking good answers, and following the evidence wherever it leads.

Beyond Survival

EVEN THE most detailed understanding of the chemical properties of paper and ink will not prepare you to understand one of Shakespeare's sonnets. No knowledge about sound waves and frequencies is sufficient to understand our emotional connection to a Bach sonata. And no examination of the human body's workings can explain the human experience.

There's so much more to being human than just our bodies and the essentials of survival and reproduction.[4] For a human, being alive means not just sensing our world but enjoying it. It means meaningful work. It means reasoning about complex ideas. It means planning and problem solving. It means creativity and invention. It means language and understanding. It means fairness and morality. We strive for goals that go well beyond mere survival. We strive for wisdom, and to know who we are.

And, importantly, being human means building and growing relationships. Our lives consist largely of talking to people, working with people, living with people.

Humans appear to be designed to interact with others, in ways that go beyond what we find in other social animals. We have dozens of muscles in our faces (far more than any ape), which have no apparent use except to express emotions to other people. Our eyes and minds are specially tuned to recognize faces and emotions. Our ears are tuned to amplify sounds in the exact range of human speech (and singing). Our hands, faces, and lips are extremely sensitive to the touch of other people. Collectively, these aspects of the human experience mark us off dramatically from any other living organism. Humans are exceptional.[5]

The amazing capabilities of the human body make these experiences possible, but they neither produce these experiences nor explain them. The body provides a platform for the human experience, and it does so mainly through processes that happen almost entirely automatically and subconsciously. The benefit is that this frees our conscious minds to explore the interesting and important "something more" that's built on top of that platform. The "something more" seems to need the platform, as a platform, but it's not *of* the platform. The platform seems to be necessary for these things, but not sufficient to explain them.

As a rough example, a basketball game needs a basketball court, with boundaries marked on the floor and hoops of a specified shape and height at each end. These are necessary to the game, but nothing about the physical structures of the game can make the game itself. The game needs the platform of the playing court, but the platform's physical structures are qualitatively different from the game itself. For the game, you also need the rules, the drive and passion of the players, and their know-how and strategies; and none of these are material.

In the same way, the things that happen "above" the body are less tangible than the body, yet they are arguably more important.

These qualities pose a troublesome challenge to those who argue that survival and reproductive success are the primary drivers behind the origin of the body, and by extension, of the human person. If their view is correct, all the qualities in the "something more" must be reduced to some emergent property of the material and must be, in effect, illusions (albeit convincing ones), preserved through some survival or reproductive advantage.

Where's the "You"?

THIS LEAVES us with another mystery. Where in all the above aspects of the human experience is the "me" that I experience? I (Steve) live inside my body, but I know I am not just a body. I reason about my body as something different from me. I can feel my body. I can tell my body what to do, and it usually obeys (though this happens less frequently the older I get).

We are blessed to live in our bodies when they're working well, yet we are also trapped in them when they don't work so well.

Neurosurgeons are in a unique position to explore such matters, because their job involves physically poking around inside other people's brains. Their observations establish a sharp and unambiguous distinction between what can be manipulated physically and what cannot.[6] Physical manipulation or injury can modify a person's emotional proclivities, memory or cognitive abilities, or ability to see or move, but can never change that person's identity. He remains the person he has always been, just with disabilities.

For example, surgically cutting the hemispheres of the brain so they function independently causes subtle impairment of coordinated neurological functions,[7] but it does not create two individuals. In this sense, the human soul is metaphysically simple, meaning that it cannot be divided like matter can be divided.[8] Neuroscience further shows that, while perception, movement, memory, and emotion are mainly caused physically, by brain matter, the human capacity for higher reason, abstract thought, and free will are not.[9]

Thus, though there is clearly a relationship between the two, the mind is distinct from the brain.[10] We don't need to plumb the depths of the mind's mysteries to realize this: the mind, however it may be connected to our brain and body, isn't reducible to matter. Your self-ness, while overlaid on your body, is in some essential way more than your body, and independent of it.

Is it possible the entire point of your body is to make the "YOU" possible, and to give it a home? This may be among the most important questions a person can grapple with, yet it seems far from the minds of most materialists. As Granville Sewell aptly put it, "But even if they could explain how animals with mechanical brains evolved out of the primeval slime, that would leave the most important question—the one evolutionists never seem to even wonder about—still unsolved: How did I get inside one of these animals?"[11]

The Causal Burden Grows

THE MORE we know about the body and how it works, the more evident becomes the astonishing engineering ingenuity involved, and the harder it becomes to explain its origin.

It's hard to make a new, coherently engineered system (at least one that works). And it's hard to make a major change to a coherent system without breaking it. Together, these realities present a doubly formidable hurdle for any proposed causal explanation.

Mix in the fact that there's a person living inside the system, and you've got a trifecta of causal problems to solve—you only win if you get them all right. Anyone who expects you to buy their origins story must account for all these things. The quality of their explanation should be compelling. Or at least intriguing. Or at least plausible.

No hand-waving allowed. And no wishful thinking.

The two competing explanatory options for the origin of the human body are not difficult to understand. The first, modern evolutionary theory, is restricted to purely material causation (the first class of causal force we introduced in the Introduction), while the second, a theory of biological design, allows for intentional causation (the second class of causal force).

The next two chapters will evaluate and compare these two alternatives, weighing each against the evidence.

21. A Theory of Billions of Innovative Accidents

I look with confidence to the future, to young and rising naturalists, who will be able to view both sides of the question with impartiality.

—Charles Darwin[1]

On November 7, 1940, the Tacoma Narrows bridge collapsed, spectacularly and famously, into Puget Sound. Films of the failure are among the most iconic film clips in engineering history. The bridge was the third longest suspension bridge in the world at the time it opened. When it failed, it had been open to traffic for barely four months.

Even during construction, the bridge deck was unstable and would move vertically in windy conditions, which earned it the nickname "Galloping Gertie." Then, on the morning of November 7, with winds steady at just forty miles per hour, the bridge deck began to oscillate and twist with increasing amplitude until the cables broke and it fell into the water below.

Tacoma's loss is instructive in two important ways.

First, the collapse resulted from unanticipated oscillations. Winds above thirty-five miles per hour caused mechanical resonance, together with aerolastic flutter that, in this case, was self-amplifying and unbounded. Once the bridge began to oscillate, the wind added energy to the oscillations, driving the amplitude of the vibrations ever higher until the structures failed.

Oscillations can occur in most complex systems, including in a complex body such as ours. In the body, oscillations may involve mechanics, chemistry, or nearly any parameter managed by a control system. These are especially difficult to avoid when multiple systems have interdependencies. And, just as with the bridge, the human body cannot survive out-of-control oscillations. We don't normally see these in the body, so its control systems must be tuned with great precision to avoid dangerous oscillations within and among its thousands of systems and subsystems.

Second, the bridge collapse was caused by a spectacular engineering failure. The failure has been the subject of much analysis and commentary and been featured in engineering textbooks and lectures ever since. Yet, to our knowledge, no one has ever claimed that nature "selected against" the Tacoma Narrows Bridge—that the wind was acting to shape the design of this bridge. This is obviously silly. Rather, the problem was that the bridge had a major engineering flaw "designed in" at the outset. Due to this inadvertent flaw, its design was simply not engineered to withstand a day with continuous forty-miles-per-hour crosswinds.

But what about in biology? Does the fact that creatures reproduce and pass on their variations give us solid grounds for believing that here, at least, nature can indeed select for or against various designs? If so, are there any limits to what can be achieved through this form of "selection"?

A Brief Review of Causality

As DISCUSSED in the Introduction, there are two jointly exhaustive classes of causal forces: Class 1: *material causes,* and Class 2: *intelligent causes.* The former work mainly from necessity so are purposeless and generally repeatable, though with some contingency due to random events. The latter work mainly from intention, so are primarily purposeful and therefore not generally repeatable.

Each of these causal classes includes multiple subsidiary forces or factors, which we'll discuss more thoroughly in this chapter and the next. Each class and each factor brings its own inherent causal capabilities and limitations. Understanding these is key to understanding how the human body may have come to be.

At the center of the mystery is this: Nearly every important system or subsystem in the human body is irreducibly complex and works coherently to achieve ingenious, fine-tuned solutions to the hard problems of life. Further, the body is brimming with interdependencies across its thousands of subsystems and between the layers in the design hierarchy. If we're ever to understand the origin of the human body (or of pretty much any other living thing), we'll need a combination of causal forces and factors that are together capable of generating these types of systems and solutions.

Clearly, since we exist, some event or series of events must have caused us. While we're unlikely to ever know all the details, we do have the means to evaluate which types of causal forces, alone or in combination, are necessary to generate the outcomes we see in life.

Neo-Darwinism and Its Tools

In 1859, Charles Darwin published *On the Origin of Species*, his seminal work on evolution in the history of life. He updated this with five more editions over the next dozen years, responding to various critics and refining the theory. Others have updated and modified the theory since, notably with the development of population genetics in the 1930s, followed by major discoveries about DNA in the 1950s and subsequent decades. The modern form of the theory is known somewhat fluidly as neo-Darwinism, a term that overlaps with an even more plastic term, modern evolutionary theory, which includes some variations on Darwinism known as the extended evolutionary synthesis. There are many variations and nuances, but they all share the same basic principles and the same causal limitations.

Darwin's theory states that the biosphere's great diversity springs from natural selection acting on random variations. As an organism generates offspring, small changes can occur, in what's known as descent with modification. Some of these changes may confer an increased sur-

358 / Your Designed Body /

vival or reproductive advantage to the offspring. Over time, traits that offer an advantage are more likely to become fixed in a population, and eventually individuals without that advantage will likely die out of the population. Darwin termed this natural selection, where material causal forces work like farmers who select which animals or plants to breed to produce desired effects in the offspring. However, in Darwin's world, unlike with animal breeders, the changes are always random and completely without guidance toward any specific outcome.

While there are additional details we won't go into here, Darwin's theory primarily involves the interplay of four causal factors, all of them in what in our taxonomy we have grouped as Class 1—that is, strictly material:

- *Variation*: A means by which differences occur in an organism. Darwin himself did not propose a mechanism for variation, but since the discovery of DNA, these changes are known as mutations and are mostly attributed to random errors in processing or copying the information in DNA.

- *Heritability*: A means by which an organism passes its traits, including its variations, to its offspring. This leads to the notion of common descent, wherein all living organisms are said to have descended from a single common ancestor, known as the last universal common ancestor (LUCA). The branching caused by descent with variation is often drawn as *a tree of life*, showing all living things descending from the hypothetical LUCA.[2]

- *Natural Selection*: In the struggle for survival, certain organisms, given their variations, are able to out-compete others in a given environment. Individuals with better survivability tend to survive, and the others tend not to. This is known more colloquially as *survival of the fittest*.

- *Time, Lots of Time*: The theory depends on eons of time. Gradual, intention-free trial-and-error evolutionary progress just doesn't happen overnight.

These four factors comprise the major drivers of what is, in essence, an evolutionary theory of *gradually innovating and diversifying by accident*. As a strictly materialist causal theory, neo-Darwinism has no place for intention or foresight of any kind: no room for goals (beyond an organism's goal of survival and reproduction), no source for guidance in whether or how to assemble a system, and no means to discern whether a partial system will be functional in the future, in the event it should ever be completed. No one is available to intend any particular outcome, evaluate partial progress, or steer things in a direction that will later prove helpful. The only possible way forward is by trial and error. However, if something useful (to survival or reproduction) should happen, natural selection will preserve it.

Assessing Neo-Darwinism's Tools

FOR NEO-DARWINISM to be causally adequate, it must explain the origin of the entire panoply of life on Earth, including all the qualities and capabilities of the human body, with all its systems, subsystems, and sub-subsystems. It must explain all the chicken-and-egg interdependencies. It must explain the generation of coherent systems at all levels, from molecular machinery to ecosystems, and how these are tuned to precise setpoints and narrow ranges. It must explain the human mind and the things that make human life worth living—love, altruism, beauty, language, music, and so much more. And it must explain the origin of many millions of other species throughout the history of life.

The causal hurdles are real. Can Darwinism's causal tools overcome them? Let's examine them one by one, considering three characteristics of each:

- *Preconditions:* The set of things that must be true before the causal factor can have any effect.
- *Capabilities:* The kinds of actions and outcomes the causal factor can bring about.

- *Limitations:* The inherent limitations of the causal factor (the kinds of actions and outcomes the causal factor cannot bring about).

Variation by Random Mutation

Neo-Darwinism focuses on variations due to random errors that occur during genetic copying.[3] Certainly, errors in a digital code like DNA will cause changes in the code. But what kinds of change will this cause in the organism? From our exploration of the body, we'd expect that, most often, multiple coding changes will be needed to generate a new feature. Further, we'd expect the vast majority of random changes in the digital code to generally degrade rather than improve the organism.

Consider, by analogy, random changes to computer programs, which have similar characteristics to DNA. How many changes would be required to add a new function to an existing program, or even just to add a new variable? As anyone with even a passing familiarity with software development knows, the overwhelming majority of random changes will degrade or destroy an existing function.[4] But making a new function would generally require many coherent changes, so achieving this by random modifications would be exceedingly rare, and thus highly unexpected.

Clearly, some beneficial changes will absolutely require multiple co-ordinated variations. Even conceptually simple hurdles like a push-pull system will likely require dozens (or more) of coherent changes in the underlying information.

But getting multiple unguided changes to produce a coherent outcome is extraordinarily unlikely—from both the probabilistic and commonsense perspectives. This is a bit like throwing bricks into a pile and expecting the result to be a house.[5] Or tossing a hundred boxes of Scrabble letter tiles on the floor and expecting a Shakespearean sonnet to form. So, for a random mutational event to generate a coherent leap in biological functionality, the change must be either trivially simple (achievable through a very small number of mutations such as, say, one or two), or it must occur gradually, over long periods of time, where each mutation gives some advantage along each step of the evolutionary pathway; if neutral or deleterious mutations are involved, this dramatically increases the amount of time required to generate the new feature (to prohibitive levels).

The mathematics of probability speak plainly here. Let's say we need to generate glutathione, the smallest known functional amino acid chain in the human body, at just three amino acids long. There are twenty amino acid "letters" in the amino acid "alphabet," so there are 8,000 (20^3) possible arrangements of three amino acids. So, choosing blindly, we have a 1/8,000 probability of getting the right one. With 4,000 tries, we'd have a 50 percent chance of finding the right one.

But what about titin, the longest known of the body's protein chains, 34,350 amino acids long? Here the numbers are too large to comprehend: 1 in $20^{34,350}$. For comparison, a recent estimate for the number of atoms in the entire universe is 10^{78}. Most calculators can't distinguish $20^{34,350}$ from infinity. (In principle, there may be so many sequences that accomplish the job that the odds of lucking onto a functional sequence are reduced to a workable level, but see below for what experimental research has revealed.)

What about all the proteins and molecular machines needed to convert glucose into ATP? What about those for the blood clotting cascade? And this is just for proteins. We still must solve all the other hard problems for the human body outlined in Chapter 19.

Any causal theory in which random causes must generate such things needs serious help from one of three quarters to tame the improbabilities: (1) *It's discovered that there are far fewer possible amino-acid sequences than supposed for a given protein.* But this one is a non-starter, since the number of sequence possibilities is easily calculated. (2) *There are far more functional amino-acid sequences possible for the given protein than supposed.* But as we saw previously and as summarized below, laboratory research appears to be pushing things in the opposite direction.

(3) *There needs to be a lot more trials available than there probably were.* Indeed, even wildly generous estimates of the number possible trials in the history of the universe are insufficient to overcome the probabilistic hurdles.[6]

The only alternative path forward for random causation is some combination of natural selection and an adaptive continuum. But as we've shown at multiple points in previous chapters, the idea of an adaptive continuum grows more and more implausible with each new discovery about the irreducible, coherent, interdependent systems of irreducible, coherent, interdependent subsystems that is the human body. Biologist Michael Behe estimates, based on the best available experimental data, that within animals it would take longer than the entire history of living organisms on Earth to get a single instance of three coherent random amino acid mutations occurring at the same time and place (in an individual organism).[7] Thus, any change that requires four or more simultaneous, coordinated changes in an animals' protein sequences in order to provide any advantage would be extraordinarily unlikely in the history of life on Earth—if they needed to occur without intention. And based on the evidence of the human body, we can reasonably conclude that even the simplest of coherent biological systems would require dozens or hundreds of coherent changes.

So it doesn't take a rocket engineer to realize that random events have limited creative power. There are so many more ways to arrange a lump of matter so that it remains a lump than there are ways of arranging it into a functional system. This is because of the degrees of freedom involved. The raw number of ways a series of parts can be assembled is mind boggling—and that's assuming you have the parts. This makes the random assembly of anything useful a combinatorial problem, where the size of the problem space grows exponentially with the number of parts required and the number of ways they're interconnected, such that solving a realistically sized problem is effectively impossible without intention.

This is why a truly random change is much more likely to damage or destroy a working system than to generate a new one or even to significantly improve an existing one. As an example, suppose a series of tornadoes sweeps through a large junkyard, and with blinding luck manages to assemble a complete Boeing 787, except for the tail section. What are the chances that the next tornado will assemble and attach the tail section rather than tear the fuselage apart or rip the wings off? This is why engineers are hired to build things, and tornados, hurricanes, and children's birthday parties aren't. Engineers apply their ingenuity, discipline, and experience to reduce the degrees of freedom, to design and build a system that achieves a desired outcome, an outcome that could never come about without their guidance.

Now let's assess the power of random mutations using the three characteristics described above:

- *Preconditions for Random Mutation:* Random mutations require something extant to mutate. Some information must exist, and it must be part of an information base that produces a living thing.
- *Capabilities of Random Mutation:* Random mutations change things in unpredictable ways, so they're contingent. Contingency is essential (but not sufficient) for creating information.
- *Limitations of Random Mutation:* Since random mutations are random, they're not working from a plan, so cannot offer direction. They cannot strive for a goal and could only generate non-trivial coherence with immense luck—the greater the coherence, the more luck is required.

Heritability

Heritability means passing variations to the next generation, then to the next, and so on, through eons of time. Darwinists insist that minor variations will accumulate over time to generate major innovations.

Heritability is itself an enormous chicken-or-egg problem. How could heritability come about gradually when it's required before changes can accumulate gradually? Realistically, this could only have occurred if reproduction with inherited traits were trivially easy. Surely Darwin believed this to be the case. But we now know that this isn't true.[8] As we saw in the chapters on reproduction, it's certainly not true for a large and complex human body, but neither is it true for a single cell. Nor, in the strictly theoretical realm, for a proto-cell, or any hypothetical self-replicating molecule.

However, it is theoretically possible for one system to gain functions from another system, through a design practice called composition (see Chapter 19)—by one organism obtaining a new function directly from another. One way this might happen is through what's known as horizontal gene transfer, but how this may have affected the history of life is unknown and remains an area of ongoing debate even among mainstream evolutionists. Still, the principle of borrowing design elements from existing systems is well known in the engineering world.

Now the assessment using our three characteristics:

- *Preconditions for Heritability*: Heritability can only happen with reproduction. Not only is reproduction among the hardest problems known, it's the mother of all chicken-or-egg problems.
- *Capabilities of Heritability*: Heritability over generations enables variations to accumulate.
- *Limitations of Heritability*: Heritability can't generate anything new.

Natural Selection

According to neo-Darwinian theory, random mutations generate changes and natural selection threshes them, separating the good from the bad, and keeping the good. More precisely, when a mutation helps an organism out-compete its brethren for limited resources like food or water, or helps it better elude predators or attract a better mate, or generate more offspring, that organism is more likely to survive, reproduce, and pass on its variations to future generations. Repeat this process millions of times and, according to the theory, life will tend to move toward greater adaptive capability over time.

But entropy happens, and that seems to fly in the face of gaining capability over time.[9]

Of course, scientists recognize that entropy tends to work against things becoming more organized, sophisticated, and capable over time, but Darwinists maintain that natural selection provides a dramatic exception to our normal understanding of nature. They believe that blind and unguided natural selection can yield dramatic increases in complex and specified information.

There are, however, a few problems with natural selection. First, natural selection cannot "act" on a trait that offers no survival or reproductive benefit. If a feature cannot be built by numerous gradual accumulations, each conferring some advantage, then it cannot be built by natural selection. Perhaps non-selective changes can occasionally be preserved by chance processes—what are collectively called genetic drift. But you have to get very lucky for this to happen. But natural selection is supposed to greatly reduce luck's role in the equation by automatically preserving traits that provide some benefit towards survival and reproduction. If that can't be done, you have to rely on sheer, dumb luck— never a good strategy for solving hard engineering problems.

So, natural selection gets stuck when it is asked to build traits which offer some clear advantage when "fully formed" but in which many parts or components are needed before any advantage is achieved. These features cannot be built in a step-by-step manner since small changes do not offer increased advantages at each step. It's all or nothing. The causal hurdles we've discussed throughout this book have this general nature.

Natural selection also struggles to explain traits which don't seem to aid in survival or reproduction. While the theory predicts that the vast majority of observed traits in life will confer some benefit, hundreds of novelties have been identified that have no adaptive purpose.[10] Examples include the extravagant coloring of male birds in many species, the radial patterns and exquisite coloring of angiosperm flowers, the radically different shapes and patterns of leaves in different species of trees, novel body plans like those of insects, and the human capacities for language and for artistic pursuits like painting and music. Similarly, many features don't seem to confer any advantage that natural selection could preserve, but rather seem to exist just for the sake of beauty.

Examples like these have been known since Darwin's day. He addressed this topic in his second book on evolution, *The Descent of Man*, attributing many such extravagances to sexual selection.[11] But he doesn't address the root problem of where these extravagances came from in the first place, or how or why these would be helpful in reproductive success. Why should a female prefer a more brightly colored male? Is there something in the DNA that drives this preference?

Modern evolutionists continue in this tradition, trying to explain such things through fantastical storytelling, mental gymnastics, and bizarre leaps of logic (and always short on concrete engineering details) as they force-fit all manner of traits into some imaginative survival or reproductive advantage.

A second problem is that "survival of the fittest" smacks of circularity. No one has proposed an objective metric for fitness, so if the starting proposition is survival of the fittest, then the survivors (whatever their particular traits) must be more fit. How do we know they're more fit? Because they survived! Logically, this reduces to "survival of the survivors"—a tautology. Darwinists minimize this embarrassing aspect of the theory by steering away from populist "survival of the fittest" talk and using the more technical language of population genetics, stressing differential survival rates and such, but it remains an awkwardness in the theory.

Third, and more fundamentally, selecting is not the same as generating. Even at its most capable, natural selection cannot generate anything new. It can only select from what's given to it. So no amount of selecting can, by itself, generate a coherent system. In the Darwinian model, the initial generating can only be done by random mutations.

Fourth, how can nature *select* anything? Selecting is an act of intention, and nature lacks the wherewithal to intend. Selection implies agency, but the theory allows no room for agency. This objection might be dismissed as a semantic quibble, but it speaks to Darwin's (and subsequent Darwinists') desire to smuggle agency into the theory, while categorically stating that the theory requires no such agency. Even Darwin, later in his life, admitted that a more appropriate term would have been *natural preservation*.[12] Thus, it appears to be a rhetorical attempt to have the cake and eat it too.

Finally, while the forces of nature cannot select anything, they continually constrain everything. As we've shown, the hard problems that life must solve to be alive are almost entirely focused on overcoming the constraints imposed by nature—to meet the often severe demands of the laws of physics and chemistry, or of punishing swings in climactic temperature, or the challenges posed by drought or famine.

Thus, it's no surprise that mutations and other degradative defects often lead organisms to short lives and limited reproductive success. Just as with the Tacoma Narrows Bridge, it's not that nature is trying to winnow the field, but that these defects limit the organism's ability to survive against the constraints imposed on it by its environment.

By imposing constraints on living systems, nature might be said to weed out the defective, the weak, and the infirm (though "weeding out" is a misleading way to describe it). But nature is at a loss when it comes to invention and innovation.

Let's see how natural selection stacks up when we consider it in the light of our three characteristics:

- *Preconditions for Natural Selection:* Natural selection, to the extent that it can do anything, only works when an organism already exists (is alive) and is able to reproduce.

368 / <small>YOUR DESIGNED BODY</small> /

- *Capabilities of Natural Selection:* Nature, by constraining life, can preserve organisms that are already capable of being alive. When a degradation occurs that weakens an individual, that individual is less likely to survive or reproduce. By this means, it's theoretically possible that a certain amount of fine tuning can occur by natural forces.

- *Limitations of Natural Selection:* (1) Natural selection cannot "act" on a trait that offers no survival or reproductive benefit. (2) Natural selection cannot generate anything new. No innovations, no new coherent information, no new body plans, no new coherent systems, no new assembly instructions. (3) Natural selection cannot actually select. Nature can only enable and constrain.

Time

Even if random mutation and natural selection could generate and fine tune organisms, their primary means of doing so mainly involves mindless trial and error, so they would need a lot of time to do anything interesting. Unintentional, undirected forces are guaranteed to make a lot of wrong turns and follow many dead ends. If any non-trivial innovation is to happen, it will take lots of time.

No worries, Darwin thought. During his day, geology was providing evidence that Earth was millions, perhaps even billions of years old. That seems like a lot of time. But even several billion years would not be nearly enough. Given the probabilities discussed above, and as Douglas Axe showed through his laboratory experiments, it would take more than the probabilistic resources of the universe to randomly generate the modestly complex protein ß-lactamase, just 150 amino acids in length.[13]

And the human body has tens of thousands of hard-working proteins averaging around three times that length (450 amino acids long). Thus, if we generalize Axe's result, Darwinians must firmly believe in many, many, many orders of magnitude worth of happy accidents. (The reader is referred back to Laufmann's *Laws of Hard Problems*.)

A second and more difficult problem with time as a resource is that time is where entropy lives. Entropy wreaks havoc over long periods of time. For engineers, time is not a friend. With more time comes more degradation. With more degradation, systems break. So, given large spans of time, it's unlikely that anything living can survive, unless it's front-loaded with resilience capabilities that can deflect or correct degradation. But blind, trial-and-error groping cannot foresee or frontload. Designer-engineers can and do, but appeals to such are anathema to evolutionary theory.

Time is much, much better at breaking things than it is at making things. In many ways, then, time is yet another problem that life must solve, rather than a solution itself.

Again, an assessment using our three characteristics:

- *Preconditions for Time:* Time here is a shorthand for duration in a universe governed by regularities and initial conditions allowing for stars, planets, and a chemistry complex enough for organic life to even be theoretically possible. These regularities and initial conditions now appear so fortuitous that they are referred to as the "fine-tuning problem" in cosmology, and this fine-tuning evidence has led several leading physicists and astronomers, including Nobel Laureates, to argue that fine tuning points to a cosmic designer.
- *Capabilities of Time:* More time gives you more chances.
- *Limitations of Time:* Since the universe had a beginning and is finite in size, there are limited opportunities for chance events to occur.[14] More importantly, time is not a causal force, so time itself cannot generate anything. Further, more time provides more chances for degradation to occur.

Some Attractions of Darwinism

THOUGH A few materialistic theories of biological origins preceded Darwin's, his was the first to propose a specific mechanism for producing change over time in a population.[15] As there are countless examples of change over time, and no other seemingly viable natural mechanisms were proposed, his theory slowly gained traction in the scientific community, and eventually spread to the general population.

The theory has an attractive simplicity and elegance. It's easy to understand and on its surface seems plausible. It addresses changes in the fossil record, including the observation that life-forms become more complex over time.

Further, for those who desire the materialist worldview to be true, Darwinism offers three attractive perks. First, for many people, one of science's primary goals is to replace superstition with natural explanations. For them, any designer-engineer, especially a transcendent one, is a quaint superstition that should be displaced by materialist science. Darwinism restricts itself to natural explanations. Second, Darwinism is an enabler for scientism, the belief that science is the only path to true knowledge. This view is desirable to many people. Third, the theory is immensely attractive to those who would prefer that no God exist. As Richard Dawkins put it, "Although atheism might have been logically tenable before Darwin, Darwin made it possible to be an intellectually fulfilled atheist."[16] The desire for facts that align with a preconceived worldview can be a powerful motivator.

Darwin's Difficulties

THE FACTORS above help explain why Darwinism persists. But the theory also has deep-rooted issues and limitations. In fact, Darwin honestly discussed evidence contrary to his theory—what in *Origin* he calls "Difficulties on Theory."

Innovation Goes Missing

The first and most glaring difficulty with Darwin's theory is that, as Gerd B. Müller and Stuart Newman put it in a MIT Press book, "It completely avoids the origination of phenotypic traits and of organismal form. In other words, neo-Darwinism has no theory of the generative."[17] Müller, at the University of Vienna, a leader in the extended-evolutionary-synthesis movement, says that "selection has no innovative capacity" and "the generative and the ordering aspects of morphological evolution are thus absent from evolutionary theory."[18]

In other words, nothing in Darwin's theory can generate any non-trivial innovation. There's simply no combination of Darwinian causal forces or factors capable of overcoming any causal hurdle of more than trivial complexity. Even combined, and with billions of years at their disposal, Darwin's causal forces are much more likely to destroy potentially helpful changes long before enough changes can accumulate to add a useful new function.

Like the Mail, the Complexity Just Keeps Coming!

In the '90s sitcom *Seinfeld*, the mailman Newman (a fictional character, not to be confused with Stuart Newman, the biologist just cited!) explains why, from time to time, a mailman flips out and goes *postal*. "Because the mail never stops," he says. "It just keeps coming and coming and coming!"

Like the mail, our understanding of the true complexities of living systems just keeps coming and coming. And this has steadily eroded the plausibility of Darwin's causal explanations. For example, in Darwin's day no one knew much about the workings inside a cell. His go-to expert on cellular biology, G. H. Lewes, referred to the cell's internal contents as a "microscopic lump of jelly-like substance" with "no trace of organization."[19] Darwin accepted this view and famously proposed, in a private letter, that the first living organism arose by chance in some "warm little pond."[20] As we showed in Chapter 1, Lewes's understanding of the cell couldn't be further from the truth. The cell is a fantastically complex factory with thousands of specialized parts, precisely organized and perfectly orchestrated.

And that's just a cell. The human body has layers upon layers of coherent interdependent systems, and with each new discovery, there are more functions, more information, more coherent systems, more interdependencies, more fine tuning. The complexity increases monotonically—always revealing more.

Each new answer raises still more questions for evolutionary theory, but Darwin's cupboard is bare. The theory's causal tools are spent, unable to overcome the sheer force of the evidence building against it.

Bounded on All Sides

IN ORIGIN, Darwin offered no specific mechanism for variation. He assumed that living organisms have unbounded plasticity—that they can gradually change from anything into anything.

It's true that information storage in DNA is practically unbounded. As a four-value digital code, it can hold any digital information. Because of this, and its extreme compactness, computer scientists are researching ways to use DNA as a computer storage system.

But it's not true that just any random combination of information in DNA will code for a living system. The hard problems that life must solve act as bounding constraints on life. Life can only exist in a very small subset of the total possible arrangements of DNA or RNA or other information codes. Rather than possessing unbounded plasticity, then, life is effectively bounded on all sides. And this makes it extremely problematic for one organism to change into a completely different organism, regardless of the time allowed. There's simply no way to be alive in the in-between stages.

A Predictions Scorecard

Darwin's theory has also faltered in its predictions. For example, Darwin predicted large numbers of intermediate forms, even though in his day the fossil record showed that most new body plans appeared suddenly, usually with no observable precursors. He placed his hope in future fossil discoveries to find the vast number of intermediate forms that his gradualistic theory predicts, and thereby validate it. Instead, a century-and-a-half of additional fossil discoveries has only confirmed the pattern that challenged Darwin's theory in the first place.

Counterintuitive

Darwin's theory is and has always been counterintuitive. Many people have an innate sense that there's more to a living creature than Darwinism alone can explain. It's hard to imagine in detail how any series of undirected accidents, in the absence of intention, could build anything like the human body, or even a molecular machine such as an ATP synthase. Obviously, common sense is not the final arbiter of truth, but it suggests that there may be a fundamental weakness in the theory and that, at the very least, it should not be embraced dogmatically.

Selecting for Death

Darwin showed a certain rhetorical genius in coining the term "natural selection"—implying agency, even while disclaiming it. The term was intended to explicitly place nature in the role of an animal breeder (an intentional actor). But the breeder's "artificial selection" is intentional.

In fact, there seems to be a limit to how far a creature's genes can bend before they break. Some species, like dogs, have enormous plasticity in their genes, but no dog breeder has so far made a distinct new species, much less an entirely new body plan. In fact, there's evidence that many of the variations in modern dogs are due to genetic degradations from the wild type they're derived from.

In evolutionary terms, nature can "do" just one thing—constrain life.[21] The environment, rather than shaping living things, simply provides the set of problems that life must solve. It can do nothing to help the organisms solve those problems. Instead, nature drives all systems toward equilibrium. Equilibrium sounds peaceful enough, but as we've seen, equilibrium with the environment means death.

So, to the extent that nature is able to select for anything, it selects everything for death. Only the internal capabilities of organisms can prevent that. And even then, only for a while.

Hard Problems

IF WE compare the prerequisites above to the hard problems as presented in these pages, it's clear that Darwin's causal factors have two additional problems, which together seem insurmountable.

First, the two hardest problems life must solve—maintaining a separate equilibrium (being alive) and reproduction (making a living copy)—must be solved *before* Darwinian causal factors can do anything. As we've shown, these are never trivial problems. Not even for the simplest bacteria.

Second, on the whole, Darwin's causal factors are not the solutions to life's problems; they are themselves problems that life must solve. Life must solve the problems that nature presents. It must be able to make a living copy of itself. It must overcome the degradations of random mutations. And it must thrive over long periods of time, even when entropy beckons.

Gradualism Revisited

DARWINIAN GRADUALISM is a sort of inevitable mashup of Darwin's four causal factors. When you look at the whole, gradualism is what you see. But we've shown that systems and subsystems in the body profoundly challenge gradualism. In particular, no system with non-trivial coherence can be built gradually, if it has to be alive at each step along the way, because it won't live long enough to reproduce.

For example, how would a creature control its salt content while it's waiting for a complete salt control system to gradually evolve and finally come online? Out-of-control salt is a killer. How many generations would be required to persist without a functioning salt control system? So, the only way to get a salt control system is to control your salt while you're waiting for a salt control system to evolve.

Logically, the only exception is where a protective system is in place to keep partial solutions from being destroyed while the whole waits to be completed. This by itself is a tall order. And more to the point, it smacks of foresight, planning, and clever engineering—reviving the problem that Darwinism was supposed to solve in the first place.

Coherence is a qualitative problem and holds true regardless of the amount of time that may or may not be available. While gradual causation may be able to make small-scale tweaks and refinements to an existing system, it can never overcome non-trivial coherence to make a new coherent system.

As a causal process, then, Darwinian gradualism fails.

Growing Discontent in the Ranks

Issues like these are thorny and increasingly hard to ignore, leading a growing number of evolutionary biologists to seek out add-ons or extensions to neo-Darwinism and even to openly express their discontent with neo-Darwinism.

Several variations have sprung up from the efforts to rescue modern evolutionary theory. Could one of them overcome the limitations of neo-Darwinism? A detailed exploration of these variations takes us beyond the scope of this book. But consider one popular variation, called neutral evolution, which relies less on natural selection. Instead, it proposes random, non-selectable allele variation and genetic drift as the main drivers of change, at least at the molecular level. In essence, this approach posits that a lot of variations (alleles) in a given gene are neutral with respect to natural selection, so the sequence of the gene can take on different states and randomly drift in a population. These changes do not require a "selective advantage."

But this elaboration on Darwin's theory only addresses the molecular level, and downplays the only natural force available to Darwinism to preserve useful features: natural selection. In doing so, it leaves no reason why useful traits should evolve other than sheer dumb luck. Sheer dumb luck is never a good mechanism, especially when you're trying to engineer machines and systems more complicated than anything ever built by a human.

376 / Your Designed Body /

Indeed, by largely eschewing natural selection, the neutral model dismisses with the very thing about Darwinism that raised it above all the previous speculations about unguided evolution, providing a way to thresh random variations and nudge a population on an upward trajectory. In this, modern evolutionary theory can't seem to live with natural selection, and it can't live without it. It faces a pick-your-poison dilemma. Without natural selection, random variations wander aimlessly in astronomically big sequence space. With natural selection, organisms cannot take a vacation from functionality while a new organ or system is being engineered. It must maintain function at every step, a demand that proves a dealbreaker for assembling via blind processes the coherent and interdependent systems of systems required of even relatively simple life-forms. Attempts to forge some sort of hybrid model, with neutral evolution doing some of the work, and natural selection swooping in as needed, have failed.

The details of neutral theory are complicated, and the capabilities are still hotly debated in the evolutionary community, but there's nothing here that can overcome the causal hurdles described in these pages, or for any other type of organism for that matter.[22]

This is typical of the variations on neo-Darwinism. They tend to focus on modest variations on the broader themes introduced by Darwin, and none have any tools with greater capabilities or lesser limitations than what we covered above. And all remain strictly in Class 1 causality—that is, restricted to purely material causes.

And as their proponents cling to a materialist framework, the situation is becoming increasingly awkward as the evidence continues to skew away from Darwin.[23] For those with an allegiance to both the evidence and to Darwinian materialism, it's like the guy who, after untying his boat, finds himself with one foot on the dock and one foot in the boat. As the gap grows, the need to choose becomes increasingly hard to ignore. And uncomfortable. And temporary.

In the search for a new theoretical foundation, in 2016 the Royal Society convened a scientific meeting in London to explore neo-Darwinism's deficiencies and ideate about new theoretical possibilities—what they call a "third way,"[24] one that hews to the dictates of methodological materialism but that isn't restricted to the neo-Darwinian causal mechanisms.

Gerd Müller, emeritus biologist at the University of Vienna, opened the conference by asserting that the modern synthesis "does not explain" what he terms "complex levels of evolution" including "the origin of... body plans" or "complex behaviors, complex physiology" and "development." According to Müller, the modern theory of evolution "is focused on characters that exist already and their variation and maintenance across populations, but not on how they originate." In his view, the standard model is "not" even "designed for addressing" questions like the origin of novelty.[25]

Neo-Darwinism "ignores much contemporary molecular evidence and invokes a set of unsupported assumptions about the accidental nature of hereditary variation," comments University of Chicago microbiologist James Shapiro and his colleagues at the Third Way website. They continue:

> Neo-Darwinism ignores important rapid evolutionary processes such as symbiogenesis, horizontal DNA transfer, action of mobile DNA and epigenetic modifications. Moreover, some Neo-Darwinists have elevated Natural Selection into a unique creative force that solves all the difficult evolutionary problems without a real empirical basis. Many scientists today see the need for a deeper and more complete exploration of all aspects of the evolutionary process.[26]

At its end, the Royal Society conference had laid out many detailed challenges to neo-Darwinism but came up empty in the search for a new theoretical foundation.[27]

A Few Thoughts

NOT ONLY did Darwin honestly discuss "Difficulties on Theory," he also offered a way to falsify his theory: "If it could be demonstrated that any complex organ existed, which could not possibly have been formed by numerous, successive, slight modifications, my theory would absolutely break down. But I can find out no such case."[28]

A lot has changed since Darwin's day. Where he could see no such case, we've explored many dozens of examples in the human body of systems that cannot reasonably be attributed to any gradual evolutionary process, in any timeframe, even if they were designed. In fact, given the kinds of causal hurdles in the human body and in all other living things that we know of, we can't find any organ or system of significance, in all of life, that could have been created gradually, one small step at a time.

In the end, then, it appears that Darwin failed to accomplish the main thing he set out to accomplish in his 1859 work—to explain the origin of species. Darwinism, together with every other theory that relies on intention-free gradualism, has failed—by Darwin's own explicit test. Or as Michael Denton put it, only slightly more gently, evolution is "a theory in crisis."[29]

For modern evolutionary theory, the causal hurdles continue to grow, in both number and magnitude. But the materialist's causal toolbox does not. If the Darwinian story ever seemed sufficient, it doesn't any longer. As a theory, Darwinism is a spent force.

So we find ourselves in an odd place with respect to biological causal theories. The evidence is skewing away from the dominant theory, but there's no acceptable new theory to take the place of the old. As of this writing, no materialist theory in the pipeline has the potential to fill neo-Darwinism's shoes.[30]

But when we let the evidence determine what is and isn't acceptable rather than being guided by a question-begging methodological rule, we find a much more interesting—and as we will argue, fruitful—way to think about these things.

22. Toward a Theory of Biological Design

When a scientific problem seems impossible to solve, it may be that a bad assumption—either implicit or explicit—is constraining our search space. In these instances, we need to think outside the box.

—Itai Yanai and Martin J. Lercher[1]

DURING THE 1984 SUPER BOWL, APPLE COMPUTER AIRED ITS NOW famous "1984" commercial. In a takeoff of George Orwell's dystopian novel *1984*, Big Brother is speaking on a large TV screen viewed by a gray army of bald-headed minions. As he drones on about pure ideology and unification of thought, an athletic blond woman wearing a bright white shirt and red shorts runs into the auditorium wielding a large sledgehammer. There's nothing gray about her. She's being chased by the Thought Police. Just as Big Brother declares, "We shall prevail!" the runner flings the sledgehammer at the screen, which explodes, leaving the audience in shock and presumably destroying Big Brother's stranglehold on "truth."[2]

In sixty seconds Apple went from being a small, geeky computer company to a national household name. The commercial captured the public's imagination and solidified Apple's branding for disruptive forward-thinking and human-centered technology. The original idea of the ad was that these new, small, and inexpensive computers would enable individuals to achieve their potential. But there is a broader point. Sometimes the dominant paradigm needs to be challenged—particularly when it has been weighed in the balances and found wanting. And dehumanizing.

Modern evolutionary theory is such a paradigm.

Think Different

THE CAUSAL capabilities of modern evolutionary theory leave much to be desired. Surely there must be a good way to explain the origin of the human body—one that better comports with the evidence. After all, we're here, so we must have gotten here somehow. To get better answers, though, we'll need to do more than just repair the old theory.

To improve on current evolutionary theory, a potential replacement must be causally sufficient—able to generate innovations in discrete leaps large enough to overcome the causal hurdles that stand in the way—to achieve coherence, interdependence, and dynamic capacity management. It also must be able to generate major leaps in body plans fast enough to align with the fossil record's pattern of sudden appearances of nearly all major body innovations. And it must be able to generate the vast array of complex specified information and the precision-defined mechanisms and machines underlying all these capabilities.

In short, any new theory will need to better explain the data, using one or more types of causes known to be capable of such outcomes. As a bonus, it also would be nice if the alternative causal explanation was intuitive and had a simplicity and elegance to rival Darwin's theory.

A Better Way

TO THIS end, a new framework is being developed to apply systems engineering thinking to living organisms—a framework that takes an outlook at least as old as Plato and updates it from a modern systems perspective. It's still early times for this work, but already there is evidence that this approach offers more compelling answers to the hard problems of the body's origins. This approach offers not only a better explanation for the origin and properties of living systems, but also a potentially more powerful predictive framework for biological and medical discovery.

In our brief overview of this theory, we'll mainly employ engineering terminology. The more we learn about biology, the more apparent it becomes that organisms are replete with exquisitely engineered solutions to hard problems. Also, the field of engineering addresses the same types of problems organisms must solve to be alive, and indeed, engineering language is uniquely suited for talking about these concepts. In fact, engineering language has become nearly ubiquitous in the biology research literature. In a curious twist, contemporary biologists cannot help but use engineering and design language, even as many of them persist in the view that none of what they're describing was actually engineered.

The Framework

THE DESIGN view has been widely held for millennia. Both Plato and Moses saw the design in living organisms. But after Darwin published *The Origin of Species*, evolution by natural selection began slowly to replace design as the dominant view of life's origins.

In the 1980s and 1990s, the modern intelligent design community took shape, drawing on recent scientific discoveries to argue that certain features of the natural world, and especially living systems, are best explained by reference to the work of a designing mind. The outcome has been a solid and increasingly fleshed-out case, based on the best data available, that life was designed.

And now that work is being extended and enriched by a theory of biological design informed by systems engineering—to explore the properties and principles of life's design, and how the design has played out over time. The new framework is conceptually simple. Living organisms are designed (and engineered) to occupy a specific range of environments. Each has the innate, pre-programmed capabilities it needs to adjust and adapt relatively quickly, as needed, within that range. Adjustments can be external, like changing colors, growing longer limbs, or having thicker beaks (how things look, which is relatively easy to observe), or the adjustments can be internal, like switching to an alternate metabolic pathway in response to a different food source (how things work, which is harder to observe). Further, each organism has adaptive resilience, to maintain its life and form over many generations.

On this view, the history of life is the unfolding interplay of four major causal factors:

- *Intentional Acts*: One or more designer-engineers have operated in space-time history to generate new body plans and novel features and, as part of that work, infused life with new information, specialized parts, organizational patterns, and process orchestrations.

- *Internal Adaptations*: Each organism has built-in capabilities for resilience and adaptation. Most of these involve controls to effect regulated change—sensing (typically of both internal and external stimuli), control logic (to decide how to respond), and effectors (to make appropriate internal changes). Such adaptations may be in function, or process, or any other relevant characteristic, including appearance.

- *Design Properties*: Every organism exhibits internal architecture—the patterns by which it's designed, assembled, and operated. Certain architectural principles and design patterns promote change, while others inhibit change. Thus, the architecture of a given organism constrains the ways it may change over time and defines the difficulties and costs associated with those changes.

- *Degradation*: Natural forces (like entropy) work constantly against living systems, continually pushing them toward equilibrium with the environment (death). Each living organism must actively counter these forces, else its life will cease. Further, it will be necessary to counter these forces across generations if a species is to last long.

As it turns out, engineers have deep experience with each of these factors. We know what each does and doesn't do. We know how each works. We know the limitations of each. We recognize the artifacts of each, and we know what happens to these artifacts over time.

In what ways might some or all these causal factors have combined to make the human body, or the millions of other known species? Let's see how these work.

Assessing the Four Factors

WHILE CONCEPTUALLY simple, the ways these four factors might have played out in the history of life are neither simple nor easy to predict. But we can make some educated inferences. Let's assess the four factors noted above and for each consider its (1) preconditions, (2) capabilities, and (3) limitations.

Intentional Acts

In artificial intelligence (AI) research during the 1980s, there was a rubric for modeling rational agents called BDI: belief-desire-intention.[3] In this approach, an actor *believes* that a specific state exists in the world (through sensors, for example), *desires* a different state for that world (one or more specific goals), then builds and acts on a plan (*intention*) to change the world from the current (believed) state to the future (desired) state.

This simple model usefully describes how intelligent agents work. The agent assesses the state of some aspect of the world, imagines it being different, and then acts to make the changes necessary to achieve the imagined state of affairs.

This causal force is simple and intuitive. People understand it because each of us does this hundreds of times every day. This is what happens when we decide to wash the dishes. This is how lumber is made from trees, and how a house is made from the lumber. This is where lawnmowers and iPhones and Atlas rockets come from. This form of causality is firmly in Class 2, intelligent causation. Simple, effective, immensely capable, not generally repeatable, and most definitely beyond the creative reach of anything in Class 1's material causes.

The BDI model illustrates the ways that an actor's capabilities can be limited—in any of the three stages (sense, plan, act). The actor's view of the world may be incorrect. The actor may not be able to design a workable new state for the world. Or the actor's plan may fail, either because the plan was flawed or because the actor lacks the ability to produce the desired outcome.

In contrast to the neo-Darwinian causal mechanisms, which work gradually over eons of time, intentional actions are able, as a matter of course, to quickly effect usefully large changes to generate coherent interdependent systems.

- *Preconditions for Intentional Acts*: To act intentionally, there must be a being—a consciousness or mind or intelligence—an entity capable of being *about* something, one capable of foresight, of setting goals, and of planning. Notably, the plan doesn't need to include a precise outcome, but may simply be directional or a set of rules to constrain an outcome. There are other preconditions. A highly capable actor would require fewer preconditions. A less capable actor, more.

- *Capabilities of Intentional Acts*: Intentional acts are capable of being about distant goals. An agent of sufficient intelligence and power can foresee possibilities, pursue a distant goal and, in so doing, bring together and reshape a wide diversity of parts in pursuit of that goal.

- *Limitations of Intentional Acts:* Intentional action is limited by either or both of two considerations: the actor's capacity to design innovative solutions, or the actor's ability to carry out the plan to achieve the desired state of affairs. Thus, an actor may have the know-how to design a solution to a given problem but lack the power to implement it. Or the actor may have the power to implement a solution but lack the know-how to design the solution. Or the actor may lack both.

Internal Adaptations

Unless dead or dying, all organisms possess adaptations needed to solve the natural hurdles to life in some form or fashion. These internal adaptations usually involve, among others, sensing, logic and rules, and programs.

To stay alive, most organisms will need to monitor and adapt to changes in both their internal states and their external conditions. As with all controls, these will require specific sensors, logic, and effectors. This is known as regulated change.

A growing range of effects have been documented in various species, from changes in metabolic processes as available food sources change, to morphological adjustments, like changing the length of a lizard's legs when it needs to avoid thorns on its food plants.

Some variations occur during an individual's lifetime. Of these, some can be passed through epigenetic signals to an individual's offspring (not yet well understood), and some may involve changes (edits?) at the genetic level. The latter is a form of what's been called natural genetic engineering, wherein the organism changes its own DNA.[4]

In an interesting case of adaptation, certain cephalopods (squid, octopus, and cuttlefish) can change almost instantly by editing their own messenger RNA (mRNA) in real time, outside their cells' nuclei. While these processes are not yet well understood, they enable surprising capabilities and challenge neo-Darwinian assumptions.[5]

These adaptive control systems are fully internal. The organism is the agent of change in the case of this mechanism.

Such regulated changes require a coherent adaptive control system. Because these are mostly non-trivial, and coherent, it's likely they were built into the organism by intentional action, but they play out solely through the agency of the organism itself—as an organic result of working through the internal control logic and effectors of the organism. These internal control systems and programming are front-loaded into the organism but play out over time in ways that may not be strictly preordained.

Taken together, an organism's adaptive control systems define the range of variations available to that organism.[6] An organism's range of effects place de facto limits on what it can become and, thus, on what environments it can survive in.

The net effect is that each organism is designed (and outfitted with the requisite internal adaptation mechanisms) for a specific range of environments. This might work something like a rubber band. As the organism's adaptations move away from its particular "sweet spot" or optimal state, the rubber band stretches and wants to draw the organism back to its optimal state. The further the rubber band is stretched, the more it wants to return to its optimal state. Though the jury is still out on this point, there is preliminary evidence that observed changes in populations often revert to their original state when the environment changes back—when the constraints placed on the organism revert to their prior condition.[7]

Critically, an organism's adaptive "range of effects" is built into the organism before it encounters a situation that requires those effects. In the most general case, to survive, the organism must be ready for challenges it has not seen before. In contrast, if the organism were required to randomly find a solution to a new metabolic problem at the time it encountered the problem, it would long be dead before a solution appeared.

One further effect to note: organisms face challenges as part of a larger population, within a diverse ecosystem. The ways that an organism's range of internal adaptations might interact with the internal adaptations of others is often unpredictable, at least to our complexity-limited minds.

Fashioning the systems necessary for internal adaptations requires, we have argued, Class 2 (intentional) input, including foresight and planning. But how these internal adaptations work over time results from their built-in rules, logic, and internal constraints, and from how they interact with the internal traits and capabilities of other organisms. And that leads to "organic" outcomes aligned with Class 1.

- *Preconditions for Internal Adaptations*: An organism's internal adaptations—that is, a capacity for regulated changes—require a front-loaded system of sensors, logic, and effectors.
- *Capabilities of Internal Adaptations*: The capabilities of this causal factor depend on the specific programming and adaptive systems built into the organism. Different organisms will have widely varying capacities for regulated change.
- *Limitations of Internal Adaptations*: The limitations of this causal factor also depend on the specific programming and adaptive systems built into the organism. Different organisms will have widely varying limitations on what regulated change is possible. That being said, the kinds of challenges this causal factor can respond to are strictly limited even in the most flexible of cases. If an organism is faced with environmental challenges beyond the range of what its internal adaptational mechanisms allow for, it will die. In general, internal adaptations that afford regulated change cannot generate substantially new organs, machinery, or functions.

We expect that most observed changes in living systems will be explained by this causal factor—a population changing in exactly the ways it's pre-programmed to change given the appropriate circumstances. The vast majority of cases where we see "evolution happening before our eyes" will turn out simply to be organisms sensing and adapting to changes in their environment using their built-in adaptive capabilities, though perhaps in ways that we don't expect.

Design Properties

Every living system exhibits some kind of design architecture. Living systems incorporate the best-known design principles with dozens of recurring design patterns. These principles and patterns dictate the level of effort required to change the system. Certain architectural principles and design patterns promote change, while others inhibit change. For example, modular design makes change easier to accomplish, while complex orchestrations (between many modules, for example) make change harder.

Further, the body's systems are organized hierarchically. Larger problems are broken into smaller subproblems, which are broken into still smaller subproblems (separation of concerns). The solutions to the smallest problems are composed into solutions to the next higher layer of problems, and so on (the rule of composition). And *voilà*, you have a design hierarchy.

Composition combines modules (standardized components), using coordination interfaces and mechanisms, to organize and orchestrate a solution to the higher-level problem or problems. This is the point at which a layer's coherence and interdependencies are defined.

The composition model is widely used in industry. It's how software developers compose different programs, by reusing the same software modules (for example, from a shared software library). In a similar way, automobile manufacturers will compose their vehicle doors by reusing the same door handles on many different vehicle models.

Interestingly, a recent study shows that the distribution of functions across species aligns much better with a composition model than with a strictly Darwinian inheritance model.[8] In Darwinism, an organism gets its traits through inheritance from its parent or parents. In a composition model, a system (including an organism) can also receive traits through other means, like horizontal gene transfer or mobile DNA.[9] But just as in industry, the best designers intentionally design their systems through a process that involves composition (among other tools). Whether the composition of modern organisms is based strictly on Class 2 factors, or on some combination of Class 2 factors and organic change over time (Class 1 factors), is not known but certainly invites fascinating new research. We predict other Class 1 functional composition mechanisms will be discovered, even as the evidence for Class 2 causation continues to grow.

Consideration of design principles leads to interesting observations. For example, a nut and bolt have quite general and reusable functions as fasteners. But their purpose is assigned to them when they're used to attach a wheel to a lawnmower. Their purpose is defined at the level above their function in the design hierarchy.

> **The Function/Purpose Axiom:** In a design hierarchy, the *function* of a module or component is defined at one level, while the *purpose* of that module or component is defined by the composition, or the ways that function is used, at the level above that function in the design hierarchy.

Given that modularity makes change easier and complex orchestrations make change harder, what's the final impact on a particular living thing's capacity for change? The outcomes from these forces are difficult to predict, but the interplay of these principles likely has enabled, and set the bounds for, much of the variation we see in life.

> **The Modularity/Orchestration Axiom:** When modules have relatively simple interfaces (modularity dominates orchestration), the net effect will be more change over time, with greater diversity of results. When modules have more complex interfaces and orchestrations (orchestration dominates modularity), the net effect will be far fewer and less dramatic changes.

The modularity/orchestration axiom shows how the design principles of life can lead in some cases to high rates of change, while in other cases to low rates of change and, for certain systems, complete stasis. Stasis should dominate in especially large and complex systems, such as we find in abundance in the human body.

- *Preconditions for Design Properties*: Design properties require an overarching design, which in turn requires an intentional designer capable of foresight and planning.
- *Capabilities of Design Properties*: The design properties of an organism are, of course, crucial to its capacity to survive, thrive, and reproduce in its environment. But a population's design properties may also afford it a capacity for a limited degree of change over time.
- *Limitations of Design Properties*: Certain architectural principles and patterns inhibit the capacity to change over time. The more complex the interfaces and orchestrations of an organism's subsystems, the less it can change over time on its own.

The architecture of a system, as we have argued, results from the foresight and planning of its designer, which would place the origin of the architecture in Class 2 of causal forces. But the ways an organism's design properties constrain and afford change in the history of life is organic. So once again we get a combination of intentional and organic causality.

In light of this study of the architectural principles observed in life, we anticipate that these design principles will increasingly be recognized as a key driver in the ways organisms change, or don't change, over time.

Degradation

Darwin put great faith in the power of time and random variation to generate innovation, but engineers have developed great faith in the power of time and random events to turn working systems into non-working systems. It doesn't take an engineer to know this—it's our universal shared experience. It happens to your TV set, your car, your home, and your body. Like everything else that is organized (at least in the physical universe), life tends to slide downhill, toward disorganization and equilibrium with the environment.

Why, then, hasn't physical degradation long ago wiped out the human race? Degradation is always lurking, so the fact that our species persists (several billion of us and counting) suggests that there are other systems actively combating the degradation of the human species. This must surely include actively preventing, pruning, or correcting many types of chance-driven degradation.

And what is true of the human species is true of other populations. This is quite an extraordinary thing. All living things must have some internal means or mechanisms (or adaptive capabilities) that assist in this regard, else they would be extinct by now. Though few details are well understood, these must surely include active controls, with all their attendant parts.

Yes, genetic diseases and dysfunctions happen. But given the persistent and ubiquitous power of degradation over all things physical, the operative question is why they don't happen much, much more often.

Finally, there are cases in the history of life where a degradation at the level of the information coding (in RNA or DNA or an epigenetic code) results in a net benefit to an organism. Several such cases have been reported, though it's not clear whether these were caused by truly random errors, or by some internal capability for finding a solution to a previously unencountered problem, analogous to the way your adaptive immune system works. But so far, the reported changes seem to be relatively simple (for example, changing a bear's fur from brown to white).

- *Preconditions for Degradation*: What we call degradation only makes sense in the context of a coherent, working system, such as we find examples of in human technology (e.g., houses, cars, airplanes), animal architecture (spiderwebs, beehives, and bird nests), and living systems.
- *Capabilities of Degradation*: While degradatory changes are expected to be relatively small at the coding level, changes to the organism from even small coding changes can be catastrophic.
- *Limitations of Degradation*: Degradation can only change functions or features that exist. It cannot build fundamentally

novel forms, systems, or even subsystems. It is a tinkerer and, at its most impactful, a destructive one.

Degradation can take many forms, with varying effects on an organism's ability to thrive in a given environment. Some organisms may need all their adaptive front-loaded capabilities just to counter the forces of degradation. We anticipate that the future holds many surprises for researchers studying the ways various organisms fend off the forces of degradation.

Important Events in History

A HELPFUL way to think about Class 1 (material) and Class 2 (intentional) causes, and about the four causal factors reviewed above, is to consider them in the light of history as a temporal accumulation of three basic types of events:

- *Insertion Events*: These insert new information into a system, for a net gain of information.
- *Neutral Events*: These change the information in a system in ways that lead to no net increase or decrease. In the case of an organism, these may be produced as an organism makes regulated changes to adapt to a new situation.
- *Degradatory Events*: These degrade or remove existing information from a system, for a net loss of information.

This rubric is helpful in asking certain questions: What type of causes or causal forces are good candidates for insertion events? What type of causes or causal forces are good candidates for neutral events? And what type of causes or causal forces are good candidates for degradatory events?

What about the Fossil Record?

WHILE THIS book is primarily concerned with the evidence from living systems, and particularly the human body, it's worth pausing to make a few brief observations about the fossil record.

The fossil record is the best physical record we have about the history of life, but there are many important details it will not provide, despite the valiant efforts of paleontologists. Because the history of life we find in the fossil record is literally set in stone, the fossils can't tell most of the details of how the bodies of these creatures functioned. The work of paleontologists has, however, allowed us to glean a few general trends—both from what's there for us to see, and from what's not there.

- New body plans and novel features don't appear gradually in the fossil record. They arrive suddenly and generally without precursor. There are currently believed to have been more than a dozen major radiations (with the Cambrian explosion being the most famous), during which all known body plans and fundamental features appear suddenly.[10]

- Between the advent of a form and its extinction, the fossil record paints a picture of a given biological form changing only within very strict limits. This pattern is known as stasis. Stephen Jay Gould and Niles Eldredge recognized this pattern, calling it punctuated equilibrium.[11]

- There is no evidence that any living thing has ever existed that is not fully coherent. Even the simplest fossil organisms provide no reason to doubt this.

- Earth's population of living forms has progressed from simpler to more complex over the history of life. Many attribute this to an unguided evolutionary process, but given the impassable casual hurdles facing blind evolution in constructing the coherent and interdependent systems of systems necessary to life at every level, other possibilities should be considered. Could this progression be so that earlier, simpler forms prepare the environment for the more complex later forms? Maybe organisms shape the environment more than the environment shapes the organisms. Could the simpler organisms be the designer-engineer's means for terraforming the planet—for instance, to establish the oxygen levels needed for later creatures, including humans?

- Transitional forms are absent from the fossil record. Neo-Darwinian theory expects to find untold millions of transitional forms scattered about in the history of life. Paleontologists have been unable to find anything of the kind, and it isn't for lack of trying. While a handful of supposed transitional forms are commonly touted, these generally come with minimal evidence and considerable controversy. But even if we were to grant all these for the sake of argument, it's far from enough. Some insist that the transitional forms are missing simply because the fossil record is incomplete, but it's mighty curious that the transitional forms seem to always hide in the parts of the fossil record that remain undiscovered.

- The scientific literature reports a major fossil gap between non-humans and *Homo erectus*, the earliest group in the genus *Homo* that is strikingly similar to modern humans. Fossilized hominids generally either are small-brained knuckle-walkers, with dramatic physiological and capacity differences from humans, or they are very human-like—including a physiology fully engineered for efficient bipedal walk, a brain size within the modern range, and exhibiting evidence of human-level intelligence. Evolutionists have tried to shrink this massive gulf with exaggerated artist renderings that make early humans look more ape-like than the evidence supports, and by depicting some fully ape-like hominids more human-like than the evidence supports. Moreover, despite the many breathless reports to the contrary in the popular press, in which all manner of fossils are heralded as the so-called "missing link" between humans and their pre-human ancestors, there are no uncontroversial and clearly intermediate pre-human ancestor fossils.[12]

- Setting aside relatively minor variations in species that could be characterized as isolated breeds or subspecies, humans appear to be the last dramatically new creature to appear in the fossil record.

The theory of biological design is fully consistent with these patterns in the fossil record, since the framework easily accounts for (1) sudden appearance of new body plans and features, (2) the fossil pattern showing a progression of discrete jumps from simpler to more sophisticated, and (3) long periods of stasis.

Evaluating the Framework

EACH OF the four causal factors described above is conceptually simple. But when we consider them together, and factor in environmental effects and the programmed interactions between organisms within a given ecosystem across historical timeframes, the complexities of biological change over time become much more interesting.

In this light, we begin to appreciate the complexities involved in distinguishing intentional effects from organic effects. Intentional effects are the direct results of intentional acts, like adding information to a system or generating a novel feature (both of which would presumably involve "insertion events," as discussed above). Organic effects are what happens when systems run on their own, based on the defined boundaries, rules, and programming built into an organism (which, in our model, are understood as the effects of intentional acts), or the collective internal programming of many organisms within an (eco)system.

As illustrated in Figure 22.1, these effects will combine over time to produce interesting outcomes—outcomes that are not strictly predefined, and which may be unpredictable (at least without mathematical superpowers). Some observed effects may be completely attributable to direct intentional acts, while others are completely organic, like random degradation events caused by, for example, stray gamma rays. But in most cases, the observed effects will be attributable to a combination of intentional and organic causes—where changes in either the environ-

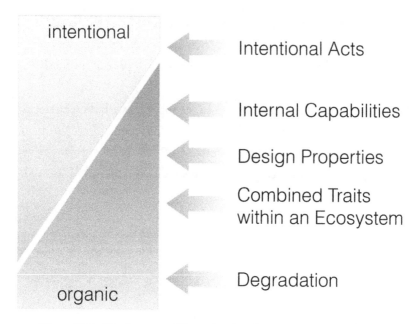

Figure 22.1. The impacts of intentional and organic causation (causal factors) on the history of life, including the effects of change within a larger ecosystem.

ment or in other creatures in the vicinity are sensed and acted on by the organisms present in the ecosystem, using their front-loaded, innate capabilities.[13]

To the extent this theory is correct, it will be difficult (but not impossible) to tease apart the ways these factors combine. Could these effects, combined, have resulted in the enormous diversity of living creatures and plants that we observe? We predict such questions will motivate many fruitful research programs in the future, though we can predict only in general terms what results will be found.

So we'll leave these questions as food for thought and return to our main concern: What are the strengths and potential difficulties of our nascent theoretical framework?

Why it Works

The design-engineering theoretical framework limned in these pages offers a much richer and more capable set of creative tools than a Darwinian materialistic framework. These tools offer a strong theory of the generative since they are fully capable of overcoming all the causal hurdles explored in these pages, and of generating coherent interdependent systems.

The theory is conceptually simple. It incorporates specific mechanisms of change, and these mechanisms are easy to understand. It gets complicated only in how the mechanisms interact.

The framework aligns well with the complexities we see in life. The framework's primary sources of capability and change, in combination, allow for far greater complexity in outcomes, and in much less time, meaning it's also capable of generating enormous diversity. Some of these adaptations may not have been specifically demanded by the original design but were enabled by the boundaries and rules of the design.

The design-engineering framework comports with the biological and medical research data on the human body. It aligns with the immense engineering complexity and coherence of living systems. And it has the potential to predict future discoveries all the way down the design hierarchy, into the physics and chemistry that undergird life. The framework also aligns well with the human design intuition, common across human cultures and generations and shared by almost everyone (until they're trained to not see it).

The framework predicts the key observations from the fossil record (listed above), notably including the rapid appearance of essentially all major body plans and innovations, and the stasis that characterizes the periods between radiations of new innovations.

In direct opposition to Darwin's approach of personifying nature and mechanizing humans, the design-engineering framework personifies humans and permits the forces of nature to remain un-personified.

Importantly, this theory leaves room to understand our human experience as real rather than illusory. It's no longer necessary to reduce all human experience to chemical reactions in the brain, or to force-fit all human behaviors and experiences, like love and altruism, into a survival-and-reproduction framework. The intent behind an organism's design may have involved considerations beyond mere survival utility, like beauty just for beauty's sake. Simply put, there's room in this framework for us humans to see ourselves as human, possessing freedom and a higher purpose, rather than as mere meat-based automatons.

Difficulties on Theory

While the design-engineering framework has the properties of a good theory, it will nonetheless be controversial in many quarters, since it relies on the intentional acts of a master designer-engineer in the history of life, and such thoughts are not allowed in today's scientistic culture. But why? It's certainly not because the data overwhelmingly support modern evolutionary theory. The evidence seems to support the design-engineering framework much better. Rather, this seems to be mainly a worldview issue. The theory of biological design flies in the face of materialist presuppositions.

Other potential detractors have a theistic framework, but when they do science they restrict themselves to the rule of methodological naturalism, according to which science can only consider purely material explanations (Class 1 causes) in its investigations of the natural world. Intentional actors need not apply. Put simply, our framework steps beyond the rule of methodological naturalism, a move that in some researchers' eyes is an unforgivable methodological sin.

However, to do science properly, it seems more reasonable to follow the evidence wherever it leads, regardless of any prior worldview commitment or methodological dictate. And the theory of biological design is offering increasing evidence that its approach is the better one, as it offers both better answers to longstanding questions, and better questions for future research.

Finally, the only real weakness in this framework that we can see is that it's still early days for it. It will take long and hard work to turn this into a mature theory. It will undoubtedly be modified and improved along the way. But that's also a strength, since it means many of the findings lie over the horizon, awaiting enterprising and capable scientific investigators to discover them.

Final Thoughts

We grouped all causes into two jointly exhaustive categories. Class 1 causes are purely material causes, lacking foresight and intention. Class 2 causes are intentional causes. The causal hurdles explored in *Your Designed Body* are real and substantial. Intelligent agency (Class 2 causation) regularly surmounts hurdles of this kind in designing and engineering systems. In contrast, Class 1 causal forces, by themselves, have never been shown to overcome such hurdles. While they've long been hypothesized to have such capabilities, such capabilities have never been observed in them. Many experiments have shown that organisms change, but no experiment has demonstrated that the change was caused by purely mindless, material forces.

So for those who wish to claim Class 1 is causally sufficient to engineer life's diversity of organisms, or even just the human body—the burden to demonstrate Class 1's sufficiency falls to you.

Since Darwinian materialists seek to wholly exclude intentional design from a comprehensive explanation for the origin of life's diversity, they would do well to eventually show how purely material processes could gradually build up, over generations, every known biological system and subsystem, including the many examples we've presented in the human body. But lest we come across as piling on, we suggest a more modest challenge to start things off: provide a detailed step-by-step pathway of even just one complex new organ, system, or subsystem discussed in these pages—where each step uses only a small, random change, and with no wishful thinking, no stretches of debilitating dysfunction, and no magic along the way.

We predict that no evolutionist will meet this challenge, or even come close, in the next twenty years, two hundred years, or ever. Not because the evolutionists lack pluck or intelligence, but for the same reason that even the most brilliant mathematician will never prove that Pi equals two, and the most brilliant engineer will never discover the engineering trick to building a perpetual motion machine. Evolutionists won't uncover any credible, causally adequate evolutionary pathways because none exist.

Anything short of the sort of demonstration urged above means that the Darwinists are asking us to trust that they'll eventually figure it out. This amounts to a promissory note, writ large. But given their inability to deliver a single such pathway even for a short enzyme cascade or complex molecular machine (never mind for a vastly more sophisticated animal system or subsystem), and given that evolutionary theory demands that untold millions of traversable evolutionary pathways exist, it's difficult to grant the Darwinists the fealty that many of them demand for their theory.

Finally, we anticipate that the theory of biological design will eventually, in a more mature form, replace Darwinism and its materialistic descendants. Because of the worldview implications, however, this may take a long while.

23. But What About All Those Botched Designs?

> If they can get you asking the wrong questions, they don't have to worry about answers.
>
> —Thomas Pynchon[1]

In 1935, famed comedian Jimmy Durante starred in a Broadway musical called *Jumbo*. In one scene, Durante leads a live elephant across the stage. A police officer stops him and asks, "What are you doing with that elephant?" Durante casually replies, "What elephant?"

If you know anything about Durante's comedic delivery, you'll know this bit always got laughs—so much so that Durante reprised the scene when the musical was made into a movie in 1962.

Elephants have long been used to make the point that some things are obvious to everyone—everyone except the foil. But sometimes obvious things do get missed, and this includes obvious problems. A problem might get overlooked due to a lack of attention, or perhaps by deliberate ignorance. But sometimes it's the opposite: getting so focused on details that one misses the big picture. You may have heard the phrase, "Strain a gnat and swallow a camel." Nowhere do we see this as clearly as with the undue attention paid to the Darwinian argument from poor design.

Some look at the human body and, rather than being amazed by its extraordinary engineering, focus instead on what they consider indications of botched design. Such arguments are typically marked by drive-by criticisms of various aspects of the human body—e.g., Kenneth Miller assuring us of "the many imperfections of the human backbone,"[2] or Nathan Lents insisting on the pointlessness of most of the ankle's seven bones,[3] or Richard Dawkins informing us that the retinal structure of the mammalian eye "would offend any tidy-minded engineer."[4]

The engineering analyses in these and similar arguments are generally so shallow that the arguments amount to little more than "I wouldn't have done it that way" or "No all-knowing God would have done it that way." Those who put forward such theological (and often subjective) arguments are writing out of a tradition going back at least as far as Charles Darwin himself.

The Devil's Chaplain

IN THE traditional telling, Darwin was merely following the evidence from nature to its logical but surprising conclusion—that people are mere accidents, shaped by purposeless, natural forces. But his private correspondence suggests a different picture, that of a man with an interest in providing a completely material explanation for the diversity of life.

In one of Darwin's letters he suggests at least part of his motivation for such a program, namely his conviction that much of the living world is riddled with misery and bad design. Writing to his friend Joseph Hooker in 1856, he commented, "What a book a Devil's chaplain might write on the clumsy, wasteful, blundering low & horridly cruel works of nature!"[5]

While the term "Devil's chaplain" was surely meant only metaphorically, it was an interesting choice of terms. It suggests that Darwin understood at least some of his theory's theological implications. Cruelties in nature have long puzzled many who are committed to the idea of a good Creator closely involved in his creation, but these cruelties struck Darwin as easily explained on the grounds of mindless evolution by random variation and natural selection.[6]

In the letter, Darwin emphasized what he saw as the deficiencies of nature and suggested that these are surely not the works we could expect from a benevolent and all-powerful creator. Better, he suggests, to suppose that the living world arose from processes that did not involve God.

The cases of apparent poor design that Darwin and subsequent Darwinists have flagged are certainly worth attending to. The problem isn't that they attend to these matters; the problem is that they attend to them superficially.

The Pathetic Design of the Bad-Design-So-No-Designer Arguments

Specific "bad-design-so-no-designer" arguments have a habit of collapsing under scrutiny, but even before this, one can recognize a more basic weakness in these arguments. Even if the human body did possess certain features that were poorly made, those features might still provide clear evidence that a designer-engineer had fashioned them. In a classic example, the Yugo automobile[7] was infamous for its shoddy quality. But even a cursory look at it, even from someone who had never seen an automobile, would reveal it to be the product of intentional design. Neither the parts nor the whole worked very well, but the coherent arrangement of the parts was clearly designed.

Logically, even a bona fide example of a badly designed system in the human body couldn't erase all the examples of masterfully engineered systems reviewed in these pages. Nor could it erase the causal challenges these systems pose to any intention-free cause. Those challenges demand real answers. Storytelling, appeals to authority, ad hominem attacks, and changing the subject won't make the challenges disappear.

Some who push poor-design arguments in biology are content to argue from poor design merely to no design; but apologists from atheistic evolution may reach further, from poor design to no *designer*. Their "poor-design-so-no-designer" argument typically follows a pattern:

1. Find a seemingly suboptimal part in a body system. This can be pretty much anything you may consider to be less than perfect. Objective criteria are not required. So, for instance, I

(Steve) don't like the way my knees make noise when I climb a flight of stairs. Good enough!

2. Ignore all research and other evidence that might explain the purpose behind the design of the "suboptimal" part.

3. Ignore the engineering disciplines concerned with reviewing designs of the sort being critiqued. (Easy, since most evolutionary biologists haven't studied engineering.)

4. Deflect criticism by ridiculing anyone who might question your argument. When possible, excoriate and denounce.

5. Draw the preordained conclusion of bad design.

6. Extrapolate from bad design to a bad designer and, from there, to no designer.

7. Further extrapolate that since there was no agent/designer, "accidental design" is a thing, which can explain just about everything.

The point of the exercise is to call into question the motives or competence of the designer, and ultimately, to conclude that the system was therefore not designed. This has been called "presumptive theology" because it asserts (typically without support) what God would or would not do. In other words, it's a theological argument (though usually cloaked beneath layers of scientific jargon), and not a very good one at that.[8]

If faced with an argument like this, ask the critic to provide a workable improvement on the design in question, one that achieves all the capabilities of the original, yet hews to real-world constraints, solving all requisite engineering problems across an organism's complete lifecycle, including its development in the womb. This is a lot harder than it looks, so examples are remarkably rare. Frankly, if anyone can manage it, a likely fortune awaits in industry. Per the above example, if you can design a better ankle than the one in the human body, the robotics industry wants to hear from you. The market potential is enormous for improvements, especially for medical implants and in building better robotic systems.[9]

Simply put, personal dissatisfaction with a design does not constitute a serious criticism. Among those putting forward a "poor-design-so-no-designer" argument, there's usually little effort given to make a serious argument, or to persuade those who don't already agree with the conclusion. Instead, the argument usually consists of storytelling, often as a form of entertainment for the neo-Darwinian faithful.[10]

With even a little creativity, one could apply this style of argument to any design, by any designer-engineer, anywhere. Take an example from my early years. The town where I (Steve) grew up was a lumber town. Chainsaws are remarkably helpful in the process of turning trees into lumber, but they're also noisy, smelly, and extremely dangerous. It would be easy to write about how poorly designed chainsaws are, with toxic exhaust fumes (making humans sick), high noise levels (damaging human hearing), and an open blade (removing a human limb as fast as it can remove a tree limb). But how could the benefits of a chainsaw be achieved with a different system? The power-to-weight ratio of its noisy two-stroke engine makes it portable to carry into rugged terrain, yet with enough power to do its job. Putting a guard over the blade would make it safer but render it unable to achieve its purpose. Adding a heavy-duty muffler or an aggressive smoke filter would compromise power and make it heavier.

Given that every real-world system is open to blinkered criticisms that ignore trade-offs, are we to conclude that nothing is designed? Of course not.

A few examples of supposed poor design in the human body include the following:

The "backward wiring" of the vertebrate retina, leading to a blind spot.

Various malfunctions in the musculoskeletal system, including the ankle/foot, spine, knee, shoulder, elbow, and wrist/hand.

The exposed testicles of human males.

The narrow pelvis and birth canal in human women.

The structure of the sinuses.

The circuitous path of the left recurrent laryngeal nerve.

The inability of humans to manufacture their own vitamin C.

Some of these arguments are approaching urban legend status. We briefly addressed a few of these in earlier chapters. Much more can and has been written exploring the shortcomings of these "botched-design" arguments.[11] We'll examine just one in more detail below—the choking hazard in the human pharynx. But using the formula above, it's not hard to invent new versions of the argument, especially if you studiously ignore the many positive facets of the design.

Such arguments are unlikely to impress actual designer-engineers of complex systems, who are accustomed to juggling multiple design goals, threading the needle between unforgiving parameters, and choosing among difficult design trade-offs. Those who are not trained to think in such terms are ill-equipped to evaluate designs, in the human body or anywhere else.

Discordance

A MORE serious counterargument to our designer-engineer thesis is called discordance.[12] We find this in Chapters 10 to 14 of Darwin's *The Origin of Species*—roughly the final third of his original treatise. There he developed a special form of his case for evolution, what Stephen Jay Gould called "one long list of examples for inferring history from the oddities and imperfections of modern objects."[13] As Darwin explained, the key clues were in "organs or parts in this strange condition, bearing the stamp of inutility."[14] The logic of the discordance arguments goes something like this: If an organism has quirks, oddities, or imperfections, or some part of it is poorly coordinated with its current circumstances (environment), but these features align with a readily inferable previous circumstance, then it's reasonable to conclude that these features are holdovers or vestiges from the former state in which the circumstances were different. Or, stated a bit more simply, one can infer that an organism's external environment changed so quickly that it hasn't yet been able to evolve to fit the new environment.

> Discordance is also invoked to explain homologies—where similar structures are used in very different ways in different organisms. For example, the bone structure of the human wrist is structurally similar (homologous) to the wings of bats and birds, the front flippers of whales and dolphins, and the forelegs of dogs and crocodiles. In these cases, the bones and their relative positions are roughly the same, but their shapes, relative sizes, and optimal uses are quite different.
>
> Darwinists claim that this must be the result of common descent. But that's not the only available explanation. A possibly better explanation is common design. The best designers reuse facets of their designs—what engineers call design patterns.
>
> Consider the case of software. A single computer program can produce very different results when invoked with different parameters. The program's algorithm remains the same, but changing the parameters can generate wildly different results. The more parameters the program allows, the more variation is possible in the results. This results in enormous design efficiencies.
>
> Could this be analogous to the ways that different homologous structures are generated in different organisms? Wouldn't this kind of thing simply be expected from a master designer-engineer?

Thus, discordance requires two steps: (1) find a feature or function that doesn't fit well in an organism's current circumstance, and (2) show that this feature did fit well with a clearly inferable past circumstance. So-called "vestigial organs," like the human appendix, are commonly cited. But these arguments have fared badly over time. Virtually all the "vestigial organs" have been shown to have an important present purpose.[15] "Junk DNA" is a similar case. It has been widely cited as evidence of evolution at its most inept, but researchers continue to discover crucial roles for the stuff.[16] As of this writing, the idea of junk DNA has been so thoroughly debunked that there's almost no talk of it anymore in the research community.

Another example in vogue involves "diseases of civilization" because the diseases seem to result from rapid changes in Western society, especially the Western diet, for which the human gastrointestinal system has not had time to properly adapt. (Presumably, in a couple million years our systems will evolve and it'll be OK to eat donuts.)

Such arguments are even worse than they may appear at first glance. Think about it. They are actually arguments that something has not evolved to fit a new environment. But to succeed, evolutionary theory needs to produce evidence of evolution actually happening, and inventing things far more novel than, say, an improved capacity for metabolizing donuts.

In one instance of an almost comically lazy discordance argument, Lents insists that the human wrist "is way more complicated than it needs to be" and that its bones are "like a pile of rocks—which is how useful they are to anyone."[17] In other words, the wrist bones are an evolutionary accident that the human body inherited from some distant ancestor, then gradually evolved into a working hand, but these specific bones no longer have any use to us. But are these bones useless?

The only way to answer with rigor is to perform a mechanical analysis of the range of movement and the stresses imposed by the various activities the hands and wrists are used for. Is it possible that every bone in the wrist serves an important purpose? It turns out the answer is yes. Kinesiologists have long understood the basics of how the human wrist works, and not surprisingly, every bone in the wrist serves a useful function. Notably (and amazingly, from the engineering point of view), the wrist contains a double hinge, in which two different joints share the same axis of rotation, allowing a wide range of motion, yet with incredible strength. The surprising part? Those "useless" bones form one of the hinges.[18] Additional research into the mechanical capabilities and functions of the wrist are ongoing, and eventually will shed still more light on the capabilities of the amazing human wrist.

So, rather than a useless "pile of rocks," what we see in the real-world human wrist is an amazingly fine-tuned system of structure, flexibility, strength, and dexterity. And thus, instead of discordance, we see superb coherence, precisely tuned to exactly match the human body, and to make it even more capable than it would otherwise be.

While discordance played a prominent role in Darwin's case for the evolution of all life, he expressed surprise—not that there are observed imperfections in some living systems, but that there are so few of them. As he put it, "The wonder indeed is, on the theory of natural selection, that more cases of the want of absolute perfection have not been observed."[19]

Also, it's important to note that Darwin's main arguments were designed to refute a version of special creation wherein forms were created much as we see them and more or less where we see them, with little to no change since then.

But our theory takes a much different approach, in which many forces and factors act on life, generating wide variation over time.

Finally, even if we were to grant for the sake of argument that a part or subsystem did come from a previous form, the ancestral part or subsystem presumably had a use back there. Did that use depend on a coherent system? If so, by what means was it generated?

Discordance solves none of the hard problems posed by coherence and interdependence—it merely punts them to an organism somewhere earlier in the timeline. And this means that discordance does nothing to lessen the challenge that sophisticated, hierarchical, interdependent biological systems pose for Darwinism.

A More Rigorous Approach

Any system can be criticized. But if the system works, and the critique is to be more than a bluff, engineering-level rigor and hard work are required.

In practice, we've yet to see an example of the poor-design argument that involves engineering-level rigor. If one is going to criticize the mechanical properties of the human wrist or the swallowing functions of the human pharynx, the critic minimally needs to perform a detailed review of the mechanical movements and stresses, and of the control systems that manage these movements.

Design Review Practices

Most biologists have no experience with an engineering design review. They don't know how this is done, so they just assume it's easy and jump right in. But engineering has a long history of rich disciplines and methodologies for reviewing and testing the quality of designs. In cases where a design failure would result in extremely high expense or systemic failures (and possible deaths), design reviews and systems testing are frequent. For example, the James Webb space telescope (launched in 2021) was deployed 1.5 million kilometers from Earth.[20] At this distance, it's not practical to service it if a subsystem fails, so it needed to work correctly on the first try. The range of engineering challenges involved ranks high on the all-time list of human engineering problems. Just the design reviews and testing procedures for this device took many years to complete (and in this case, it really did take a rocket scientist, or rather, thousands of them).

Of course, rigorous critiques are more difficult in biology than with a space telescope. As sophisticated as the James Webb telescope is,[21] biological systems are far more so. Thus, any claim that a biological system or subsystem is poorly designed is best undertaken with a healthy dose of humility.

"This Design is Stupid" Arguments Lose Their Way

INVARIABLY, WHEN a "this design is stupid" argument is trotted out against a biological system, the conclusion has less to do with actual bad design and more to do with one of the following wrong turns:

1. Not Understanding the Design

Without a proper understanding of the design, it's hard to claim the design doesn't pass muster. In our example of the chainsaw above, in the absence of the design objectives and real-world trade-off choices, it's easy to argue that the machine—noisy, smelly, dangerous—is badly designed. But the argument collapses when one considers all the design objectives and trade-off choices that went into the chainsaw's design.

Naïve criticisms of some bodily feature or system tend to be similarly misguided. To avoid such mistakes, knowledge of key design criteria is required: the design objectives for the system, its functional requirements, the relevant set of design constraints, and what engineers call its "non-functional requirements" (requirements that go beyond mere function, like continuity, resilience, robustness, and adaptability). This must include considerations that non-engineers might not think of, like the placement, packaging, and serviceability of subsystems. With human vision and hearing, for example, placement and ingenious packaging are essential to function, since the nerve impulses for both sight and sound need to be instantaneously received and processed, and this affects where they can be placed. (See Chapters 10 and 11.)

Sadly, we have no access to the design documentation for the human body (or for any other living creatures). We don't understand all the design trade-offs that were involved. We simply don't have enough information to perform an exhaustive analysis. So we must infer most of these things. Fortunately, experienced engineers are accustomed to making these kinds of inferences, so it's possible to do a serviceable job in many cases. Further, we know that the human body (and most everything else that's alive) is packed with systems interdependencies, and these contribute to what is sometimes described as elegant design—

where multiple objectives are achieved with the same set of features and structures. Proponents of "poor-design-so-no-designer" arguments often overlook this aspect of good design, as for example in their critique of the human pharynx, which we explore below.

Finally, remember that the function of a part or subsystem is defined at one level in the design hierarchy, while its purpose is defined at the level above. It's therefore necessary in any rigorous assessment of a design to begin at least one level higher in the design hierarchy than where the part or subsystem resides. This consideration also is frequently overlooked.

2. Not Considering Trade-Offs

A related error in many poor-design-so-no-designer arguments is a demand (typically implicit) for perfect design. The idea is that if a system is not "perfect," then it must be poorly designed. But engineers know that perfect design is not conceptually possible for any non-trivial system. So this concept is simply not in the engineer's vocabulary.

All complex systems involve conflicting design objectives, so design trade-offs must be weighed and carefully selected. Decisions that are optimal for the whole—the design objectives taken together—may be suboptimal for a given subsystem or component. A well-designed solution to one engineering problem might easily exacerbate another engineering problem. For example, the same blood pressure needed to force blood to flow uphill to the brain will tend to cause blood to pool in the feet (when we're standing), so other subsystems are required to overcome these issues. Is this good design or bad design? In effect, the sweet spot of a particular part or subsystem may not be so sweet when dozens of considerations must be balanced in every design decision.

It's easy for non-designers to trivialize these considerations, but doing so betrays a naïve view of the complexities of the real world. This is always a mistake and one that neither doctors nor engineers can afford to make. A good physician must carefully weigh potential side effects of a treatment—for instance, asking whether the cure is worse than the disease. And engineers spend a good deal of their professional lives choosing the right mix of trade-offs for a complex system.

In reality, most cases of inferring bad design in the case of various biological systems are simply the result of good design decisions evaluated in isolation. We anticipate that more and more biologists will come to terms with this, because doing so will accelerate their progress in understanding living systems.

3. Not Acknowledging Degradation over Time

To WHAT extent is any given "bad design" example the result of degradation over time, either in an individual or in a species? Even in systems with the finest possible design, degradation occurs as the laws of nature inexorably take effect. All living systems, including the human body, degrade over time.

Errors during critical periods in development can lead to catastrophic systems failures. Features needed for fetal development may get in the way once the body matures. Diseases can degrade function. Knees that worked well in your twenties may complain when you reach your sixties. In the human body, these are often exacerbated by user abuse. Degradations also can occur in heritable ways, and these will naturally accumulate over many generations.

Do any of these mean the body is poorly designed? Or undesigned? No. Engineers know that degradation is relentless. It happens everywhere, all the time, and everyone understands this. We've all seen those cars with the sheet of plastic where a window used to be, held on with duct tape, but no one says that no "tidy-minded engineer" would design a car that way.

We echo Darwin's sentiment when he expressed surprise "that more cases of the want of absolute perfection" in the forms of various species "have not been observed."[22] Organisms seem to be equipped with capabilities that counter the effects of degradation and slow degradation in a species. How do they do that? We anticipate that this will become a burgeoning field of research.

4. Jumping from Poor Design to No Intentional Design

As NOTED above, "poorly designed" is not the same as "not designed." Even if it could be proved that a body system or component was poorly or even terribly designed, this would be insufficient to draw any conclusions about the possible participation or quality of any designer(s). And it's hardly proof that non-intentional causes were able to generate the system in the first place. In other words, the poor-designer-so-no-designer argument is at best counterintuitive, and at worst, a non-sequitur.

5. Aesthetic Considerations

Any design can easily violate subjective considerations, which some people cannot seem to distinguish from bad design. You can argue about the designer's vision or taste, but this is not sufficient warrant to say that the system wasn't designed.

The Supposed Bad Design of the Human Pharynx

THE ABOVE considerations can be applied as a five-part test for evaluating ostensible instances of bad design. This test can help determine whether we're looking at a bad design, or simply a bad argument.

Let's apply the five-part test above to the claim that the human pharynx is poorly engineered. Figure 23.1 shows that the pharynx is the common entry for both the respiratory and gastrointestinal tracts. Whatever is ingested can potentially go down the airway and cause obstruction, which can result in death by choking.

Some insist that the pharynx is therefore miserably designed, something no wise designer would engineer, but that evolution, with its trial-and-error messiness, very well might. "The biggest danger in the human throat's design is choking," writes Nathan Lents. "If we had separate openings for air and food, this would never happen. Swallowing is a good example of the limits of Darwinian evolution. The human throat is simply too complex for a random mutation—the basic mechanism of evolution—to undo its fundamental defects. We have to resign ourselves to the absurdity of taking in air and food through the same pipe."[23]

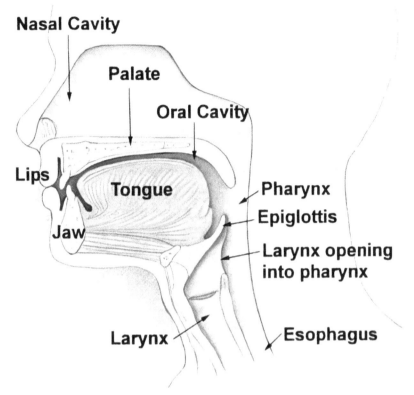

Figure 23.1. The anatomical relationship of the nose, mouth, and throat showing that the pharynx is a shared pathway for air to enter the respiratory system and for liquids and solids to enter the gastrointestinal system.

Abby Hafer, in her pointedly titled book, *The Not-So-Intelligent Designer: Why Evolution Explains the Human Body and Intelligent Design Does Not*, sounds a similar note. "A better designed system would keep the tubes for air and food separate to avoid unnecessary fatalities," she writes. "If we were designed why did the Designer do this job so badly? Or is it that the Creator likes other animals better? There are creatures in which the air passages and food passages are entirely separate. The whale's respiratory system is separate from its digestive system. This means that a whale, unlike a human, can't choke on its food by inhaling it. If the Creator could do that for the whales, I don't know why he couldn't do it for us?"[24]

These arguments are riddled with problems. To see why, we need to take a closer look at the human pharynx.

How it Works

IN ADDITION to the structures identified in Figure 23.1, fifty different pairs of muscles, controlled by six different nerves, are needed to swallow. After food in the mouth has been formed into a small ball (bolus), the tongue voluntarily moves it to the pharynx, which automatically triggers the involuntary swallow reflex.

As the bolus enters, the pharynx sends sensory information to the swallow center in the brainstem, which immediately turns off respiration so that air is not breathed in during swallowing. This prevents the lungs from drawing food into the airway. The brainstem also sends precisely ordered signals telling the various muscles to contract and move the bolus downward into the esophagus, bypassing the airway. This takes about a second.

As swallowing begins, several muscles contract to move the bolus into the pharynx, while moving the back of the palate and the upper pharynx close together to close off the path to the nose.

Next comes the tricky part. The bolus has been blocked from going up into the nose, and muscular contraction is hurtling it down towards the airway and the esophagus. Three separate actions take place to protect the airway. First, muscles contract to close the larynx, which is the gateway to the lungs. Second, other muscles move the larynx up and forward (which you can feel in the front of your neck while swallowing) to hide it under the floor of the mouth and the base of the tongue while being protected by the epiglottis. Third, this action, combined with other muscular activity, opens the upper esophagus to allow the bolus to enter.[25]

The timing and coordination are remarkable. The swallow center must send the right signals via the right nerves to the right muscles, with the exact right split-second timing. Since all this is triggered by the bolus entering the pharynx, the signals from throat to brainstem and back to the many muscles involved (with their reaction times) must be fast enough to prevent choking.

While critics seem to miss the amazing design of this system, it should give the reader pause. Somehow, swallowing happens, usually without incident, a thousand times a day.

Where did the information come from that specifies the size, shape, position, and range of movement of the pharynx, each of its nearby structures, and the fifty pairs of muscles involved in swallowing? How could such a system come about gradually, by accident?

Where did the information come from to make the swallow center in the brainstem and the logic it uses to control safe swallowing? Where is the repository for the information needed to orchestrate the precisely ordered, well-coordinated contraction sequence of fifty pairs of muscles?

Scoring the Pharynx-Is-Poorly-Designed Argument

WITH THAT primer on the pharynx and the swallowing system of which it's a part, let's now score the argument that the pharynx is badly designed and therefore not intentionally designed.

Not Understanding the Design of the Pharynx

The pharynx affords us the dual abilities to breathe and swallow food and water, but it does much more. It affords the ability for speech, language, and tonal activities like lyrical speech and singing. The percussion and acoustic shaping of the tongue, teeth, throat, oral and nasal cavities, and most of the other parts of the pharynx, are absolutely required for the nuanced communication that's essential to the human experience. So the pharynx has at least three major functional design objectives. If you were asked to design a system with these capabilities, how would you approach it? How would your design make the trade-offs needed to do all this with a single system? If you used separate systems, as advocated by the critics above, how would you achieve the right kinds of functions, and how would this affect how these functions are packaged into the body as a whole? The critics ignore these questions, apparently because they haven't bothered to understand the design of the system, *as a system*—either its core objectives or the orchestration of its many parts.

Not Considering Trade-Offs when Criticizing the Pharynx

Clearly, the pharynx's main three functions cause design conflicts that must be solved. We could use two or maybe even three separate systems to achieve these vastly different goals. However, since all three functions need similar components, two or possibly three copies of many of these structures would be necessary. If, as the critics recommend, we were structured to use the mouth only for swallowing food and water, and not for breathing, thereby precluding speech and language as we know it, the nasal passageways would need to be much larger to bring in enough oxygen during high levels of activity.

To keep all three functions, duplication of parts may be an option. We'd need two mouths, one for eating and another for breathing and speaking, and we'd need two large pipes, one for air and the other for food. We'd need two tongues, one for manipulating food in the eating mouth, and another for speaking in the breathing/speaking mouth. For making the hard consonant sounds in speech, we'd need something like teeth in the breathing/speaking mouth, but we'd also need teeth for chopping up food in the eating mouth. For making complex tonal sounds, the nasal cavities would need to be attached to the breathing/speaking mouth. But we'd also need the nose's smell sensors in the eating mouth in order to fully experience the taste of our food. We could go on, but you get the idea.

In the end, the anatomical changes for either scenario, precluding or preserving speech and language as we know it, would require a complete reconfiguration of the head and neck and possibly also some parts of the lungs and stomach in the body's core. At a minimum, an increase in the size of the nasal passageways would require the head and face to be much wider. But to house duplicate systems, the volume of the head and neck would need to roughly double, and depending on the positioning of the two mouths, the passageways to the lungs and stomach would likely need to be rearranged too.

Maybe if our bodies were shaped more like a whale, this would work better, but of course this might make it harder to climb mountains. Or even to turn our heads quickly.

Building these different functions into a single set of components, with the programming and orchestration to make them work properly, is another example of elegant invention. The obvious trade-off is that it's possible to choke, never mind how well-designed the system that's in place to avoid this problem. Of course, the critics also neglect to consider whether it would be easier or harder to choke in a system with two mouths, as the risk of this happening would depend on their positions relative to each other.

The marvel is that the system combines these three separate functions in such a compact space, and the whole works so well at all three of its core functions.

Not Acknowledging Pharynx Degradation over Time

How and why do humans die from choking? One common cause of swallowing problems is neuromuscular injury or degeneration related to aging or disease. Since swallowing requires precisely orchestrated contractions of many different muscles, any condition that compromises nerve or muscle function can lead to difficulties in swallowing. Common conditions include stroke, Parkinson's disease, and multiple sclerosis (MS), each of which puts the person at risk for aspirating food into their lungs and choking to death. These represent about half of the annual deaths by choking. One could argue that the body's inability to fight off Parkinson's or MS is also a design flaw, but these are also instances of degradation. As we've seen, complex systems always degrade over time and generations, so it's unrealistic to think this should never happen to the human body if it were well designed.

Another common cause of choking is user abuse. When a healthy adult takes in too large a piece of food, or doesn't chew sufficiently, or a child takes in a foreign object like a small toy, these objects can get stuck in the airway and choking results. One could insist that the design should have been foolproof against such abuses, but this merely takes us back to the question of trade-offs.

To even hope to make the system abuse-proof, the three functions of the pharynx would have to be divided out into two or three separate systems, and we've already seen the problems that attend that strategy. Moreover, no matter how carefully an engineer designs a product, it's always at risk of being misused and, due to wear and tear, its functional capacity lessening over time.

Jumping from Poor Design of the Pharynx to No Intentional Design

Even if we were to grant for the sake of argument that the pharynx is a case of shoddy engineering, it wouldn't follow from this alone that it wasn't intentionally designed (as the Yugo car and Tacoma Narrows Bridge aptly illustrate). The evolutionists who reach this unsound conclusion perhaps get there by embracing the false premise that poorly designed things must be unintentionally designed things, and combining it with the equally mistaken view that the pharynx is a botched design. But perhaps the error is a bit more subtle.

In logic, one of the formal fallacies is known as affirming the consequent. That logical fallacy runs like this:

Major Premise: If A is true, then B is true.

Minor Premise: B is true.

Conclusion: Therefore, A is true.

That's an invalid syllogism. For it to be valid, the major premise would need to be "If B is true, then A is true." As it is, the conclusion simply doesn't follow. This is affirming the consequent, or put more generally, it's a non sequitur. This may be how the evolutionists above have reached their invalid conclusion, thus:

Major Premise: If A (something came about without intention), then B (it is poorly constructed).

Minor Premise: B is the case: the human pharynx is poorly constructed.

Conclusion: A is true: the pharynx came about without intention. Even if we granted both premises, the conclusion wouldn't follow, since it's an invalid syllogism guilty of affirming the consequent.

It's not clear that this is exactly how evolutionists are reasoning, but it well may be close to the mark based on their statements.

But wait, there's more. Lents asserts that "if we had separate openings for air and food, [choking] would never happen." But in any system which requires breathing air into the body, the opening for the air can become blocked—no matter where you put it on the body or how it's configured. How will these critics' "improved" system prevent choking from ever happening?

Even a design that is truly suboptimal in one respect cannot demonstrate that it's a poor design, since the "suboptimal" feature may simply be the natural outcome of a perfectly reasonable design trade-off. (And as noted, even if a suboptimal feature were a true design blunder, this would not be sufficient warrant to claim that it wasn't intentionally designed.)

Another error in reasoning: "The human throat is simply too complex for a random mutation—the basic mechanism of evolution—to undo its fundamental defects,"[26] Lents insists. But if the human throat is too complex for a random mutation to undo a "design defect," how could random mutations have built such a complex feature in the first place? And if it works and the species thrives, can it be called a defect?

Or recall this argument from Hafer: "If the Creator could [separate the respiratory from the digestive systems] for the whales, I don't know why he couldn't do it for us?"[27] Being capable of doing something doesn't make it a good idea. We could design an iPhone with tires, but this may not be helpful to that device's purpose. Whales are also able to live their whole lives in the ocean. Why couldn't the Creator give humans that ability, too? It would certainly cut down on skateboard injuries and fatal traffic accidents. Maybe it just wasn't the plan.

While the above are likely intended as arguments to poor design, they come across as logical "rubbish," to borrow a phrase from our British colleagues.

Aesthetic Considerations in Evaluating the Pharynx

The two critics above, at least in the quotations above, do not level aesthetic objections against the design of the pharynx. The irony is that if the designer of the human body had taken their advice and used the vastly clunkier and less elegant approach of creating two or three separate systems for breathing, eating/drinking, and communicating in order to minimize choking, the anti-design critics might have lodged an aesthetic argument against such a choice, namely that no properly ingenious "tidy-minded engineer" would have failed to elegantly combine the three primary functions into a single clever system.

Engineers know this game—damned if you do and damned if you don't, with critics ignoring the question of trade-offs. Engineers develop thicker skins as a natural coping mechanism. (Which, come to think of it, is another clever adaptive design feature of the human body!)

Ingenious Design

Most people swallow a thousand times a day without incident, all the while breathing in enough air, swallowing enough food and water, verbally communicating with nuance, and sometimes even singing. Thus, the rare possibility of choking to death provides little actual evidence of incompetent design. Rather, the human pharynx is more accurately viewed as a clever, elegant solution to a complicated set of competing design objectives, with justifiable choices regarding design trade-offs, within rigid constraints. Further, the solution is profoundly well packaged and even provides a way to equalize the air pressure in the middle ear. This is ingenious design.

Conclusions and Disqualifications

THE PHARYNX is but one example of how the poor-design-so-no-design-er arguments for mindless evolution fall apart on close inspection. There are dozens of other similarly shoddy arguments of this sort, some of which were exposed in early chapters of this book, and all of which make one or more of the same kinds of mistakes enumerated above.

This class of argument is generally offered as part of a grand evolutionary narrative. You're not supposed to notice that the narrative is built on a panoply of questionable presuppositions, educated and sometimes not-so-educated guesses, cherry-picked data, selective ignorance of key details, and dubious factoids. The grand narrative resembles the proverbial description of a fishing net: *a bunch of holes tied together with string.*[28] The narrative may play well with the Darwinian faithful. It may even convince the uninformed that all is in order with evolutionary theory, so no need to ask any questions. But the attentive will notice that there's more storytelling than science going on here.

> To any biologist enamored of poor-design-so-no-designer arguments, we offer the following friendly opportunity and challenge: Let's work together on a serious research proposal to assess the living system you see as your most compelling example of poor design in the human body. We will include team members from all the relevant medical and engineering disciplines, perform a rigorous design analysis of the system, in the context of the whole (including the creature's entire lifecycle), and jointly publish the results.

The bad-design-so-no-designer argument is a bit like diligently reading and rereading *War and Peace*, looking for grammatical errors, typos, and other mistakes. Of course, you're likely to find examples, whether real or contrived. But in the process, you may have missed the point of the book, and its genius. The analogy isn't perfect. The human genome contains roughly 150 times more information than *War and Peace*, one of the longest novels in Western literature. Further, *War and Peace* can't generate its own power, maintain a chemical equilibrium different from its environment, or make copies of itself. But the analogy does make our point: fixating on error, real or apparent, can lead to overlooking the most important and impressive aspects of a work, whether a novel or an organism such as the human body.

A focus on finding poorly designed features may result in key questions that go begging. Why are there any good designs in the biosphere? Why does every living thing contain so much coherent design? For the human body, why do the trillions of parts work, and why do they just happen to make up a whole that can accomplish tasks that none of the parts can do by themselves?

Anyone who examines the human body's design without fully considering such questions has missed the mark—and the elephant in the room.

24. Two Questions

This is one of the most important intellectual issues of modern times, and every thinking person has the right and duty to judge for himself.

—David Gelernter, "Giving Up Darwin"[1]

A NTONY FLEW WAS HAILED BY MANY AS THE WORLD'S MOST INFLU-ential philosophical atheist. The son of a famous Methodist minister in England, he was raised in a Christian home but turned to atheism at the age of fifteen.

His quick intellect won him awards and prestige. He was a leading advocate of atheism for the bulk of his career, authoring twenty-six books upon which generations of atheists and agnostics built their belief systems.

But early in 2004, at the age of eighty-one, he changed his mind.

Flew announced his conversion to deism, launching seismic waves throughout the philosophic community. Ardent supporters denounced him. Jay Leno got laughs on *The Tonight Show*, saying, "Of course he believes in God now. He's eighty-one years old."

Despite the attacks, Flew persisted. He had become convinced that life would not be possible without the extreme fine tuning of the universe, and this was only possible with a designer. In addition, he concluded that new discoveries about DNA made it impossible that life could be an accident. As he put it, "It now seems to me that the findings of more than fifty years of DNA research have provided materials for a new and enormously powerful argument to design."[2]

While Flew did not convert to a revelation-based religion,[3] his change of mind was both startling and, to many who had formed their lives around his views, disturbing. Why, after investing his entire professional life in the opposite view, did he change his mind? "Since the beginning of my philosophical life I have followed the policy of Plato's Socrates," he explained. "We must follow the argument wherever it leads."[4]

As Flew gained more information about the particulars of life, he realized that his earlier stance was mistaken. In his words to an interviewer, "I've always engaged in inquiry. If I am shown to have been wrong, well, okay, so I was wrong."[5]

Flew offers a model for all of us. All who seek truth should strive to process new information in the same way, even when it means admitting to having gone down a wrong path before. Like him, we should always ask questions, carefully and diligently weigh alternate answers, and make the best choices we can.

The Sticking Point

THIS BOOK has set out a systematic argument for what's needed for life, at least for the human body. Viewed as a set of solutions to hard problems, the body presents much more that must be explained by origins science than is generally discussed, especially in the popular press. This is all the more true when taken in the aggregate. Physicians and engineers must deal with the whole, but biologists usually specialize, focusing more narrowly on a part or small set of parts, and this tendency trickles down into the popular press. As a result, most people, even many trained biologists, have little sense of the enormous coherent and interdependent sophistication of the human body.

There are hundreds of systems and subsystems in the human body for which there is neither a known nor even a theorized gradual evolutionary pathway to generating function—no adaptive continuum along which life is viable and reproducing at every step. Without this, no gradual approach can ever fashion the individual systems in the human body, much less orchestrate the irreducibly complex ensemble of systems essential to our existence.

If no gradual pathway is possible for overcoming a substantive causal hurdle (given the "life" plus "reproduction" constraints of the real world), then the burden falls to raw luck to overcome that hurdle, and to do so in more or less a single shot for a given function or feature, lest a partial solution be lost by degradation while waiting for the rest of the solution to appear. Overcoming the causal hurdles inherent to a single coherent subsystem is hard enough, but the interdependencies between coherent subsystems raise the bar to levels that further exceed any reasonable inference to blind luck. Appeals to the contrary violate the First Law of Hard Problems—no amount of wishful thinking can solve a problem this hard, much less all of them.

We need another framework, then, if we are to ever understand where the body came from and how it works. There is a suitable framework available—one with intuitive simplicity and causal sufficiency; one consistent with the data; one that aligns with our sense of ourselves as agents possessing personal freedom and moral responsibility, in a universe where good and evil are more than a mirage.

This framework has one element, however, that is anathema to many. It requires an intelligent designer-engineer who creatively acts at one or more points in the history of life.

Planned or Accidental?

WE HAVE two competing ideas before us: life, in all its incredible diversity, was formed purely by a series of gradually occurring accidents, absolutely without intention, foresight, or planning of any kind. Or life came about in significant measure by the intentional acts of a master designer-engineer.

They cannot both be true.

The first approach is firmly rooted in materialist philosophy, so it cannot permit intention in its origins story. On this view, the material universe is all that exists, so there was simply no one available to do the

428 / <small>YOUR DESIGNED BODY</small> /

intending. This restriction is not an inherent constraint of science, at least not in the original definition of science as a careful study of the natural world. Rather, this constraint is imposed by an *a priori* worldview commitment to materialism.

Science does not deal in absolute proof, and as such it cannot absolutely show that no intentional acts were involved in the history of life. But science can demonstrate that there are no detectable instances of design in life and that no intentional acts were needed to achieve these outcomes. But the earnest endeavors of generations of biologists and materialist philosophers have shown no such thing. So far, these materialists have failed to explain how their causal forces could have overcome any of the hurdles we've described, much less all of them.

What the leading proponents of modern Darwinism do offer in abundance are bluffs and promissory notes, something like, "Trust us, we're scientists. The problem is basically solved and we're very close to disentangling the final few difficulties."

Not true. Not even close.

Yes, science has a long history of dispelling folklore and superstition, but the quandaries presented by living systems are in a completely different class from explaining, say, the cause of lightning, and they demand a completely different approach. Moreover, scientists are only human, so are not immune to their own preferred superstitions.

In contrast, the second approach allows for intention in the origin of living systems. The incredible diversity of life, the adaptive capabilities of life, and the relative stasis of life-forms across thousands and sometimes millions of years are possible only through the creative work of a master designer-engineer, acting intentionally to bring about a desired (though not necessarily pre-ordained) result.

The first approach, to prove that intention is not required, must account for the many amazing bodily systems we've discussed, plus countless more in the rest of the biota.

The second approach, however, needs just a single example of a system that cannot be produced gradually or by accident, and which therefore requires a coherent leap in information and functionality reflecting the need for forethought, intention, planning, and design. We've provided nearly two dozen chapters filled with such examples.

No matter how much it's desired, or how earnestly it's sought, there is simply no third alternative that can achieve intentional outcomes without meaning to. In other words, there's no alternative that can overcome a logical impossibility.

So, this is the sticking point. If intent truly is necessary in the history of life, a lot of people will need to rethink their worldviews.

Magical Thinking, Billiards, and the Miraculous

THIS RAISES an obvious objection. We have said that magical thinking is not allowed, but we appear to be invoking instances of design, which some might characterize (possibly pejoratively) as miracles. Aren't miracles a form of magical thinking? What's up with that? Moreover, the objection continues, the laws of nature are regular and, by all accounts, immutable. Doesn't this rule out the possibility of intentional actions by a cosmic designer-engineer?

It does not. C.S. Lewis used the example of billiards. The laws of physics tell us what will happen when a moving ball strikes a second, stationary ball. But "the physicist, as a physicist, does not know how likely I am to catch up a cue and 'spoil' his experiment with the billiard balls: you had better ask someone who knows me."[6]

Nancy Pearcey expounds: "The laws do not tell us what will happen *if* a mischievous child grabs the ball. The laws are still true, of course, but the child has interfered with the physics."[7]

In Pearcey's illustration, a child acted with intent to modify her world. Of course we do this kind of thing all the time. No one says an engineer violates the laws of nature when he builds a bridge over a river. Rather, the engineer is simply working within the laws to achieve a desired outcome that the laws can neither intend nor produce by themselves.

None of this violates the laws of nature. The laws permit this kind of involvement. According to Lewis, "The divine art of miracle is not an art of suspending the pattern to which events conform but of feeding new events into that pattern."[8]

At the same time, we shouldn't fall into the mistake of regarding the laws of nature as necessary truths on par with such necessary and eternal truths as $2 + 2 = 4$. Modern cosmology makes clear that the universe had a beginning, so there's no longer any question that the laws of nature themselves had a beginning. Something, or someone, brought them into existence. And since they are fine tuned to an extraordinary degree to enable life, they also give every appearance of being intended. This is a reasonable conclusion from the evidence.

Magical thinking, in contrast, involves causal effects without a causal link. This especially includes attributing special powers to inanimate objects, like when I (Steve) wear my orange socks to ensure that the Denver Broncos will win their football game. (Note: not really. I don't *have* orange socks.) Or claiming that a universe can spring from nothing. Or claiming that life can overcome insuperable odds, *time and time again*, to generate new proteins just when they're needed. Avoiding magical thinking, as we mean the term, is to avoid just such nonsense.

Of Captains and Sinking Ships

THERE'S THE old saying that the captain always goes down with his ship. The saying, hopefully an exaggeration, does carry with it an insight into human psychology. Those who are most invested in a venture are the least likely to abandon it when both prudence and reason urge them to do so. Darwin encountered some serious problems with his theory, but he refused to abandon his ship. In the 160-plus years since he published his theory, the evidential challenges to the theory have grown, including the sort explored in these pages. Committed evolutionists who have invested their careers in the modern form of the theory may also choose to stay with the ship.

But why should the rest of us stay on board as the ship founders?

The designer-engineer framework offers an alternative that turns the tables 180° on Darwin's theory. Or, since Darwin was trying to turn the tables 180° on the design-based theories of his day, perhaps this is more like coming full circle—only this time we have a far richer and deeper understanding of the engineering and fine tuning required for life, and with a superior set of creative tools to factor into the exploration: intentional design with organic growth.

If this new framework is on the right track, the scientific (and engineering, and medical) objective must be to discover and formulate the "rules of engagement" for living systems. How do these creative tools interact to affect the ways living systems change over time? A research program built around such questions would be rich in potential.

Cultural Implications

DISCARDING DARWINISM in favor of an intention-based framework has implications far beyond science, just as embracing Darwin's theory had larger philosophical and cultural implications for his followers. These larger implications touch on the big questions: Who am I? Why am I here? Is there anything more than nature? Is death really the end of me, or is there more?

Worldviews are about ultimate questions and ultimate answers. Every worldview identifies something that it holds as the prime reality, from which all else flows. Is that something material, such as the physical stuff of the universe, or is it a mind, such as a transcendent designer-engineer? If the prime reality is material, nothing is greater than the material universe. All is derived from matter and energy, including you. If the material universe caused you, then you are merely the sum of your molecules. No more, no less. There is no other option.

If the prime reality is a mind, a person, then all is derived from that person, including you. If this is true, maybe the "you" that you sense so strongly is real.

It's hard to imagine any two ideas more at odds with each other. From start to finish, these are polar opposites. In the first, we are mere accidents (in the sense of chance events), the outcome of countless accidents in an uncaring universe—uncaring because it has no means to care. The "me" that I experience is merely an illusion caused by chemical changes in "my" brain. All of which makes the "me" a biomechanical automaton, lacking free will and autonomy. Importantly, when yoked to Darwinism this view reduces the entire human experience to survival advantage. The elements that make life worth living are robbed of their significance. Human life is bereft of inherent purpose or higher meaning.

The second view accommodates a richer set of possibilities. To see why, compare a gas-powered lawnmower engine with a radio. A lawnmower engine can be well understood by examining its parts and how they're organized, along with a basic understanding of chemistry and combustion. But with a radio, no amount of knowledge about the physical components, how they're organized, or how radio waves work will ever reveal where the music is coming from, much less explain the purpose of the music. This requires knowledge of things far beyond the radio itself. In the same way, biological life—and human life especially—exists at the intersection of the seen and the unseen, of the material and the immaterial. The materialistic framework can't follow this path because it refuses to include the immaterial on any of its maps. For materialists, humans can be nothing more than really complicated lawnmower engines.

But for those willing to entertain notions of the immaterial, the search has only begun.

The Purpose Pay-off—What's the Point of Having No Purpose?

PURPOSE IS defined at a level above mere existence. Purpose is always defined top-down—from the designer-engineer of the body, to the inhabitant of the body, to the body itself. And from there to the body's systems and down through the design hierarchy to the cells and cellular organelles, and from there to the molecules, ions, and chemical reactions. This view offers hope that our lives have some higher purpose than mere survival and reproduction.

But is the evidence of purpose in life real or an illusion? The only causal forces allowed in the materialist worldview are purposeless. For these causal forces to achieve functionality of any kind, by themselves, would be astonishing. But to achieve purpose?

These forces are not agents. They do not care whether life exists. They do not desire to generate life. If they did do so, it would be purely by happenstance (if such were possible), and they would have no qualms about immediately destroying that life.

But what if reality is larger than philosophical materialism allows? Life is brimming with evidence of purpose. Life appears to come from purpose and to serve a purpose. The various elements of an organism—its systems, its subsystems, and the various parts of those subsystems—each fulfills a function that serves a purpose. Even parts that were assumed to be vestigial have been shown to serve important purposes.

This pattern of purpose is so pervasive that biology researchers increasingly find themselves working from a foundation of teleology, of purpose: *Why is this part here? What does it do? How does it work?* The most productive research in biology nowadays occurs when investigators assume that everything they observe is there for a reason, and that their job is to figure out what that reason is. In this regard, biology (and medicine) are largely exercises in reverse engineering. The goal is to figure out how these astoundingly capable things work. As pioneering evolutionist J. B. S. Haldane is said to have commented, "Teleology is like a mistress

YOUR DESIGNED BODY /

to a biologist; he cannot live without her but he's unwilling to be seen with her in public."[9]

Two Questions, Four Outcomes

A CENTRAL inference of this book is that intentional actions were required at one or more points in the history of life to generate the systems of the human body.

As you reflect on this proposition, consider two questions:

1. *Is the proposition true?* As with most serious questions about complex matters, it's a challenge to sift through the evidence and weigh competing theories in search of the truth. Adding to the confusion are those who habitually obfuscate and mislead. Red herrings, sleights of hand, and blowing smoke are among the common tools of that trade. Appeals to authority will sway some, since it saves them the hard work of wading through the evidence themselves. Given all this, it's not surprising that so many people avoid wrestling with this question altogether.

2. *Do I like it?* What would I like to be true? Which answer would best serve my personal interests and preferences? If the answer upends my worldview, am I willing to deal with that? Will this affect my lifestyle? This question is typically much easier to answer. We know instantly whether we like or hate anchovies on our pizza, whether we like or dislike flannel shirts in the winter. For most of us, the same goes for whether we like or dislike the idea of a designer-engineer of life.

Since the first question is hard and the second one easy, most people skip over the first question and jump straight to the second. This has the advantage of saving a lot of time (and thinking, which is known to hurt), and it allows a person to believe (and do) what he wants, rather than what the facts might suggest.

For those who have answered for themselves these two questions about human origins and design, we can see that there are four possible

	Is it true? NO	Is it true? YES
Do I like it? NO	Q1	Q2
Do I like it? YES	Q3	Q4

Figure 24.1. Answering two questions about the proposition, *Intentional actions were required at one or more points in the history of life to generate the systems of the human body.*

combinations (quadrants) of answers to the question of whether design in life is real.

Quadrant 1: Life is an Accident—Drat!

Those in this category are convinced that no designer-engineer was involved in the history of life, and they are disappointed by this. This category includes many who were persuaded by unrelenting materialist propaganda in college, were unaware of the substantial contrary evidence, and resigned themselves to a cosmos without higher purpose. They wish that the cosmos were the result of foresight and design, and that humans were more than meat machines, but hey (they think to themselves), we all wish we were billionaires, too.

Quadrant 2: Life was Designed—Drat!

Those in this category are convinced that a designer-engineer was involved in the history of life, and they're disappointed. Perhaps they picture a cold and distant cosmic designer, not unlike a cold and distant father figure, and they'd prefer that no such being exist. Or perhaps they picture the cosmic designer as all too interested in the affairs of men but as stern and cruel, quick to punish and full of rage.

Others in this category may have fallen in love with the idea of the living world evolving on its own toward ever-greater complexity and wonder, but reluctantly conclude that the idea is a secular myth without evidential grounding. This comes close to describing distinguished American philosopher Thomas Nagel. In 1997 Nagel made a frank admission:

> I want atheism to be true and am made uneasy by the fact that some of the most intelligent and well-informed people I know are religious believers. It isn't just that I don't believe in God and, naturally, hope that I'm right in my belief. It's that I hope there is no God! I don't want there to be a God; I don't want the universe to be like that. My guess is that this cosmic authority problem is not a rare condition and that it is responsible for much of the scientism and reductionism of our time. One of the tendencies it supports is the ludicrous overuse of evolutionary biology to explain everything about human life, including everything about the human mind.... This is a somewhat ridiculous situation.... [I]t is just as irrational to be influenced in one's beliefs by the hope that God does not exist as by the hope that God does exist.[10]

Then fifteen years later he penned the book *Mind and Cosmos*, subtitled *Why the Materialist Neo-Darwinian Conception of Nature is Almost Certainly False*. Here is a well-trained thinker who clearly is having trouble believing that all of life's diversity emerged according to a purely materialist framework, without the aid of a designer-engineer, and he is none too pleased. That said, it's probably going too far to say that Nagel is in this second category, since he appears to be holding out against theism. Still, Nagel is a fascinating case study of someone whose exploration of the scientific evidence, on the one hand, and his preference for materialism, on the other, pull strongly in opposite directions.

Quadrant 3: Life is an Accident—Yay!

Those in this category are convinced that no designer-engineer was involved in the history of life, and they're glad. They have concluded that the evidence in origins biology and paleontology supports atheism, and they want to remain atheists.

Quadrant 4: Life was Designed—Yay!

Those in this category are convinced that the diversity we find in the biosphere required the work of a designer-engineer, and they're happy about it. The conclusion may support deism with its picture of a distant and uninvolved Creator, a non-religious theism, or the theism of one of the world's monotheistic religions (including Judaism, Islam, and Christianity), which see God as both transcendent over nature and immanent in nature.

If you land in Q3 or Q4, your beliefs and your desires are aligned. If you're in Q1 or Q2, you have some tension in your belief system.

Of course, some people aren't sure what they want. Others aren't sure what they believe. And some aren't sure what they want or believe. If that describes you, perhaps it's time to add "ponder the meaning of life" to the To Do list.

Further, this four-part matrix only covers this one proposition. Of course, life is much more complex than this, so other propositions may weigh as well. For example, some committed materialists may secretly worry that a designer-engineer was involved in the history of life, but they are immensely unhappy about this possibility, so they refuse to acknowledge the possibility. They land in Q2, but steadfastly refuse to let anyone know, possibly including themselves. For them, another question supersedes this one in importance.

Interestingly, as Antony Flew became convinced that some form of intentional design was required in the history of life, he moved from atheism toward a secular deism rather than to traditional theism, because he found some of the implications of the latter personally objectionable. As he put it, "I don't want a future life. I have never wanted a future life…. I want to be dead when I'm dead and that's an end to it."[11] On several occasions he expressed revulsion for various Judeo-Christian doctrines.

This is a form of the "I don't like it" argument. Apparently Flew found himself in Quadrant 2, convinced that a designer-engineer was required for life but less than thrilled about it. Deism offered him a way to minimize the discomfort without denying what he regarded as unambiguous scientific evidence of design.

Where do you land in these four quadrants? Or are you still trying to figure that out? Which of the two questions do you struggle with the most?

These small questions expose the big questions about life, so they're worth examining carefully. Regardless of our personal views or preferences, truth is bigger than we are, so it's best to struggle honestly with both questions, and in the right order.

Remember that, in the end, the truth gets to win.

Ideas Have Consequences

The big questions may seem far away from our real, day-to-day lives, but the answers touch everything.

According to philosophical materialism, you are a cosmic accident. No intention was involved in making you, because there was no one to intend anything. You can have no inherent purpose, because purpose is not material and is therefore at best a froth on reality, an illusion. There is no free will because cognition is a trick played on you by your brain.

There is no objective basis for good or evil, or for right and wrong, but only emotions based on some ill-defined evolutionary "advantage" from the distant past, or social contracts, wherein we huddle in tribes with like-minded individuals.

On this view, everything you experience and everything you are must ultimately be reduced to chemical reactions in your brain and body. Your mind and your will, along with love, nobility, and altruism, are all illusions (albeit convincing ones).

Under philosophical materialism, you are more like a gasoline engine than a radio.

If you're a materialist, this is true not just for people in the abstract, but it's true for *you*. There's no escape from this implication as long as you remain a materialist.

A few leading materialists publicly acknowledge this. The late William Provine was known for his brutal honesty in this regard. "Let me summarize my views on what modern evolutionary biology tells us loud and clear—and these are basically Darwin's views," he said. "There are no gods, no purposes, and no goal-directed forces of any kind. There is no life after death. When I die, I am absolutely certain that I am going to be dead. That's the end of me. There is no ultimate foundation for ethics, no ultimate meaning in life, and no free will for humans, either."[12]

This, then, is the materialist's quandary: How can he live his life consistently with the logical conclusions of his own worldview? Is any materialist willing or able to do so? Unsurprisingly, most supporters of materialism shy away from the logical conclusions of their own theory. Why is that? It may be that they are aware that such implications are bad PR for their position, hence it's better to leave such things unspoken. For others it may simply be a desire to disregard these implications.

A Band of Theologians

THERE IS one more question to address, one that everyone wants to know the answer to: If life was indeed designed, who, exactly, is this designer-engineer?

The science of biological design cannot answer this question. As a means to explore the universe, the sciences that work so well within the universe simply cannot reach beyond it. Science cannot tell us if the physical rules that apply inside our universe apply outside our universe, because the rules beyond our universe are not observable by us. So to answer this question in any depth we would need investigative and epistemological tools other than science, such as revelation, theology, and philosophy, and these are beyond the scope of this book.

That being said, using reason we can glean some additional clues about this designer.[13] First, remember that life would not be possible without the extreme fine tuning of the laws of physics and chemistry. Since the designer-engineer of life needs this fine tuning for living systems, and there's no other proposed reason for the fine tuning to have the precise values for life, we can reasonably infer that the designer of life may well be the designer of the universe, and therefore exists outside the universe, transcending space, time, matter, and energy as we know them. (Note that it does not follow that this same designer would be precluded in any way from later contributing additional information to the universe, existing in and through the universe as well as outside it, or entering into the universe.)

Let the above points about fine tuning and transcendence sink in. To make even the simplest living creature, the master designer-engineer must have intended for life to exist, planned the deepest foundations of the universe to make this possible, and acted to make it so.

Second, in our experience life always comes from life, never from non-life. Thus, we can reasonably hypothesize that the designer of the human body is also the original source of its life.

Third, the designer-engineer must profoundly understand physics, chemistry, biology, medicine, and engineering—all the way down and all the way up. To design life, the math alone must be unimaginably complicated.

The worldview implications of all this are enormous. It suggests the possibility that there is an immaterial, even a spiritual, component to everything we are. And maybe also to everything we do.

Intriguingly, long before these scientific discoveries, the Christian theological tradition spoke of "the Author of Life," "the Author of Creation," and "the book of nature." In this tradition the designing agent through which the universe came to be is known as the "Logos," from which we get our word "logic" and which translates into English as "word," "reason," or "plan." The picture is of a grand author writing into existence an information-rich and reasonable universe, a view very much in sync with the discoveries of twentieth and twenty-first century science.

This view of nature as the rational product of a rational mind, by the way, was the view held by the very men who launched the scientific revolution in the Renaissance and Enlightenment, almost all of them Christians. Their worldview inspired them to go looking for the hidden, rational order of nature through careful observation and experiment.

The late Robert Jastrow, a world-renowned astronomer and planetary physicist, was the founding director of NASA's Goddard Institute for Space Studies. As an agnostic, he long held at arm's length the framework of traditional Christian theology described above. But he found himself deeply impressed with the cosmological discoveries surrounding the Big Bang, the instant when the universe came into existence and its fine-tuned parameters took their values—the exact values needed to support life. In light of these discoveries Jastrow made the following observation:

> At this moment it seems as though science will never be able to raise the curtain on the mystery of creation. For the scientist who has lived by his faith in the power of reason, the story ends like a bad dream. He has scaled the mountains of ignorance; he is about to conquer the highest peak; as he pulls himself over the final rock, he is greeted by a band of theologians who have been sitting there for centuries.[14]

We could not have said this better.

Which Deal to Take?

You MAY have been told, often and with force, that you and every other human being—indeed, every other living thing—are a cosmic accident. You were also likely told that this is the only reasonable and properly modern view of things. It isn't.

We've shown that there's another option available. The evidence we've presented clearly shows that your body could not have been an accident, that a master designer-engineer must have been involved.

So where does this leave us? There are two deals on the table. You are either a cosmic accident, or you are the result of intentional acts by a master designer-engineer. You cannot, of course, be both. You can, however, freely consider both possibilities rather than merely accepting materialism on faith.

So there is one final question to grapple with: What will you do with the information and arguments we've presented? Even if based only on the evidence for design in the human body, there is sufficient warrant to give the design-engineering framework serious consideration.

We think the evidence is overwhelming, and we are not alone. Apparently, Antony Flew did, as did famous polymath David Gelernter, who in 2019 announced publicly that he had left the Darwinian fold. In fact, recent years have seen a growing number of prominent defections from the Darwinian-materialist viewpoint, and in many cases these people have risked their careers and livelihoods to do so.[15]

For many of these who are changing their views, the effort required to maintain belief in the Darwinian status quo simply became too much in light of recent scientific discoveries. This book has explored additional evidence, and when combined, the weight of the evidence is difficult to ignore. So we put the key question to you: How hard are you willing to work to avoid the obvious?

For those who insist that the case for mindless evolution of all life is "overwhelming," the burden is on them to answer the many hard questions we've asked in these pages. If they cannot answer with anything more than hand-waving, storytelling, and appeals to authority, a person should think twice before following them.

In our experience, openly considering the evidence for a designer-engineer can "de-constrain" our thinking from materialist philosophy and open us up to new possibilities, both in our scientific research and in our personal lives. It also offers an escape from the dreary nihilism lurking in the warp and woof of the materialist worldview.

We hope these pages have challenged you to think about these things in new ways. As we conclude, we encourage you to embrace what we consider to be your rightful place in the universe as a real, living person, made for a purpose. But for most of us, getting there is a journey. As you ponder these questions, lean in. Explore the options. Evaluate the trade-offs. Consider the implications and outcomes.

The rest is up to you.

END MATTER

ENDNOTES

INTRODUCTION

1. Max Planck, *Scientific Autobiography and Other Papers*, trans. Frank Gaynor (New York: Philosophical Library, 1949), 33–34.
2. Richard Dawkins, *The Blind Watchmaker: Why the Evidence of Evolution Reveals a Universe without Design* (New York: W. W. Norton, 1986), 9.
3. Dawkins, *The Blind Watchmaker*, x. As we'll show, the idea that biological systems are merely "complicated" profoundly understates the matter. Living systems are more than complicated; they're coherent and finely tuned, and these properties are fundamental requirements for life, not a result of life.
4. Our human descriptions of the regularities of the material world are themselves immaterial, including our formulations of mathematics and the laws of physics and chemistry. The fact that the physical universe hews so closely to this kind of regularity has astonished physicists for centuries. So perhaps even the material universe is less material than is often supposed.
5. We can, it should be stressed, make repeatable observations that when intelligent agents act to create artifacts, they produce complex specified information or, in Michael Behe's formulation, a "purposeful arrangement of parts." Such tell-tale signs allow us to reliably detect the prior action of intelligence in the past. Michael Behe, "Recognizing Design by a 'Purposeful Arrangement of Parts,'" *Evolution News and Science Today*, June 10, 2021, https://evolutionnews.org/2021/06/recognizing-design-by-a-purposeful-arrangement-of-parts/.
6. In addition to materialism and theism, there are two other classes of worldview. One is known generally as pantheism—in which the universe is all that exists, but the universe is God. We won't address this worldview in much detail in this book, as it shares materialism's view that the universe is impersonal, and no transcendent, personal being exists. A fourth worldview, deism, posits a transcendent God but one who (at least in deism's contemporary formulation) is distant and uninvolved except in the creative act that brought the finely tuned universe into existence. We will touch on that perspective but, again, will primarily focus on materialism and theism.
7. The differences between materialism and naturalism are relatively minor, and not relevant to our purposes herein. Hence, we'll use these terms interchangeably.

1. BEING ALIVE

1. As quoted in Marco Piccolino, "Biological Machines: From Mills to Molecules," *Nature Reviews Molecular Cell Biology* 1 (November 2000): 149–153.

2. Michael Denton, *Evolution: A Theory in Crisis* (Chevy Chase, MD: Adler & Adler, 1986), 249–250.

3. For a more thorough treatment of Denton's thinking on the subject, see *Evolution: A Theory in Crisis*, Chapter 11, and *Evolution: Still a Theory in Crisis* (Seattle, WA: Discovery Institute Press, 2016), 112 ff. In the first of these two books, on page 249, he distills the same idea when he writes that "the existence of a break between the living and non-living world... represents the most dramatic and fundamental of all the discontinuities of nature."

4. Howard Glicksman, "Each Cell in Your Body is a Walled City Besieged by Enemies," *Evolution News and Views*, March 2, 2015.

5. There are sixty-four (4^3) possible three-letter codons. Since only twenty amino acids need to be specified, most of the amino acids may be specified by multiple codons. For example, the codons CAA and CAG both code for glutamine. This may seem suboptimal and inelegant, but ongoing research is discovering how this redundancy is not only useful, but possibly also necessary for life.

6. Douglas Axe's experiments showed that, for every DNA sequence that generates a relatively short (150 amino acid) functional protein fold, there are about 10^{77} combinations of the same length that will not yield a stable, useful protein. This means that it would take more than the probabilistic resources of the universe to randomly find even a single useful protein of moderate length. Douglas Axe, "Estimating the Prevalence of Protein Sequences Adopting Functional Enzyme Folds," *Journal of Molecular Biology* 341 (2004): 1295–1315. For perspective, there are an estimated 10^{78} atoms in the entire universe, spread across hundreds of billions of galaxies. Several other studies have corroborated Axe's numbers using different methods. See, for example, Sean V. Taylor et al., "Searching Sequence Space for Protein Catalysts," *PNAS USA* 98 (2001): 10596–10601.

7. Problems of this kind exhibit combinatorial explosion—a relatively small change in the size of the problem leads to exponential growth in the size of the solution space. For example, a standard Sudoku game in a 9x9 grid can have 6,670,903,752,021,072,936,960 possible answers (~6.67×10^{21}). But in a 16x16 grid, the number of possible solutions is about 6×10^{98} (that is the number six followed by ninety-eight zeroes). The combinatorial problem for proteins is similar, though in most cases the numbers are much, much larger.

8. In an arresting display of how much we don't know about how much we don't know, estimates of the number of proteins in the human proteome vary widely, from a few tens of thousands to around six billion. One paper calculates that the number will be in the range of 600,000 to 6,000,000. Elena A. Ponomarenko et al., "The Size of the Human Proteome: The Width and Depth," *International Journal of Analytical Chemistry* (2016), https://doi.org/10.1155/2016/7436849. As of this writing (in 2022), the Human Protein Reference Database (http://www.hprd.org) has experimentally catalogued 30,047 different human proteins. Regardless of the actual number, we know it won't be less than that, and that by itself is a challenge to any narrative of origins that does without intent.

9. Discovery Science, "Molecular Machines—ATP Synthase: The Power Plant of the Cell," *YouTube*, January 21, 2013, video, 3:21, https://youtu.be/XI8m6o0gXDY.

10. This is called "moving down the concentration gradient," naturally moving from an area of higher concentration to an area of lower concentration, just like what the meteorologist tells us about how the movement of air from an area of higher atmospheric pressure to an area of lower pressure determines the prevailing winds and our weather.

11. The chemistry here is fascinating—and yet another facet of chemistry that the cell must get right. Osmolarity is the total number of chemical particles (regardless of type or size) that are dissolved in a given volume of water. This includes Na, K, proteins, and pretty much everything else in the cell's fluid. The laws of nature say that the osmolarity (all the chemical particles in solution) on either side of the cell membrane (the fluid inside the cell and the fluid outside the cell) must always be equal. As Na and K pass through the membrane to equalize their concentrations on either side (diffusion), the higher concentration of proteins inside the cell compared to outside causes the osmolarity inside the cell to rise. Since proteins can't simply cross the membrane, water has to enter the cell (osmosis) to keep the osmolarity the same on both sides. If the cell can't manage this "expanding" situation, it will continue to build up its water content (and pressure), eventually causing the cell to explode.

12. For each ATP molecule, a pump pushes 3 Na^+ ions out of the cell and brings in 2 K^+ ions.

13. Discovery Science, "The Workhorse of the Cell: Kinesin," *YouTube*, May 15, 2014, video, 3:32, https://youtu.be/gbycQf1TbM0.

14. See an animation showing the ribosome transcription of mRNA into an amino acid chain ready for folding, at DNA Learning Center, "mRNA Translation (Advanced)," *YouTube*, March 22, 2010, video, 3:03, https://youtube.com/watch?v=TfYf_rPWUdY. Another animation of the ribosome function: WHI Movies, "Ribosome," *YouTube*, March 31, 2017, video, 1:00, https://youtube.com/watch?v=morl5e-jBNk

15. The Human Protein Atlas, "The Human Cell," *YouTube*, November 29, 2016, video, 4:07, https://youtu.be/P4gz6DrZOOI.

2. TRILLIONS OF CELLS WORKING TOGETHER: THE BODY

1. Edwin Conklin, "The Mechanism of Heredity," *Science* 27, no. 691 (January 17, 1908), 89–90.

2. While many sources count twelve major body systems, we've chosen to treat the immune and lymphatic systems as a single larger system because they operate so seamlessly together.

3. For more about irreducibility and the challenge it poses to evolutionary theory, see Michael J. Behe, *Darwin's Black Box: The Biochemical Challenge to Evolution*, 10th Anniversary Edition (New York: Free Press, 2006) and *A Mousetrap for Darwin: Michael J. Behe Answers His Critics* (Seattle, WA: Discovery Institute Press, 2020).

3. STRUCTURE AND SUPPORT

1. Kim Stearns, quoted in "Thirteen Strange and Interesting Facts about Your Bones," Cleveland Clinic, December 22, 2020, https://health.clevelandclinic.org/13-strange-interesting-facts-bones-infographic/.

2. The distinguished Brazilian chemist Marcos Eberlin suggested this line of thought to us. See *Foresight: How the Chemistry of Life Reveals Planning and Purpose* (Seattle, WA: Discovery Institute Press, 2019), 23. When talking about aquaporin power he asks, "But

if Nobel-caliber intelligence was required to figure out how this existing engineering marvel works, what was required to invent it in the first place?"

4. The Respiratory System

1. Ezekiel 37:5 (Revised Standard Version).
2. When CO_2 enters the blood, the red blood cells use an enzyme called carbonic anhydrase to speed up the reaction in which CO_2 combines with water (H_2O) to form carbonic acid (H_2CO_3). H_2CO_3 quickly splits into positive H^+ ions (acid) and negative HCO_3^- ions (bicarbonate). When the CO_2 level rises due to respiratory problems, so does the H^+ ion (acid) level. This can result in something called respiratory acidosis.

5. The Cardiovascular System

1. Andrée Seu Peterson, "The Mystery of Our Body Temperature," *World*, April 24, 2014, https://wng.org/articles/the-mystery-of-our-body-temperature-1617286018.
2. Since the fetus doesn't really change its activity levels much at this point in its development, the more complex and capable mechanisms for changing the heart's rate and strength aren't yet needed. As of this writing, much about how all this works remains unknown.
3. How can the red blood cell elongate in this way without being damaged? In a precisely orchestrated multi-step process, after a new red blood cell is generated and matures in the bone marrow, it ejects its nucleus, mitochondria, and ribosomes, thereby making it small and flexible enough to squeeze through the capillaries. But this also means it can no longer make new hemoglobin (or any other proteins). For a discussion of this amazing process, see Michael Denton, *Evolution: Still a Theory in Crisis* (Seattle, WA: Discovery Institute Press, 2016), 130–136.

6. Hemoglobin

1. Michael Denton, *Nature's Destiny: How the Laws of Biology Reveal Purpose in the Universe* (New York: Free Press, 1998), 202.
2. Hemoglobin is a multimer, a molecular system composed of four proteins bound tightly together: two alpha-globins and two beta-globins.
3. The average human body has 20–30 trillion red blood cells, which make up 70–80 percent of the total number of cells in the body. This number may seem high, but given how critical oxygen delivery is to everything else in the body, and given that it takes time for each red blood cell to make its round trip from heart to lungs, to heart, to tissues, and back to the heart, it only makes sense that it would take a lot of them to get the job done.

7. Getting the Raw Materials for Life

1. Grace L. Lawrence and the Geo. H. Nettleton Home Association, *The Nettleton Cook Book* (Kansas City, Missouri: The Little Craft & Stationary Shop, 1909), 138.

8. Sugar, Water, and Other Key Chemical Substances

1. Gerald H. Pollack, Ivan L. Cameron, and Denys N. Wheatley, eds., *Water and the Cell* (Dordrecht, The Netherlands: Springer, 2006), viii.

2. We'll be using US units in mg/dL instead of international units in mmol/L. To convert mg/dL to mmol/L of glucose divide the former by eighteen. To convert mmol/L to mg/dL multiply the former by eighteen.

9. Temperature

1. "Goldilocks and the Three Bears," *Storynory*, September 13, 2016, https://www.storynory.com/goldilocks-and-the-three-bears/.

10. Seeing Is Believing

1. Isaac Newton, *Opticks: Or, A Treatise of the Reflections, Refractions, Inflexions and Colours of Light. The Second Edition, with Additions* (London: 1718), Book III, Query 28. Available at the Newton Project, August 2006, https://www.newtonproject.ox.ac.uk/view/texts/normalized/NATP00051.

2. This summary borrows from Michael Behe, *Darwin's Black Box* (New York: Simon and Schuster, 1996) 18–22.

3. Behe, *Darwin's Black Box*, 18.

4. Jonathan Wells, *Zombie Science: More Icons of Evolution* (Seattle, WA: Discovery Institute Press, 2017), 131–148.

5. A skeletal muscle is generally attached to the bones across a joint by two different tendons. The tendon on the bone that doesn't move when the muscle contracts is called the "origin," and the tendon that attaches to the bone that moves is called the "insertion." In the case of the eyeball, the origin tendons for the six extra-ocular muscles are attached to the bones making up the orbital cavity, and the insertion tendons are attached to the eyeball itself.

6. The inside half of the visual field and retina is called "nasal" because it is close to the nose, and the outside visual field and retina is called "temporal" because it is close to the temporal bone in the skull.

7. Michael Denton, *Children of Light* (Seattle, WA: Discovery Institute Press, 2018), 26.

8. This matches which side of the brain controls sensory and motor function. The right brain senses and controls the left side of the body, and the left brain senses and controls the right side of the body (see Chapter 12).

9. Charles Darwin, *On the Origin of Species by Means of Natural Selection* (London: John Murray, 1859), 186. In this passage Darwin confesses that applying natural selection to the mammalian eye "seems absurd in the highest possible degree." But still he held out hope that an adaptive continuum would one day be found that could explain the gradual appearance of so perfect an eye. Of course, he had a hopelessly simplistic understanding of the physics and mechanics of vision, including the molecular chemistry and visual processing involved. One might also note that, even 160 years after Darwin wrote this, our understanding of the ins and outs of vision is still grossly incomplete. But we can safely infer that as that understanding grows, the picture of the human vision system will continue to grow more complex, and we will continue to uncover still more engineering solutions all working together.

11. HEARING IS BELIEVING

1. Pratap Sriram Sundar, Chandan Chowdhury, and Sagar Kamarthi, "Evaluation of Human Ear Anatomy and Functionality by Axiomatic Design," *Biomimetics* 6, no. 2 (June 2021): 31, https://doi.org/10.3390/biomimetics6020031.

2. Recent research suggests that Beethoven may not have been completely deaf. However, his hearing loss is well documented, and began quite early in his adulthood.

12. BALANCE AND MOVEMENT

1. Cai Emmons, *His Mother's Son* (Orlando, FL: Harvest Books, 2003), 286.

2. Stuart Burgess, *The Design and Origin of Man* (Leominster, UK: Day One Publications, 2004), 24–28.

3. Burgess, *The Design and Origin of Man*, 30. The hole where the spinal cord exits the cranial cavity is called the foramen magnum. It opens at the bottom of the skull so that "the most natural position for the human head is looking forward in the upright position" (on two legs), as opposed to the ape where the foramen magnum is towards the back of the skull "so that the most natural position of the head is looking forward in the horizontal position" (on four legs).

13. CLOTTING

1. William James, *The Varieties of Religious Experience: A Study in Human Nature* [1902] (New York: The Modern Library, 1929), 133.

14. IMMUNITY

1. Richard Saunders [pseud.], *Poor Richard: An Almanac for the Year of Christ, 1736* (Philadelphia: B. Franklin, 1736). Available at https://founders.archives.gov/documents/Franklin/01-02-02-0019.

2. The neutrophil's method of locomotion is an open question. A few hypotheses exist, but the exact mechanism of motion remains a mystery.

3. Tony Goldberg quoted by Rachel Nuwer, "Why the World Needs Viruses to Function," *BBC Future*, June 17, 2020, https://www.bbc.com/future/article/20200617-what-if-all-viruses-disappeared.

15. VIVE LA DIFFÉRENCE

1. Erasmus Darwin, *Phytologia: or the Philosophy of Agriculture and Gardening* (London: J. Johnson, 1800), 103. Erasmus Darwin was Charles Darwin's grandfather. In a widely read book written in poetic form, *The Temple of Life* (1803), Erasmus set forth a vision of the natural evolution of all life, though without the mechanism of natural selection working on random variations later proposed by his grandson and Alfred Russel Wallace.

16. FERTILITY

1. For more details, see Howard Glicksman, "The Neo-Darwinian Chronicles: Tall Tales of 'Bad Design' in the Human Body—The (Descended) Testicles," *Access Research Network*, 2022, http://www.arn.org/docs/glicksman/bad-design/04/bda-04.html.

18. From 1 Cell to 30 Trillion

1. Alexander Tsiaras, "Conception to Birth—Visualized," INK Conference, December 2010, TED, video, 9:21, https://www.ted.com/talks/alexander_tsiaras_conception_to_birth_visualized. This portion begins at time marker 7:24.

2. See early in Chapter 1 of the present book, under the subheading "The Greatest Discontinuity," including endnotes 2 and 3 there.

19. Looking at the Whole

1. Uri Alon, *An Introduction to Systems Biology: Design Principles of Biological Circuits* (Boca Raton, FL: CRC Press, 2006), 2.

2. These things are so complicated (and important) that I (Steve) wrote a book about ways to manage them: *Breaking Through the Agility Barrier* (Erie, CO: Barebulb, 2015).

3. Michael Denton refers to this requirement of gradualism as an "adaptive continuum." Whatever series of events may have led to the human body, it's essential that the body was alive at each step. Michael Denton, *Evolution: Still a Theory in Crisis* (Seattle, WA: Discovery Institute Press, 2016), 42.

4. What size of discrete jump in functionality is needed to achieve functionality? Must functional plans arise all at once, even if some of the modules have been borrowed and adapted from other systems? The minimum size of any given functional leap varies depending on the specific systems in question. But for any system of even modest complexity, the size will generally be far larger than the leaps one could reasonably expect from any gradual, non-intentional activity. Much more research is needed to explore this question. This is an area where engineers have a lot to offer to biology.

5. Separation of concerns allows optimization around a specialized skill, which leads to enormous efficiencies. Interestingly, Adam Smith explored this principle in his classic 1723 work, *The Wealth of Nations*, though he called it the "division of labour."

20. But Wait, We've Only Scratched the Surface

1. Frank Sonnenberg, "The Secret to Happiness," *Frank Sonnenberg Online*, December 8, 2015, https://www.franksonnenbergonline.com/blog/the-secret-to-true-happiness/.

2. Gene regulatory networks (GRNs) use gene expression with chemical signaling in ways that parallel the logic gates and feedback loops of computer chips. GRNs are beyond the scope of this book, but it's interesting to note that even a relatively simple GRN may represent complex logic, so the total effects of a given GRN can be difficult to establish. See also the brief discussion of GRNs in Chapter 18.

3. In fact, so much about the human genome is unknown that most scientists in the field are unwilling to estimate how much of it is actually known. Some research has suggested that there are multiple layers of information overlaid on the same genes, making this number even harder to estimate. Thus, on the question of how much of the human genome is known, about the only thing we can say at this point is that there's not much we can say (definitively) at this point. A 2021 paper in *Nature* does a good job of at least showing how few genes and non-coding genetic elements have actually been subjected to intense study. See Alexander J. Gates et al., "A Wealth of Discovery Built on the Human Genome Project—by the Numbers," *Nature* 590, no. 7845 (February 11, 2021), 212–215.

4. This is a property sometimes called "over-design," where the design seems to far exceed the qualities strictly needed for survival. It demonstrates a sort of exuberance of design. See Stuart Burgess, *The Design and Origin of Man* (Leominster, UK: Day One Publications, 2004), 9.

5. While the evidence for human exceptionalism is abundant and obvious, there is a movement to convince people that we are unexceptional. Perhaps because the materialist worldview has difficulty accommodating those aspects of the human person that most clearly mark us off from other animals, its proponents seek to deflect and diminish them. Their argument is that humans differ from other living things only in degree. Such ideas are counterintuitive and flatly implausible, so the materialists' campaign to mainstream them has been a long and bitter one, involving all manner of rhetorical tricks, propaganda, and enticements. For a more thorough treatment of this topic, see Richard Weikart, *The Death of Humanity and the Case for Life* (Washington, DC: Regnery, 2016), especially Chapter 2.

6. These ideas date back at least as far as Aristotle, who distinguished between "substance" and "accidents," where "accidents" refer not to mishaps but to characteristics an entity has contingently—that is, characteristics the entity could lose and still retain its identity. Professor of neurosurgery Michael Egnor has written extensively about the lessons from neuroscience about distinctions between the brain and the mind, based on decades of clinical experience. See, for example, Michael Egnor, "A Map of the Soul," *First Things*, June 29, 2017, https://www.firstthings.com/web-exclusives/2017/06/a-map-of-the-soul.

7. Yair Pinto et al., "Split Brain: Divided Perception but Undivided Consciousness," *Brain* 140, no. 5 (2017): 1231–1237.

8. Michael Egnor, "More than Material Minds," *Christianity Today*, September 14, 2018, https://www.christianitytoday.com/ct/2018/september-web-only/more-than-material-minds-neuroscience-souls.html.

9. There is a rich literature describing these effects. See Michael Egnor, "Pioneering Neuroscientist Wilder Penfield: Why Don't We Have Intellectual Seizures?" *Evolution News and Science Today*, April 21, 2016, https://evolutionnews.org/2016/04/wilder_penfield/. Penfield showed that abstract thought is not produced by any region of the brain. See also, Wilder Penfield, *The Mystery of the Mind: A Critical Study of Consciousness and the Human Brain* (Princeton, NJ: Princeton University Press, 2015), 53. Neurophysiologist Benjamin Libet has shown that free will is a power of the mind that is independent of brain function. On this, see Michael Egnor, "Do Benjamin Libet's Experiments Show that Free Will Is an Illusion?" *Evolution News and Science Today*, January 15, 2014, https://evolutionnews.org/2014/01/do_benjamin_lib/.

10. This is known as mind-body dualism. This is a philosophical position that comports well with the evidence, though a thorough discussion is well beyond our remit here.

11. Granville Sewell, "A Summary of the Evidence for Intelligent Design," YouTube, January 8, 2021, video, 9:23, https://youtu.be/izfyYYXCLjY.

21. A Theory of Billions of Innovative Accidents

1. Charles Darwin, *On the Origin of Species by Means of Natural Selection* (London: John Murray, 1859), 187.

2. The data do not fit a clean and unambiguous tree of life topology, and for this reason, among others, no one has been able to reverse engineer the traits the LUCA might have had.

3. It's beyond the scope of this book to delve into the kinds of changes that have been observed from genetic mutations, but most result from errors in storing, retrieving, or processing either DNA or RNA. Note, however, that in general for complex body plans like the human form, only the variations that occur in the reproductive cells will be inherited—either the sperm or the egg cells. Mutations elsewhere in the body would not affect the offspring unless they're occurring in some epigenetic information.

4. Marcel P. Schützenberger, "Algorithms and the Neo-Darwinian Theory of Evolution," in *Mathematical Challenges to the Darwinian Interpretation of Evolution*, Wistar Institute Symposium Monograph No. 5, eds. P. S. Morehead and M. M. Kaplan (Philadelphia: Wistar Institute Press, 1967), 73–80. While random changes will almost always be harmful to a computer program, causing it to malfunction or crash, this is not necessarily true for random changes to the values assigned to the program's variables. While a thorough discussion of this is beyond our scope here, we think this is likely the cause of many observed allele variations. Of course, random changes in specific locations of the code (like modifying only the values) are not truly random. If and where this occurs in a living system, it's likely directed in some way by an organism's internal systems.

5. C. H. Waddington used this colorful example in a 1952 article: "To suppose that the evolution of the wonderfully adapted biological mechanisms has depended only on a selection out of a haphazard set of variations, each produced by blind chance, is like suggesting that if we went on throwing bricks together into heaps, we should eventually be able to choose ourselves the most desirable house." C. H. Waddington, *The Listener*, November 13, 1952, quoted in Arthur Koestler, *The Ghost in the Machine: The Urge to Self-Destruction: A Psychological and Evolutionary Study of Modern Man's Predicament* (London: Arkana, 1967), 127.

6. William A. Dembski, *The Design Inference: Eliminating Chance through Small Probabilities* (Cambridge, UK: Cambridge University Press, 1998); William A. Dembski, *The Design Revolution: Answering the Toughest Questions about Intelligent Design* (Downers Grove, IL: IVP Books, 2004), Chapters 8–21.

7. Michael Behe presents a fascinating analysis, based on observational data, in Chapters 3 and 7 of *The Edge of Evolution*. Michael Behe, *The Edge of Evolution: The Search for the Limits of Darwinism* (New York: Free Press, 2007) 44–63, 123–147, 195. See also Michael J. Behe and David W. Snoke, "Simulating Evolution by Gene Duplication of Protein Features That Require Multiple Amino Acid Residues," *Protein Science* 13 (2004): 2651–2664.

8. Readers interested in pursuing the complexity of self-reproduction are referred to Eric Anderson's compelling and readable essay, "A Factory That Builds Factories That Build Factories That…" in *Evolution and Intelligent Design in a Nutshell* (Seattle, WA: Discovery Institute Press, 2020), 65–86.

9. Historically, evolution and entropy have had a somewhat strained relationship. The basic disagreement goes something like this. For decades it's been argued that Darwinian processes violate the second law of thermodynamics because those processes require an increase in order and complexity—a decrease in entropy—which should not be possible in the general case, according to the laws of physics. Evolutionists argue that the second

law only applies within a closed system, and because the Earth is not a closed system (e.g., planet Earth is richly bathed in constant radiation from the sun), the objection isn't valid. Moreover, they maintain, Darwinian evolution doesn't necessarily even require an increase in "complexity"—it just requires whatever helps you survive. But clearly, life is unimaginably complex, and at some point this must be accounted for. Life requires both an increase in free energy and a decrease in entropy. Merely adding energy isn't enough. As Granville Sewell has aptly pointed out, shining a light for all eternity on a pool of chemicals will never yield a living cell. See Granville Sewell, "Entropy and Evolution," *BIO-Complexity* 2 (2013), and Granville Sewell, "On 'Compensating' Entropy Decreases," *Physics Essays* 30 (2017). For more on this topic, see Brian Miller, "Free Energy and the Origin of Life: Natural Engines to the Rescue," *Evolution News and Science Today*, June 22, 2017, https://evolutionnews.org/2017/06/free-energy-and-the-origin-of-life-natural-engines-to-the-rescue/.

10. Michael Denton explores many examples of non-adaptive features in depth in *Evolution: A Theory in Crisis* (Chevy Chase, MD: Adler & Adler, 1986) and *Evolution: Still a Theory in Crisis* (Seattle, WA: Discovery Institute Press, 2016), and in the short film "The Biology of the Baroque," Discovery Institute, December 4, 2017, https://www.discovery.org/v/baroque/.

11. Charles Darwin, *The Descent of Man and Selection in Relation to Sex* (New York: D. Appleton and Company, 1871).

12. In a September 1860 letter to Charles Lyell, Charles Darwin wrote, "Talking of 'Natural Selection', if I had to commence de novo, I would have used 'natural preservation'." Charles Darwin to Charles Lyell, September 28, 1860, Darwin Correspondence Project, University of Cambridge, Letter 2931, https://www.darwinproject.ac.uk/letter/DCP-LETT-2931.xml.

13. In the entirety of possible amino acid sequences, only a minuscule number will produce a stable folded protein form, and only a minuscule number of these will provide a specific function that is useful to a living organism. Douglas Axe published groundbreaking research on the rarity of these proteins. Douglas D. Axe, "Estimating the Prevalence of Protein Sequences Adopting Functional Enzyme Folds," *Journal of Molecular Biology* 341, no. 5 (2004): 1295–1315, https://doi.org/10.1016/j.jmb.2004.06.058. For a more informal assessment, see Brian Miller, "Mistakes Our Critics Make: Protein Rarity," *Evolution News and Science Today*, July 2, 2020, https://evolutionnews.org/2020/07/mistakes-our-critics-make-protein-rarity/.

14. Dembski, *The Design Inference*.

15. Darwin and his contemporaries were in the dark about what might be causing variation, but in his work with animal and plant breeders, he was keenly aware that variation happens all the time. So, while his theory requires variation, he did not propose a specific mechanism for variation.

16. Richard Dawkins, *The Blind Watchmaker: Why the Evidence of Evolution Reveals a Universe without Design* (New York: W. W. Norton & Company, 2015), 18.

17. Gerd B. Müller and Stuart A. Newman, "Origination of the Organismal Form: The Forgotten Cause in Evolutionary Theory," in *Origination of Organismal Form: Beyond the Gene in Developmental and Evolutionary Biology*, eds. Gerd B. Müller and Stuart Newman (Cambridge, MA: MIT Press, 2003), 7.

18. Gerd B. Müller, "Homology: The Evolution of Morphological Organization," in *Origination of Organismal Form: Beyond the Gene in Developmental and Evolutionary Biology*, eds. Gerd B. Müller and Stuart Newman (Cambridge, MA: MIT Press, 2003), 51.

19. G. H. Lewes, *Fortnightly Review*, November 1, 1868, 508. Available at http://darwin-online.org.uk/converted/Ancillary/reviews/1868_Lewes_A604.html.

20. Charles Darwin to Joseph Hooker, February 1, 1871, Darwin Correspondence Project, Letter no. 7471, University of Cambridge, https://www.darwinproject.ac.uk/letter/?docId=letters/DCP-LETT-7471.xml.

21. In fact, nature also enables life. The laws of physics and chemistry are fine tuned to make life possible, but they can do nothing to make life.

22. For more thorough discussions of neutral evolution, see Stephen C. Meyer, *Darwin's Doubt: The Explosive Origin of Animal Life and the Case for Intelligent Design* (New York: HarperOne, 2013), 321–329 and Michael J. Behe, *Darwin Devolves: The New Science about DNA That Challenges Evolution* (New York: HarperOne, 2019), 94–102.

23. To some extent, this movement away from Darwin is being held in check by sheer application of force, through (often indirect) threats about loss of jobs or denial of tenure. For more on this, see the documentary *Expelled: No Intelligence Allowed*, directed by Nathan Frankowski, with host Ben Stein (Premise Studios, 2008). Available at *YouTube*, June 14, 2012, https://www.youtube.com/watch?v=V5EPymcWp-g). At some point, the sheer pressure of the data will overwhelm these artificial forces, and the Darwinian house of cards will collapse. We are convinced that this is closer than most people realize.

24. The Royal Society dedicated an issue of their journal to the conference. See Denis Noble et al., "Introduction: New Trends in Evolutionary Biology: Biological, Philosophical and Social Science Perspectives," *Interface Focus* (August 18, 2017), https://royalsocietypublishing.org/toc/rsfs/2017/7/5. For a different perspective of the meeting's outcomes, see Paul Nelson and David Klinghoffer, "Scientists Confirm: Darwinism is Broken," *CNSNews*, December 13, 2016, https://www.cnsnews.com/commentary/david-klinghoffer/scientists-confirm-darwinism-broken.

25. For more on the 2016 Royal Society meeting and other rumblings of dissent from orthodox neo-Darwinism, see Casey Luskin, "*Nature Communications* Retroactively Concedes a Lack of Evidence for Darwinian Gradualism," *Evolution News and Science Today*, March 8, 2022, https://evolutionnews.org/2022/03/nature-communications-retroactively-concedes-a-lack-of-evidence-for-darwinian-gradualism/.

26. James A. Shapiro et al., *The Third Way: Evolution in the Era of Genomics and Epigenomics*, accessed September 12, 2022, https://www.thethirdwayofevolution.com/.

27. For a news account of this, see Nelson and Klinghoffer, "Scientists Confirm: Darwinism Is Broken," *CNS News*. See also Kevin Laland, "Schism and Synthesis at the Royal Society," *Trends in Ecology and Evolution* 32, no. 5 (May 2017): 316–317; and Susan Mazur, "Pterosaurs Hijack Royal Society Evo Meeting," *Huffington Post*, November 21, 2016, https://www.huffpost.com/entry/pterosaurs-hijack-royal-s_b_13131246.

28. Darwin, *On the Origin of Species*, 189. However, even in Darwin's day, sometimes referred to as the Golden Age of Engineering, enough was known to provide him with more than ample cases to abandon his theory. He should have talked to a few of his contemporary engineers.

29. Denton, *Evolution: A Theory in Crisis* (1986) and *Evolution: Still a Theory in Crisis* (2016).

30. See Meyer's *Darwin's Doubt*, Chapters 15 and 16.

22. TOWARD A THEORY OF BIOLOGICAL DESIGN

1. Itai Yanai and Martin J. Lercher, "What Puzzle Are You In?," *Genome Biology* 23, no. 179 (2022): 5, https://doi.org/10.1186/s13059-022-02748-1.
2. "Apple's 1984 Super Bowl Commercial Introducing the Macintosh Computer," Certell, *Vimeo*, accessed September 8, 2022, video, 1:03, https://vimeo.com/251318529.
3. Anand S. Rao and Michael P. Georgeff, "Modeling Rational Agents within a BDI-Architecture," *Proceedings of the 2nd International Conference on Principles of Knowledge Representation and Reasoning* (San Mateo, CA: Morgan Kaufmann, 1991), 473–484.
4. James A. Shapiro, *Evolution: A View from the 21st Century. Fortified.* (Chicago, IL: Cognition Press), 2022.
5. For a formal treatment of this subject, see N. Liscovitch-Brauer et al., "Trade-Off between Transcriptome Plasticity and Genome Evolution in Cephalopods," *Cell* 169, no. 2 (April 6, 2017), 191–202, https://doi.org/10.1016/j.cell.2017.03.025. For a more informal discussion of these discoveries, see Cornelius Hunter, "More on Massive RNA Editing and the Octopus," *Evolution News and Science Today*, April 10, 2017, https://evolutionnews.org/2017/04/more-on-massive-rna-editing-and-the-octopus/.
6. The idea that an organism's adaptive control systems define the range of variations available to that organism is a modern variation on that of Fleeming Jenkin, a leading engineer, in his 1867 critique of Darwin's *Origin*. Jenkin proposed that species function like "spheres," with an archetypical configuration at the center and insurmountable limits to variation representing the surface. Jenkin thus directly opposed Darwin's core argument for smooth extrapolation to unlimited variation. Though experimental evidence for Darwin's view of limitless change was lacking, Darwin wrote, "What limit can be put to this power, acting during long ages and rigidly scrutinizing the whole constitution, structure, and habits of each creature—favoring the good and rejecting the bad? I can see no limit to this power, in slowly and beautifully adapting each form to the most complex relations in life" (*On the Origin of Species*, 469). In our view, Darwin should have conferred with more engineers to consider the real-world limitations of his theory. Fleeming Jenkin, "Review of 'The Origin of Species,'" *The North British Review* 46 (June 1867): 277–318.
7. For a non-technical and eye-opening introduction to the internal adaptive capabilities of living systems, see Brian Miller, "Nearly All of Evolution Is Best Explained by Engineering," *Evolution News and Science Today*, September 24, 2021, https://evolutionnews.org/2021/09/nearly-all-of-evolution-is-best-explained-by-engineering/.
8. In a 2018 *BIO-Complexity* paper, Winston Ewert presented a dependency graph model that better explains the relationships in the biological data than does a more traditional Darwinian inheritance model. Ewert's hypothesis is "that different biological species share modules." In other words, Ewert's data indicate that living systems are composed of modules, and these modules may have been acquired by composition rather than inheritance. These results support our contention that the body was likely designed using the classic engineering practices of separation of concerns and the rule of composition, as discussed in Chapter 19. Winston Ewert, "The Dependency Graph of Life," *BIO-Complexity* 3 (2018), 1–27, https://bio-complexity.org/ojs/index.php/main/article/view/BIO-C.2018.3/BIO-C.2018.3.

9. While proponents of evolutionary biology's "third way" see these composition-like mechanisms as important factors in the history of life, their worldview prevents them from considering what we're proposing here: the possibility that these organisms were designed through a composition process, as intentional acts of design.

10. Günter Bechly and Stephen C. Meyer, "The Fossil Record and Universal Common Ancestry," in *Theistic Evolution: A Scientific, Philosophical, and Theological Critique*, eds. J. P. Moreland et al. (Wheaton, IL: Crossway, 2017), 331–362; James Valentine, *On the Origin of Phyla* (Chicago: University of Chicago Press, 2004).

11. Niles Eldredge and Stephen J. Gould, "Punctuated Equilibria: An Alternative to Phyletic Gradualism," in *Models in Paleobiology*, ed. T. J. M. Schopf (San Francisco: Freeman Cooper, 1972), 82–115. Reprinted in Niles Eldredge, *Time Frames* (Princeton, NJ: Princeton University Press, 1985), 193–223. For a critical discussion of this theory, see Chapter 7 of Stephen C. Meyer, *Darwin's Doubt: The Explosive Origin of Animal Life and the Case for Intelligent Design* (New York: HarperOne, 2013), 136–152.

12. The question of "missing links" between humans and our purported fully ape-like ancestors is a complex subject, which to cover adequately would take us far afield of this book's primary focus. For more information on this topic, see Casey Luskin, "Missing Transitions: Human Origins and in the Fossil Record," in *Theistic Evolution: A Scientific, Philosophical, and Theological Critique*, eds. J. P. Moreland et al. (Wheaton, IL: Crossway, 2017), 437–474.

13. We have ample evidence that such things happen around us all the time. For an interesting example of how organic changes follow an intentional act, consider what happened when wolves were reintroduced into the Yellowstone National Park ecosystem. "How Wolves Change Rivers," [remastered HD] Sustainable Human, *YouTube*, February 4, 2022, video, 4:11, https://www.youtube.com/watch?v=W88Sact1kws. While we can't vouch for all the specific claims in the video, the phenomenon of trophic cascades is firmly established in the field of ecology.

23. But What About All Those Botched Designs?

1. Thomas Pynchon, *Gravity's Rainbow* (New York: Viking, 1995), 251.

2. Kenneth Miller, *Finding Darwin's God* (New York: Cliff Street Books, 1999), 101.

3. Nathan H. Lents, *Human Errors: A Panorama of Our Glitches, from Pointless Bones to Broken Genes* (New York: Houghton Mifflin Harcourt, 2018), 29.

4. Richard Dawkins, *The Blind Watchmaker* (New York: W.W. Norton, 1986), 93. Tasked with solving a truly hard problem, few engineers would view tidiness as a primary design goal. One wonders how many engineers Dawkins consulted with before making this statement.

5. Charles Darwin to Joseph Hooker, July 13 [1856], Darwin Correspondence Project, Letter no. 1924, University of Cambridge, https://www.darwinproject.ac.uk/letter/DCP-LETT-1924.xml.

6. For more on Darwin's wrestling with the problem of suffering in the natural world, see Cornelius G. Hunter, *Darwin's God: Evolution and the Problem of Evil* (Grand Rapids, MI: Brazos Press, 2001), 13–18; and Charles Darwin, *The Autobiography of Charles Darwin* (New York: Harcourt, Brace and Co., 1958), 90.

7. For the story of the Yugo, see Jason Vuic, "A Quick Look at the Yugo, the Worst Car in History," *Car and Driver*, June 6, 2018, https://www.caranddriver.com/features/a21082360/a-quick-history-of-the-yugo-the-worst-car-in-history/.

8. Readers interested in a more thorough exploration of the theological component of Darwinian theory are referred to Hunter's 2001 book *Darwin's God*, cited above.

9. Of course, improving on the design of a particular bodily system is relatively easy if you're allowed to jettison some of the system's capabilities. Removing key goals in the design will almost always open the possible solution space to completely new approaches. For example, why improve the ankle and foot if you can just use a wheel? It may not be so good for rock hopping or spelunking, but if you take those objectives off the list, a wheel might work well. In the extended example of the human pharynx, which we discuss later in this chapter, how would a better solution work if it needs to meet all the objectives met by the pharynx? What design trade-offs would be made? What would a "better solution" do better, and what would it do less well?

10. For an example of this kind of thing, see the embarrassingly naive video on "Stupid Design" from astrophysicist Neil deGrasse Tyson, "Neil DeGrasse Tyson—Stupid Design," *YouTube*, November 8, 2009, video, 4:55, https://www.youtube.com/watch?v=4238NN8HMgQ. He mentions several of the examples we mention in this chapter, including the choking hazard of the pharynx. Also note the responses from his audience. This is clearly meant to entertain rather than educate.

11. For a book laying out some of the most common bad-design-so-no-designer arguments regarding the human body, see Nathan Lents's 2018 book *Human Errors*. For several articles pointing up the shortcomings of such arguments, and explicitly responding to Lents, search "Lents Human Errors" at *Evolution News and Science Today* (evolutionnews.org).

12. The concept of discordance is closely related to what Ernst Haeckel (1834–1919) called dysteleology, the philosophical view that existence has no *telos*—no purposeful design or goal—and thus pretty much anything can happen. However, the many constraints nature imposes mean it's much more likely that the range of things that can actually happen is quite limited.

13. Stephen Jay Gould, *The Structure of Evolutionary Theory* (Cambridge, MA: Belknap Press, 2002), 111–112.

14. Charles Darwin, *On the Origin of Species by Means of Natural Selection* (London: John Murray, 1859), 450.

15. Jonathan Wells, *Zombie Science: More Icons of Evolution* (Seattle, WA: Discovery Institute Press, 2017), 115–124.

16. Ann Gauger et al., *Theistic Evolution: A Scientific, Philosophical and Theological Critique* (Wheaton, IL: Crossway, 2017), 485–486.

17. Lents, *Human Errors*, 28.

18. In any serious evaluation, the many structures and capabilities of the human wrist, including the many ways its joints are hinged to move in three dimensions, provide a lesson in the highest possible design prowess. If there are any imperfections in this design, it's hard to imagine what they might be. For a fascinating discussion of the wrist, see Chapter 7 in the textbook below, and especially note Figure 7–15 (227), which shows one dimension of the amazing double hinge of the human wrist, illustrating how two different joints share the same axis of rotation. Donald A. Neumann, *Kinesiology of the*

Musculoskeletal System: Foundations for Rehabilitation, 2nd ed. (St. Louis, MO: Mosby Elsevier, 2010), 216–243.

19. Darwin, *On the Origin of Species*, 472.

20. The telescope is deployed at the second LaGrange point, 1.5 million kilometers from the Earth. This special (non-random) location relative to the sun and Earth offers a stable orbit well away from interferences caused by the light and heat of the sun, Earth, and moon.

21. The engineering of the James Webb space telescope boggles the mind. Read more about this project at NASA's web page for the telescope, all the better to appreciate the design of complex systems: https://www.jwst.nasa.gov/index.html.

22. Darwin, *On the Origin of Species*, 472.

23. Lents, *Human Errors*, 19–20.

24. Abby Hafer, *The Not-So-Intelligent Designer: Why Evolution Explains the Human Body and Intelligent Design Does Not* (Eugene, OR: Cascade Books, 2015), 72–73. Others employing the pharynx to plump for evolutionary theory could be cited. Ardea Skybreak, for example, insists that if the human pharynx had been designed, then the designer was "really stupid (or perversely sadistic)." *The Science of Evolution and the Myth of Creationism: Knowing What's Real and Why It Matters* (Chicago: Insight Press, 2006), 109.

25. To see the amazing and beautiful coordination that occurs in swallowing, see "Swallowing Reflex, Phases and Overview of Neural Control, Animation," Alila Medical Media, *YouTube*, April 19, 2014, video, 2:58, https://www.youtube.com/watch?v=YQm5RCz9Pxc.

26. Lents, *Human Errors*, 19–20.

27. Hafer, *The Not-So-Intelligent Designer*, 72–73.

28. The origin of this joke is unknown—attributed to a "jocular lexicographer."

24. TWO QUESTIONS

1. David Gelernter, "Giving Up Darwin: A Fond Farewell to a Brilliant and Beautiful Theory," *Claremont Review of Books*, Spring 2019, https://claremontreviewofbooks.com/giving-up-darwin/.

2. Gary R. Habermas, Antony Flew, and David J. Baggett, *Did the Resurrection Happen?: A Conversation with Gary Habermas and Antony Flew* (Westmont, IL: InterVarsity Press, 2009), 75.

3. Antony Flew often pointed out that while he did not become a Christian, he held the person of Jesus in high regard.

4. James A. Beverley, "Thinking Straighter: Why the World's Most Famous Atheist Now Believes in God," *Christianity Today*, April 8, 2005, https://www.christianitytoday.com/ct/2005/april/29.80.html.

5. Beverly, "Thinking Straighter."

6. C. S. Lewis, *Miracles: A Preliminary Study* [1947] (New York: HarperOne 2015), 91.

7. Nancy Pearcey, "Stephen Hawking's Final Salvo Against God," *CNS News*, October 26, 2018, https://www.cnsnews.com/commentary/nancy-pearcey/stephen-hawkings-final-salvo-against-god.

8. Lewis, *Miracles*, 95.

9. The quotation is commonly attributed to Haldane but without mention of any specific book, article, speech, or other occasion, so it may be apocryphal. Haldane, however, is known to have been a quotable conversationalist. Biologist C. S. Pittendrigh, regarded by some as the "father of the biological clock," describes the quotation as "that famous old quip of Haldane's," hinting perhaps at an oral tradition. See Pittendrigh's note at the end of Ernst Mayr, "Teleological and Teleonomic: A New Analysis," *Boston Studies in the Philosophy of Science* 14 (1974): 91–117.

10. Thomas Nagel, *The Last Word* (Oxford, UK: Oxford University Press, 1997), 130–131.

11. Antony Flew, quoted in Beverly, "Thinking Straighter."

12. William Provine, from a 1994 debate with Phillip Johnson at Stanford University. "Provine/Johnson Debate Excerpts," *Origins Research* 16, no. 1, 1995, http://arn.org/docs/orpages/or161/161main.htm.

13. This topic is much too broad to be explored in depth here. For a deeper discussion, interested readers are referred to Stephen C. Meyer, *Return of the God Hypothesis: Three Discoveries That Reveal the Mind Behind the Universe* (New York: HarperOne, 2021).

14. Robert Jastrow, *God and the Astronomers* (New York: W.W. Norton, 1978), 116.

15. While it's beyond the scope of this book to explore the stories behind these defections from Darwin, it's no secret that publicly abandoning Darwinism can jeopardize your career, especially a career in one of the life sciences. Still, as a testament to the growing force and reach of the design arguments, the number of people in this company continues to grow and now includes scientists, intellectuals, and thought leaders from many backgrounds: Dean Kenyon, Richard Sternberg, Günter Bechly, Dennis Prager, Ben Shapiro, Thomas Nagel, and many others. Meanwhile, Nobel Laureate scientists such as Charles Townes and Brian Josephson have explicitly endorsed intelligent design in physics and cosmology, with the latter endorsing two intelligent design books that made ID arguments in both physics and biology, *Return of the God Hypothesis* by Stephen Meyer and *Foresight* by Marcos Eberlin, which was also endorsed by two other Nobel Laureate scientists. A less widely known trend: many others have abandoned Darwin but are in sensitive career positions that make it difficult to issue public declarations to this effect. For more on the defectors from Darwin, see the theatrically released film *Expelled: No Intelligence Allowed* (2008), directed by Nathan Frankowski, with host Ben Stein (Premise Studios, 2008). Available at *YouTube*, June 14, 2012, video, 1:37:59, https://www.youtube.com/watch?v=V5EPymcWp-g). See also David Klinghoffer, "High-Level Defectors from Evolutionary Theory Leave a Top Darwin Defender Feeling 'Disturbed,'" *Evolution News and Science Today*, August 30, 2012, https://evolutionnews.org/2012/08/high-level_defe/; and John West, "Do Scientists Have the Intellectual Freedom to Challenge Darwinism?" in *The Comprehensive Guide to Science and Faith: Exploring the Ultimate Questions about Life and the Cosmos*, eds. William Dembski, Casey Luskin, and Joseph Holden (Eugene, OR: Harvest House, 2021), 399–406.

ACKNOWLEDGMENTS

FIRST, WE MUST THANK OUR WIVES FOR THEIR UNFLAGGING SUPport and encouragement, even when we worked long hours instead of taking them out for dinner. Without them this book would not exist.

Without Jonathan Witt's skill and perseverance as editor, project director, and chief antagonist, this book would be much the worse, and we'd likely have been sitting on a beach somewhere drinking sarsaparillas with our wives. We were never quite sure on any given day whether to hug him or strangle him, as he has a way of being annoyingly right. But we're thankful for him just the same.

This book results from our respective (and very different) decadeslong professional careers, mixed with the inspiration and wise counsel of many colleagues. Though there are too many to name here, these include Brian Miller, Casey Luskin, Eric Anderson, Randy Guliuzza, Stuart Burgess, David Klinghoffer, John West, Dennis Wagner, Art Battson, Ann Gauger, Rebecca Keller, Donald Calbreath, David Kruger, Jonathan Wells, and Ray Bohlin.

And of course, we cannot forget a hearty thank you to the many blind peer reviewers, whose names we don't know, but who offered their time and expertise to make the final result all the better.

ABOUT THE AUTHORS

Steve Laufmann

Steve Laufmann is a speaker, author, computer scientist, and consultant in the design of enterprise-class systems, with expertise in the difficulties of changing complex systems to perform new tasks. He leads the Engineering Research Group at Discovery Institute and chaired the program committee for the 2021 Conference on Engineering in Living Systems.

Howard Glicksman

Dr. Howard Glicksman is a general practitioner with more than forty years of medical experience in office and hospital settings, who now serves as a hospice physician seeing terminally ill patients in their homes. He received his MD from the University of Toronto and is the author of "The Designed Body" series for *Evolution News and Science Today*.

Figure Credits

Figure 1.1. A typical human cell. "Components of Eukaryotic Cell." Image by Christoph Burgstedt, Adobe Stock. Standard license.

Figure 1.2. Kinesin motor protein. "3D Rendered Illustration of a Motor Protein." Image by SciePro, Adobe Stock. Standard license.

Figure 1.3. Ribosome. "Ribosome mRNA Translation." Image by Mariana Ruiz Villarreal (Lady of Hats), June 29, 2009, Wikimedia Commons. Public domain.

Figure 2.1. Hierarchical layers of the human body. Image by Steve Laufmann.

Figure 2.2. A few of the cell types in the human body. "Cell Set." Image by Designua, Adobe Stock. Standard license.

Figure 3.1. Types of epithelium. "Types of Epithelium. Squamous, Cubic, Ciliated, Glandular." Image by Timonina, Adobe Stock. Standard license.

Figure 4.1. Respiratory system. "The Respiratory System." Image by the Canadian Lung Association, 2021. Used with permission.

Figure 4.2. Alveolus gas exchange. "Alveolus Gas Exchange." Image by Designua, Adobe Stock. Standard license.

Figure 4.3. Cellular respiration. "Cellular Respiration Medical." Image by VectorMine, Adobe Stock. Standard license.

Figure 5.1. The human heart. "Human Heart Anatomy." Image by BlueRingMedia, Adobe Stock. Standard license.

Figure 5.2. The arterioles and capillaries. "Illustration of Blood Vessels." Image by National Cancer Institute, Wikimedia Commons. Public domain.

Figure 5.3. Arterioles. Image by Thomas Appleton for Discovery Institute.

Figure 6.1. Hemoglobin multimer. "Hemoglobin in Red Blood Cells." Image by VectorMine, Adobe Stock. Standard license.

Figure 7.1. Overview of gastrointestinal system. "Medical Anatomy Illustration of Human Gastrointestinal Digestive System." Image by Christos Georghiou, Adobe Stock. Standard license.

Figure 9.1. The hypothalamus-pituitary-thyroid axis. "Thyroid Hormones Diagram." Image by Pikovit, Adobe Stock. Standard license.

Figure 10.1. Main parts of human eye. "Structure of the Human Eye." Image by K3Star, Adobe Stock. Standard license.

Figure 10.2. Tissues at the back of human eye. "Eyeball in Section, Structure of Retina." Image by Lavreteva, Adobe Stock. Standard license.

Figure 10.3. Trochlea. "Human Eye Anatomy / Vintage Illustration from Meyers Konversations-Lexikon 1897." Image uploaded by Hein Nouwens, Adobe Stock. Standard license. Modified by Steve Laufmann.

Figure 10.4. The optical inversion of the image at the retina. "Vision." Image by Andrea Danti, Adobe Stock. Standard license.

Figure 10.5. Pathway for visual information. "Visual Pathway Medical." Image by VectorMine, Adobe Stock. Standard license.

Figure 11.1. Amplitude and frequency in sound waves. "Amplitude and Pitch." Image by VectorMine. Adobe Stock. Standard license.

Figure 11.2. The parts of the ear. "Anatomy of Ear." Image by Lucky-Soul, Adobe Stock. Standard license.

Figure 11.3. Middle ear. "Middle Ear." Image by Bruce Blaus, October 15, 2013, Wikimedia Commons. CC-BY-3.0 license, https://creativecommons.org/licenses/by/3.0/.

Figure 11.4. Inner ear. "The Internal Ear." Image by Bruce Blaus, October 15, 2013, Wikimedia Commons. Free cultural work license.

Figure 11.5. Cochlea. "Cross Section of the Cochlea." Image by Oarih, March 27, 2010, Wikimedia Commons. CC-BY-SA 3.0 license. Modified by Steve Laufmann.

Figure 12.1. Center of gravity. Image by Thomas Appleton for Discovery Institute.

Figure 12.2. The central nervous system. "Central Nervous System Anatomy." Image by LuckySoul, Adobe Stock. Standard license.

Figure 12.3. The spinal cord's segmentation. "Skeleton Spine." Image by Sveta, Adobe Stock. Standard license.

Figure 12.4. The stretch reflex process. "The Stretch Reflex." Image by Joshya, Adobe Stock. Standard license.

Figure 12.5. The homunculus. Image by Thomas Appleton for Discovery Institute.

Figure 13.1. Blood clotting. "Blood Clotting Process." Image by Alila Medical Media, Adobe Stock. Standard license.

Figure 13.2. Blood clotting pathways. "The Clotting Cascade." Image by Angela, Adobe Stock. Standard license.

Figure 14.1. The lymphatic system. "Lymphatic Circulation System." Image by VectorMine, Adobe Stock. Standard license.

Figure 14.2. Multi-faceted signaling between a B-cell and a helper T-cell. "T-Dependent B Cell Activation." Image by Altaileopard, December 1, 2010, Wikimedia Commons. Public domain.

Figure 14.3. The structure of an antibody. "Antibody Structure." Image by AlexandraDaryl, Adobe Stock. Standard license.

Figure 15.1. Male and female reproductive systems. "Human Reproductive System." Image by VectorMine, Adobe Stock. Standard license.

Figure 15.2. Hypothalamus-pituitary-gonadal axis. Image by P. Koopman. Used and modified with permission.

Figure 16.1. Cross-section of human penis. "Human Reproductive System Anatomy... Male Penis with Text." Image by Tasty_Cat, Adobe Stock. Standard license.

Figure 16.2. Process of fertilization. "Process of Human Fertilization." Image by Olando, Adobe Stock. Standard license.

Figure 17.1. Fetal and maternal interface. "Placental Structure and Circulation." Image by Sakurra, Adobe Stock. Standard license.

Figure 17.2. Chambers and valves of human heart. "Heart Anatomy." Image by Designua, Adobe Stock. Standard license.

Figure 17.3. Fetal heart. "Module 13: Heart and Great Vessels." Image by Rice University, Anatomy 337 eReader. CC-BY-4.0 international license, https://creativecommons.org/licenses/by/4.0/.

Figure 18.1. The three germinal layers of a developing embryo. "Module 9: Human Development and Anatomy Through Lifespan." Image by Rice University, Anatomy 337 eReader, https://creativecommons.org/licenses/by/4.0/. CC-BY-4.0 international license.

Figure 19.1. Partial problem cascade for cellular respiration. Image by Steve Laufmann.

Figure 22.1. The challenge of distinguishing intentional effects from organic effects in living systems. Image by Steve Laufmann.

Figure 23.1. Pharynx. "Head and Neck Overview." Image by Arcadian, February 15, 2007, Wikimedia Commons. Public domain.

Figure 24.1. Answering two questions. Image by Steve Laufmann.

INDEX

CPSIA information can be obtained
at www.ICGtesting.com
Printed in the USA
BVHW062001061122
651208BV00002B/9